BEST-LOVED
CHRISTMAS STORIES
OF THE LDS PEOPLE

BEST-LOVED
CHRISTMAS STORIES
OF THE LDS PEOPLE

Edited by Linda Ririe Gundry, Jay A. Parry,
and Jack M. Lyon

DESERET BOOK COMPANY
SALT LAKE CITY, UTAH

Library of Congress Cataloging-in-Publication Data

Best-loved Christmas stories of the LDS people / [compiled by] Linda Ririe Gundry, Jay A. Parry, Jack M. Lyon
    p.   cm.
  ISBN 1-57008-722-9 (hardbound : alk. paper)
    1. Christmas stories, American.   2. American fiction—Mormon authors.
3. Mormons—Fiction.   I. Gundry, Linda Ririe. II. Parry, Jay A.   III. Lyon, Jack M.

PS648.C45 B47 2001
813'.0108334—dc21

    2001004017

Printed in the United States of America   72082-6851

10   9   8   7   6   5   4   3   2   1

CONTENTS

CONTENTS

Classic Christmas Tales

Christmas Stories in Poetry

True Stories of Christmas Present

PREFACE

What Christmas would be complete without a story—and especially *the* story of the Savior's birth from Luke, Matthew, and 3 Nephi? As President David O. McKay said, "The announcement of the first Christmas is the sweetest story ever told—the sweetest story because of the eternal principles enunciated—the 'glad tidings of great joy'—were to be 'unto all people.' The Light of the world was to shine in every heart" (*Steppingstones to an Abundant Life* [Salt Lake City: Deseret Book Co., 1971], 422).

But the story doesn't end there. As Elder Neal A. Maxwell has noted, "The larger Christmas story is clearly not over. It is not solely about some other time, some other place, and some other people. It is still unfolding, and we are in it!" (Cory H. Maxwell, ed., *The Neal A. Maxwell Quote Book* [Salt Lake City: Bookcraft, 1997], 46).

In that spirit we present the stories in this collection—stories of love, caring, and giving from the time of the Savior up to our day. Some of the stories are fictional. Some of the stories are true. Some simply had to be included because they are Christmas classics, even though to modern sensibilities they may seem a little outdated or sentimental. Some are even told in poetry rather than prose. But all of the stories, in one way or another, illustrate the true meaning of Christmas.

Some readers may question the inclusion of Clement Moore's "'Twas the Night Before Christmas" or other stories that mention Saint Nick. But we must remember that Santa Claus represents the spirit of giving. As Elder John A. Widtsoe wrote, "There are men who object to Santa Claus, because he does not exist! Such men need spectacles to see that Santa Claus is a symbol; a symbol of the love and joy of Christmas and the Christmas spirit. In the land of my birth there was no Santa Claus, but a little goat was shoved into the room, carrying with it a basket of Christmas toys and gifts. The goat of itself counted for nothing; but the Christmas spirit, which it symbolized, counted for a tremendous lot" ("Temple Worship," *The Utah Genealogical and Historical Magazine,* Apr. 1921, 62).

We hope you will take time to feel that spirit during the Christmas season, to read with your family the story of the Savior's birth, and to enjoy the stories in this volume that show his continuing influence in our lives.

A Note about Sources

Where stories are no longer under copyright but are in public domain, we have often not given a source. Such stories are generally easy to find in most libraries. We have included original sources in three instances: (1) when the story comes from a Latter-day Saint publication (even if the story is in public domain), (2) when the story is under copyright protection, and (3) when the source may be of special interest to the reader (for instance, many readers will be interested to note that Kenneth Grahame's *"Dulce Domum"* is excerpted from his *Wind in the Willows*).

The authors and the publisher have made every reasonable effort to locate and contact owners of copyrighted material, that appropriate permission may be obtained.

STORIES OF THE FIRST CHRISTMAS

GOD'S GIFT, OUR SAVIOR:
THE TESTIMONY OF THE PROPHETS*

I

In the due time of the Lord
He sent an angel to a city in Galilee, named Nazareth,
To a virgin named Mary, a precious and chosen vessel.
And the angel said,
Hail, thou that art highly favored, the Lord is with thee:
blessed art thou among women.
And the angel said,
Thou shalt conceive in thy womb, and bring forth a son,
even the Son of God, and shalt call his name JESUS.
And he shall reign over the righteous for ever;
and of his kingdom there shall be no end.

Then Mary said,
How shall this be, seeing I know not a man?

And the angel answered,
The Holy Ghost shall come upon thee,
and the power of the Highest shall overshadow thee:
therefore that holy child who shall be born of thee shall be
     called the Son of God.
For with God nothing is impossible.

And Mary said,
Behold the handmaid of the Lord;

---

*From Luke 1:26–37, 46–49; 2:1–19; Mosiah 3:5–9; Alma 7:10–15; 1 Nephi 19:9–10; Luke 24:1–12, 33–40; John 20:1–7, 19; 1 Corinthians 15:6–8; 19–22; 55, 57; 3 Nephi 11:1, 15; Alma 38:9; 5:33; Moroni 10:32–33; and D&C 76:22–24; arranged and adapted by Jay A. Parry.

be it according to thy word.
And the angel departed.
And Mary said,
My soul doth magnify the Lord,
And my spirit hath rejoiced in God my Savior.
From henceforth all generations shall call me blessed.
For he that is mighty hath done to me great things;
*   and holy is his name.*

II

And it came to pass in those days, that Caesar decreed
    that all the world should be taxed.
And all went to be taxed, every one into his own city.
Joseph also went up unto Bethlehem, the city of David,
to be taxed with Mary, his espoused wife,
who was great with child.
And while they were there, the days were accomplished
    that she should be delivered.
And she brought forth her firstborn son,
and wrapped him in swaddling clothes,
and laid him in a manger;
because there was no room for them in the inn.

III

There were in the same country shepherds abiding in the field,
    keeping watch over their flock by night.
And, lo, the angel of the Lord came upon them,
and the glory of the Lord shone round about them:
and they were sore afraid.
And the angel said unto them,
Fear not—
for, behold, I bring you good tidings of great joy,
*   which shall be to all people.*

For unto you is born this day in the city of David a Savior,
    who is Christ the Lord.
And this shall be a sign unto you:
Ye shall find the babe wrapped in swaddling clothes,
lying in a manger.
And suddenly there was with the angel
a multitude of the heavenly host praising God, and saying,
Glory to God in the highest,
and on earth peace, good will toward men.

And it came to pass that the shepherds said one to another,
Let us now go even unto Bethlehem,
and see this thing which is come to pass.
And they came with haste,
and found Mary, and Joseph,
and the babe lying in a manger.
And when they had seen it, they made known abroad all they had
    heard and seen.
But Mary kept all these things,
and pondered them in her heart.

IV

And thus it was that with power, the Lord Omnipotent,
who was, and is from all eternity to all eternity,
came down from heaven among the children of men,
to dwell in a tabernacle of clay.
And he went forth amongst men,
working mighty miracles,
healing the sick,
raising the dead,
causing the lame to walk,
the blind to receive their sight,
the deaf to hear,
and curing all manner of diseases.
And he cast out devils,

or the evil spirits that dwell in the hearts of the children of men.
And he suffered pains
and afflictions
and temptations of every kind,
yea, pain of body, hunger, thirst, and fatigue,
even more than man can suffer, except it be unto death;
for behold, blood came from every pore,
so great was his anguish for the wickedness of his people.

And thus did he take upon him the pains
and the sicknesses of his people.
And he took upon him their infirmities,
that his bowels would be filled with mercy,
that he could succor his people.
And he took upon him the sins of his people,
that he could blot out their transgressions.
And he took upon him death,
that he could loose the bands of death.

But even after all this they considered him a man,
and said he had a devil,
and scourged him,
and crucified him.
Yea, the world, because of their iniquity,
judged him to be a thing of naught;
wherefore they scourged him,
and he suffered it;
and they smote him,
and he suffered it;
And they spat upon him,
and he suffered it,
because of his loving kindness
and his long-suffering towards the children of men.
And the God of our fathers,
yea, the God of Abraham, and of Isaac, and of Jacob,
yielded himself as a man into the hands of wicked men,

to be lifted up,
and to be crucified,
and to be buried in a sepulcher.

V

Now in those days, on the third day after his burial,
Mary Magdalene, and Mary the mother of James, and certain other
    women of faith,
came unto his sepulcher,
bringing the spices they had prepared for his body.
But when they entered in, they found not the body of the Lord Jesus.
And as they wondered,
behold, two men stood by them in shining garments:
And they said unto them,
Why seek ye the living among the dead?
He is not here, but is risen.
And they made haste and told all these things unto the eleven,
    and the other disciples.

The same day at evening, as the eleven were gathered together,
    and others with them, speaking of these things,
Jesus himself stood in the midst of them, and said unto them,
Peace be unto you.
But they were terrified and affrighted,
and supposed that they had seen a spirit.
And he said unto them,
Why are ye troubled?
Why do fears arise in your hearts?
Behold my hands and my feet; it is I myself:
handle me, and see;
a spirit hath not flesh and bones, as ye see me have.
And he shewed them his hands and his feet.

After that, he was seen of above five hundred brethren at once;
And then he was seen of the people of Nephi,

BEST-LOVED CHRISTMAS STORIES OF THE LDS PEOPLE

who did see with their eyes

and feel with their hands,

and did know of a surety that it was Jesus Christ;

And last of all he was seen of Paul,

as of one born out of due time.

Wherefore, Paul wrote truly,

If in this life only we have hope in Christ,

we are of all men most miserable.

But now is Christ risen from the dead,

and become the firstfruits of them that slept.

For as in Adam all die,

even so in Christ shall all be made alive.

O death, where is thy sting?

O grave, where is thy victory?

But thanks be to God,

who gives us the victory through our Lord Jesus Christ.

VI

And now, ye must learn wisdom;

ye must learn that there is no other way or means

whereby man can be saved, only in and through Christ.

Behold, he is the life and the light of the world.

He is the word of truth and of righteousness.

Behold, he sendeth an invitation unto all men,

for the arms of mercy are extended towards them,

and he saith:

Repent, and I will receive you.

Yea, he saith:

Come unto me

and ye shall partake of the fruit of the tree of life.

Come unto me

and ye shall eat and drink of the bread and the waters of life freely.

Therefore, come unto Christ, and be perfected in him,
and deny yourselves of all ungodliness;
and if ye shall deny yourselves of all ungodliness,
and love God with all your might, mind, and strength,
then is his grace sufficient for you,
that by his grace ye may be perfect in Christ.
And if ye by the grace of God are perfect in Christ,
and deny not his power,
then are ye sanctified in Christ by the grace of God,
through the shedding of the blood of Christ,
unto the remission of your sins,
that ye become holy, without spot.

VII

And now, after the many testimonies which have been
    given of him,
this is the testimony, last of all, which we give of him:
That he lives!
For we saw him, even on the right hand of God;
and we heard the voice bearing record
that he is the Only Begotten of the Father—
That by him,
and through him,
and of him,
the worlds are and were created,
and the inhabitants thereof are begotten sons and
    daughters unto God.
Amen and amen.

The First Christmas

DAVID O. McKAY

When the weary, travel-worn couple, Joseph and Mary, entered their old home-town of *Bet Lahm,* they anticipated securing comfortable lodgings, but "there was no room for them in the Inn." Only mothers can realize Mary's keen disappointment and fearful anxiety as she and Joseph left the Inn and again entered the darkness to seek lodgings elsewhere. The city was crowded, but among the throngs there were no friends to help, no familiar faces to alleviate their heavy feelings of loneliness—an expectant mother in need of the best, the most comfortable of accommodations, yet not an open door, not even a couch on which to rest!

Well, to quote a modern writer, Herbert Spough: "Providence has a way of overruling the best laid plans of men, and turning their errors to fit the greater, divine plan. The hour has struck for the advent of the world Deliverer, and the Lord of all is ushered into the world in a stable.

"How the guiding hand of the Ruler of worlds directed the stage setting of this greatest of world dramas time has borne testimony."

Humble shepherds informed by revelation said: "Let us now go even unto Bethlehem and see this thing which has come to pass, which the Lord hath made known unto us, . . . and they found Mary, and Joseph, and the babe lying in a manger."

Wise men from the east, were guided to him through the channel of learning—"and when they were come into the house (not the manger) they saw the young child with Mary, his mother, and fell down and worshipped him: and when they had opened their treasures they offered unto him gifts: gold and frankincense and myrrh."

When, after eight days, Mary, in conformity with the Mosaic law, took her child to the Temple, Simeon, a "just and devout" man, receiving witness by the Holy Ghost, recognized the babe as "the Lord's Christ." Taking him in his arms, he blessed God and said: "Lord, now lettest thou thy servant depart in peace, according to thy word: for mine eyes have seen thy salvation."

Thus was it shown even on the first Christmas that all people—the humble, the learned, the rich, the great—who sincerely seek the Christ will find him and become of one mind in a divine brotherhood of which the Lord is the acknowledged head.

THE BIRTH OF JESUS CHRIST

JAMES E. TALMAGE

The Annunciation to the Virgin

Six months after the visitation of Gabriel to Zacharias, and three months prior to the birth of John, the same heavenly messenger was sent to a young woman named Mary, who lived at Nazareth, a town in Galilee. She was of the lineage of David; and though unmarried was betrothed or espoused to a man named Joseph, who also was of royal descent through the Davidic line. The angel's salutation, while full of honor and blessing, caused Mary to wonder and to feel troubled. "Hail, thou that art highly favoured, the Lord is with thee: blessed art thou among women" [Luke 1:28]; thus did Gabriel greet the virgin.

In common with other daughters of Israel, specifically those of the tribe of Judah and of known descent from David, Mary had doubtless contemplated, with holy joy and ecstasy, the coming of the Messiah through the royal line; she knew that some Jewish maiden was yet to become the mother of the Christ. Was it possible that the angel's words to her had reference to this supreme expectation and hope of the nation? She had little time to turn these things in her mind, for the angel continued: "Fear not, Mary: for thou hast found favour with God. And, behold, thou shalt conceive in thy womb, and bring forth a son, and shalt call his name JESUS. He shall be great, and shall be called the Son of the Highest: and the Lord God shall give unto him the throne of his father David: and he shall reign over the house of Jacob for ever; and of his kingdom there shall be no end" [Luke 1:30–33].

Even yet she comprehended but in part the import of this momentous visitation. Not in the spirit of doubt such as had prompted Zacharias to ask for a sign, but through an earnest desire for information and explanation, Mary, conscious of her un- married status and sure of her virgin condition, asked: "How shall this be, seeing I know not a man?" The answer to her natural and simple inquiry was the announcement of a miracle such as the world had never known—not a miracle in the sense of a happen- ing contrary to nature's law, nevertheless a miracle through the operation of higher law, such as the human mind ordinarily fails to comprehend or regard as possible. Mary was informed that she would conceive and in time bring forth a Son, of whom no mortal man would be the father:—"And the angel answered and said unto her, The Holy Ghost shall come upon thee, and the power of the Highest shall overshadow thee: therefore also that holy thing which shall be born of thee shall be called the Son of God" [Luke 1:35].

Then the angel told her of the blessed condition of her cousin Elisabeth, who had been barren; and by way of sufficient and final explanation added: "For with God nothing shall be impossible." With gentle submissiveness and humble acceptance, the pure young virgin replied: "Behold the handmaid of the Lord; be it unto me according to thy word."

His message delivered, Gabriel departed, leaving the chosen Virgin of Nazareth to ponder over her wondrous experience. Mary's promised Son was to be "The Only Begotten" of the Father in the flesh; so it had been both positively and abundantly pre- dicted. True, the event was unprecedented; true also it has never been paralleled; but that the virgin birth would be unique was as truly essential to the fulfillment of prophecy as that it should occur at all. That Child to be born of Mary was begotten of Elohim, the

Eternal Father, not in violation of natural law but in accordance with a higher manifestation thereof; and, the offspring from that association of supreme sanctity, celestial Sireship, and pure though mortal maternity, was of right to be called the "Son of the Highest." In His nature would be combined the powers of Godhood with the capacity and possibilities of mortality; and this through the ordinary operation of the fundamental law of heredity, declared of God, demonstrated by science, and admitted by philosophy, that living beings shall propagate—after their kind. The Child Jesus was to inherit the physical, mental, and spiritual traits, tendencies, and powers that characterized His parents—one immortal and glorified—God, the other human—woman.

Jesus Christ was to be born of mortal woman, but was not directly the offspring of mortal man, except so far as His mother was the daughter of both man and woman. In our Lord alone has been fulfilled the word of God spoken in relation to the fall of Adam, that the *seed of the woman* should have power to overcome Satan by bruising the serpent's head [Genesis 3:15].

In respect to place, condition, and general environment, Gabriel's annunciation to Zacharias offers strong contrast to the delivery of his message to Mary. The prospective forerunner of the Lord was announced to his father within the magnificent temple, and in a place the most exclusively sacred save one other in the Holy House, under the light shed from the golden candlestick, and further illumined by the glow of living coals on the altar of gold; the Messiah was announced to His mother in a small town far from the capital and the temple, most probably within the walls of a simple Galilean cottage. . . .

Mary and Joseph

The visit [with Elisabeth] lasted about three months, after which time Mary returned to Nazareth. The real embarrassment of her position she had now to meet. At the home of her cousin she had been understood; her condition had served to confirm the testimony of Zacharias and Elisabeth; but how would her word be received at her own home? And especially, how would she be regarded by her espoused husband? Betrothal, or espousal, in that time was in some respects as binding as the marriage vow, and could only be set aside by a ceremonial separation akin to divorce; yet an espousal was but an engagement to marry, not a marriage. When Joseph greeted his promised bride after her three months' absence, he was greatly distressed over the indications of her prospective maternity. Now the Jewish law provided for the annulment of a betrothal in either of two ways—by public trial and judgment, or by private agreement attested by a written document signed in the presence of witnesses. Joseph was a just man, a strict observer of the law, yet no harsh extremist; moreover he loved Mary and would save her all unnecessary humiliation, whatever might be his own sorrow and suffering. For Mary's sake he dreaded the thought of publicity; and therefore determined to have the espousal annulled with such privacy as the law allowed. He was troubled and thought much of his duty in the matter, when, "behold, the angel of the Lord appeared unto him in a dream, saying, Joseph, thou son of David, fear not to take unto thee Mary thy wife: for that which is conceived in her is of the Holy Ghost. And she shall bring forth a son, and thou shalt call his name JESUS: for he shall save his people from their sins" [Matthew 1:20, 21]. . . .

The Birth of Jesus

. . . Bethlehem, though small and of little importance in trade or commerce, was doubly endeared to the Jewish heart as the birthplace of David and as that of the prospective Messiah. Mary and Joseph lived in Nazareth of Galilee, far removed from

Bethlehem of Judea; and, at the time of which we speak, the maternity of the Virgin was fast approaching.

At that time a decree went out from Rome ordering a taxing of the people in all kingdoms and provinces tributary to the empire; the call was of general scope, it provided "that all the world should be taxed" [Luke 2:1]. The taxing herein referred to may properly be understood as an enrollment, or a registration, whereby a census of Roman subjects would be secured, upon which as a basis the taxation of the different peoples would be determined. This particular census was the second of three such general registrations recorded by historians as occurring at intervals of about twenty years. . . . Joseph and Mary went to Bethlehem, the city of David, to be inscribed under the imperial decree.

The little town was crowded at the time, most likely by the multitude that had come in obedience to the same summons; and, in consequence, Joseph and Mary failed to find the most desirable accommodations and had to be content with the conditions of an improvised camp, as travelers unnumbered had done before, and as uncounted others have done since, in that region and elsewhere. We cannot reasonably regard this circumstance as evidence of extreme destitution; doubtless it entailed inconvenience, but it gives us no assurance of great distress or suffering.* It was while she was in this situation that Mary the Virgin gave birth to her first-born, the Son of the Highest, the Only Begotten of the Eternal Father, Jesus the Christ.

Jesus Born Amidst Poor Surroundings.—Undoubtedly the accommodations for physical comfort amidst which Jesus was born were few and poor. But the environment, considered in the light of the customs of the country and time, was far from the state of abject deprivation which modern and western ways would make it appear. "Camping out" was no unusual exigency among travelers in Palestine at the time of our Lord's birth; nor is it considered such today. It is, however, beyond question that Jesus was born into a comparatively poor family, amidst humble surroundings associated with the inconveniences incident to travel. Cunningham Geikie, *Life and Words of Christ,* chap. 9, pp. 112, 113, says:

" . . . Traveling in the East has always been very different from Western ideas. As in all thinly-settled countries, private hospitality, in early times, supplied the want of inns, but it was the peculiarity of the East that this friendly custom continued through a long series of ages. On the great roads through barren or uninhabited parts, the need of shelter led, very early, to the erection of rude and simple buildings, of varying size, known as khans, which offered the wayfarer the protection of walls and a roof, and water, but little more. The smaller structures consisted of sometimes only a single empty room, on the floor of which the traveler might spread his carpet for sleep; the larger ones, always built in a hollow square, enclosing a court for the beasts, with water in it for them and their masters. From immemorial antiquity it has been a favorite mode of benevolence to raise such places of shelter."

THE BIRTH OF THE MORTAL MESSIAH

BRUCE R. McCONKIE

Angels, Alma says, come to men, women, and children to impart the word of God. (Alma 32:23.) And never was there a case when angelic ministration was more deserved, or served a greater purpose, or was manifest in a sweeter and more tender way, than when Gabriel, who stands in the presence of God, came to Mary to announce her divine call to be the mother of the Son of God. She at the time dwelt in Nazareth, a city of Galilee, located some eighty miles northward from the Holy City and the Holy Temple, where last the angelic form had been seen and the angelic voice heard.

Mary was espoused to Joseph, meaning she had made a formal contract of marriage with him that yet had to be completed in a second ceremony before they would commence living together as husband and wife. She was, however, considered by their law to be his wife; the contract could be broken only by a formal "bill of divorcement," and any infidelity on her part would be classed as adultery, for which Jehovah had of old decreed death as the penalty.

Faithful Jews prayed in their homes three times daily—at the time of the morning offering, at noon, and at the time of the evening sacrifice. Perhaps at such a time (for the veil grows thin when prayers flow from the heart) the man Gabriel "came in" to her humble home. She was alone; her spiritual eyes were open; and she saw the minister from heaven. He spoke: "Hail, thou virgin, who art highly favoured of the Lord. The Lord is with thee, for thou art chosen and blessed among women."

Understandably the humble, perhaps even shy and timid, Maid of Nazareth was troubled by such lavish praise from one sent from the other world and who spoke only the truth. Sensing her feelings, Gabriel continued: "Fear not, Mary: for thou hast found favour with God. And, behold, thou shalt conceive in thy womb, and bring forth a son, and shalt call his name Jesus."

Jesus, blessed name—signifying *Jehovah is salvation*—her Son to be a Savior! Had she ever hoped or thought that the Messiah, expected by her people, would be born as her Son? Had the Spirit, even before Gabriel came, whispered any message of hope or comfort or expectancy to the soul of one so attuned to spiritual things as she was?

But there was more, telling her in plain words the status and mission and dominion of him who was to be her Son: "He shall be great, and shall be called the Son of the Highest: and the Lord God shall give unto him the throne of his father David: And he shall reign over the house of Jacob for ever; and of his kingdom there shall be no end."

"The Son of the Highest"—the Supreme God shall be his Father! "The throne of his father David"—the symbol of all Jewish hope and triumph and glory and freedom and deliverance! An eternal kingdom—the kingdom of our God and of his Christ, and they shall reign forever and ever!

Mary asked, "How shall this be, seeing I know not a man?" Obviously she could, at the proper time, know Joseph, and he could be the father of all her children, not just those who would come after the Firstborn. She knew that. But already the concept was framed in her mind that the promised Son was not to originate from any power on earth. This offspring was to be himself almighty—God's Almighty Son. How and by what means and through whose instrumentality does such a conception come?

Gabriel explains: "The Holy Ghost shall come upon thee, and the power of the Highest shall overshadow thee: therefore also that holy thing [better, that holy child] which shall be born of thee shall be called the Son of God."

Again the answer is perfect. There is a power beyond man's. When God is involved, he uses his minister, the Holy Ghost, to overshadow the future mother and to carry her away in the Spirit. She shall conceive by the power of the Holy Ghost, and God himself shall be the sire. It is his Son of whom Gabriel is speaking. A son is begotten by a father: whether on earth or in heaven it is the same. . . .

. . . But what does it mean to be "with child of the Holy Ghost"? Who is the Father of Mary's Son? . . . The Father is a personage of tabernacle; he has a body of flesh and bones as tangible as man's; he is in one place at one time; he lives and moves and has a being; his influence is spread through all immensity, but he is a personal Being in whose image man is created, and he is the Father of the spirits of all men. . . .

The Son, existing first as a spirit man, was born into mortality as a mortal man; and he has now risen in the resurrection as an immortal man. As far as this life is concerned, he was born of Mary and of Elohim; he came here as the offspring of that Holy Man who is literally our Father in heaven. He was born in mortality in the literal and full sense as the Son of God. He is the Son of his Father in the same sense that all mortals are the sons and daughters of their fathers. . . .

When Mary told Joseph that she was with child by the power of the Holy Ghost, his reaction was one not only of shock, of sorrow, and of dismay, but also of disbelief. His soul had yet to feel the flames of the refiner's fire before so great a spiritual truth could rest easily in his heart; as with all men, his faith and his willingness to submit to the divine will in all things must be tested.

For Mary it was no easy thing to tell the man she loved that their relationship was different from that of other faithful couples. And yet Gabriel himself had brought the word! When she recited to Joseph what the aerial ambassador had told her, great and wondrous as the promises were, it must yet have been as a sword piercing her soul, a sword that would wound her feelings time and again, until that day when she, at the foot of a cross, would weep for the Son whom she had brought into the world.

For Joseph it was the beginning of a period of agony and uncertainty. That he wanted to believe Mary, but did not, is shown by his determination "to put her away privily" with as little embarrassment as possible. He planned to give her a letter of divorce in the presence of two witnesses only, as the law permitted, rather than to make the dissolution of their contract to marry a matter of public knowledge and possible gossip. It must have been at this point that Mary sped hastily to Hebron to find comfort in the arms of Elisabeth.

Joseph pondered and prayed. Was Mary with child by the power of the Holy Ghost or in some other way? As to the true father of the unborn child, Mary knew; Elisabeth knew; Zacharias knew. They all gained their testimonies by revelation, and Joseph must now learn for himself in the same way. As we have seen, there is no way for anyone—neither Joseph, nor Mary, nor any living soul—to know and declare the generation of the Son of God, except by the whisperings of the Holy Spirit. Joseph must learn by powers beyond those exercised by mortal men that Mary's child was God's Son. Until this happened, their marriage could not be completed and their union consummated; until this occurred the Holy Family could not be perfected according to the divine plan. This knowledge must come to Joseph to prepare him to provide proper paternal influence in Mary's home during the infant and maturing years of the Son whose Father is above.

It was at this point of hope and faith that Joseph prevailed with the Lord. His prayers were answered. "The angel of the Lord appeared unto him in a dream." His message: "Joseph, thou son of David"—for Joseph, like Mary, was of the house and lineage of Israel's greatest king—"Fear not to take unto thee Mary thy wife: for that which is conceived in her is [by the power] of the Holy Ghost. And she shall bring forth a son, and thou shalt call his name Jesus: for he shall save his people from their sins."

Joseph now knew! Doubt fled. The circle of true believers was growing. He had the same testimony, from the same source, as did Mary and Elisabeth and Zacharias; and, according to their law, in the mouths of two or three witnesses shall every word be established. The Lord was providing his witnesses, and soon the whole nation and the whole world would be bound to believe, and that at the peril of their salvation. How often Joseph bore the special witness that was his we do not know, but that he remained true to every trust and that he performed the mission assigned him by the Lord, there can be no doubt. . . .

Mary—in whose womb the Child was growing, within whose

flesh the Eternal One was in process of making flesh his tabernacle—dwelt in love and peace in Nazareth of Galilee. She was sheltered and steadied by the kind arm of Joseph, her husband, for the marriage was now completed; Joseph had obeyed the command of Gabriel and taken the young virgin as his wife. His name and his influence now gave comfort to the one who would soon be a mother, to the one who would bear a Son, conceived under the most unusual circumstances ever known on earth. With Joseph's name and comforting assurances she no longer feared the gossip and shame that otherwise might have attended her forthcoming ordeal.

But Bethlehem, more than eighty dusty, dreary miles away, was the destined place for the birth of the great Deliverer. So it was written by the prophets; so it must be. Out of this small place, insignificant among the villages of Judea, must come Him whose goings forth have been from of old, from everlasting. Mary knew this and Joseph knew it; both had seen an angel; both knew, by means beyond mortal comprehension, that the Holy Thing that was in her was to "be called the Son of the Highest," who should rule on the throne of David his father forever. They must go to Bethlehem and there attend to the coming forth of a Son, lest any of the Messianic prophecies, by so much as a hair's breadth, should fail.

And so to Bethlehem they went. Was it to be taxed? Yes, for Octavian—the great Caesar Augustus—had so decreed all the world must be taxed. . . . Joseph and Mary—both descendants of David, both of the tribe of Judah—must enroll in the land of Judah and in the City of David, in Bethlehem.

They went to Bethlehem because they had no choice: Caesar had spoken, and Herod was echoing the word. But this was only the occasion, the vehicle, the excuse, as it were. They would have moved heaven and earth, if need be, to place themselves in the

City of David when the hour arrived for the coming of the Son of David. We cannot suppose that a considerate and loving husband, having a wife big with child, would cause her to walk, or ride a slow stepping donkey, or traverse in any manner the dusty roads of Palestine, camping out overnight as they traveled—all as the hour of her confinement approached—unless there was a reason. Joseph and Mary were going to Bethlehem for a purpose. It was the one and only place where the Messiah could be born, and we cannot but suppose that they knew it and acted wittingly.

As to why they did not reside in this city of Judah in the first instance, we can only say that the providences of the Lord called for them to live in Nazareth where Joseph carpentered for a living. Jesus was to be a Nazarene; so also was it written. And as to why they did not leave Nazareth earlier, we are left to assume that Divine Providence planned a late arrival, an arrival when there would be no room in the inns, when the new baby would be brought forth under the most humble circumstances. . . .

. . . Of this most important of all births, Luke says simply: "And she brought forth her firstborn son, and wrapped him in swaddling clothes, and laid him in a manger, because there was none to give room for them in the inns."

No room in the inns! Hospitality was universal, freely extended, and everywhere to be found. People in all walks of life took strangers into their homes, fed them, washed their feet, and cared for their beasts of burden. It was a way of life. No one can fault the Jewish practice of caring for travelers, whether they were kinfolk or strangers. Had Joseph and Mary come days earlier, they might have found lodgment in the home of a relative, a friend, or a hospitable stranger, any one of whom would have summoned a midwife and prepared a cradle for the Coming One. Had they even arrived earlier in the day, there would have been a place in the rooms or inns rather than in the court, where those beasts were tethered among whom the Coming One came.

No room in the inn—not an inn of western or modern make, but a *kahn* or place of lodgment for strangers, a *caravanserai* or place where caravans or companies of travelers bedded down for the night. It may have been a large, bare building, built of rough stones, surrounding an open court in which animals could be tied up for the night. A foot or two above this courtyard were the small recesses or "low small rooms with no front wall" where the humans tethered themselves.*

In the area of Bethlehem, sometimes the whole kahn, sometimes only the portion where the animals were kept, was located within a large cave, of which there are many in the area. But unless or until some of the saints—and such a thing is by no means improbable or beyond the realm of expectancy—see in a dream or a vision the inn where Joseph and Mary and Jesus spent that awesome night, we can only speculate as to the details.

For the present also, we have no way of knowing how or in what manner the Babe of Bethlehem was delivered. Was there a midwife among the travelers who heard the cries of travail and came to Mary's aid? Did Mary alone wrap the swaddling clothes around her infant Son, or were there other hands to help? How were her needs cared for? Needless to say, the Gospel narratives are silent on these and a lifetime of personal matters relative to the greatest life ever lived. All we can now know—perhaps all we need to know—is that he was born in the lowest conceivable circumstances.

Though heaven was his habitation and earth his footstool, he chose to lie as an infant in a manger, surrounded by horses and camels and mules. Though he laid the foundations of the earth,

---

*In the only other place where this word is found in the New Testament, it was translated as *guestchamber*. There is no real English equivalent.

and worlds without number had rolled into orbit at his word, he chose to come into mortality among the beasts of the field. Though he had worn a kingly crown in the eternal courts on high, he chose to breathe as his first mortal breath the stench of a stable. Though he would one day come forth—born then in glorious immortality—with all power in heaven and on earth, for now, as the helpless child of a peasant girl, he chose to begin the days of his probation as none of Adam's race had ever done before. And there, even in such a birth, he was rejected by his people, symbolically at least, for none in the recesses and rooms of the inn had seen fit to make room for a weary woman, great with child, who needed above all at that hour the kind hands and skill of those who had attended her cousin Elisabeth in more fortuitous circumstances.

But with it all, a God had come into mortality, inheriting from his mother the power of mortality and from his Father the power of immortality. Soon the infinite and eternal atonement—sought and desired by the righteous for four thousand years—would be a living reality. Soon all that had been hoped and promised and foreseen would come to pass. Is it any wonder that angelic choirs, even now, were awaiting the cue to sing forth great anthems of praise, some of which would be heard by shepherd ears on the nearby Judean hills! . . .

. . . In the fields of Bethlehem, not far from Jerusalem and the Temple of Jehovah, there were shepherds watching their flocks by night. These were not ordinary shepherds nor ordinary flocks. The sheep there being herded—nay, not herded, but watched over, cared for with love and devotion—were destined for sacrifice on the great altar in the Lord's House, in similitude of the eternal sacrifice of Him who that wondrous night lay in a stable, perhaps among sheep of lesser destiny. And the shepherds—for whom the veil was then rent: surely they were in spiritual stature like Simeon and Anna and Zacharias and Elisabeth and Joseph and the growing group of believing souls who were coming to know, by revelation, that the Lord's Christ was now on earth. As there were many widows in Israel, and only to the one in Zarephath was Elijah sent, so there were many shepherds in Palestine, but only to those who watched over the temple flocks did the herald angel come; only they heard the heavenly choir. As Luke's idyllic language has it: "And, lo, the angel of the Lord came upon them, and the glory of the Lord shone round about them: and they were sore afraid." . . .

> And the angel said unto them, Fear not: for, behold, I bring you good tidings of great joy, which shall be to all people. For unto you is born this day in the city of David a Saviour, which is Christ the Lord. And this shall be a sign unto you; Ye shall find the babe wrapped in swaddling clothes, lying in a manger.

His message delivered, the angel—was it Gabriel again?—ceased to speak; the shepherds must heed the heavenly voice, find the Savior, and then commence the infinitely great and eternally important work of taking the "good tidings of great joy . . . to all people." How they will tell the message to their wives and children! How they will explain it to their neighbors and friends, and even to strangers! How they will gather the people in the courts of the temple, at the time of the morning and evening sacrifice—when the very sheep they had cared for so tenderly are attaining their divine destiny on the holy altar—and tell their fellow Jews what they have heard from heaven! . . .

Then the shepherds find the Child and begin to make known what God has revealed to them. "But Mary kept all these things, and pondered them in her heart," awaiting the day when she too will bear witness of all that she feels and believes and knows concerning the Son of David, who was born in the city of David, and who came to reign on the throne of David forever.

THE NATIVITY

FREDERIC W. FARRAR

The associations of our Lord's nativity were all of the humblest character, and the very scenery of His birth-place was connected with memories of poverty and toil. On that night, indeed, it seemed as though the heavens must burst to disclose their radiant minstrelsies; and the stars, and the feeding sheep, and the "light and sound in the darkness and still-ness," and the rapture of faithful hearts, combine to furnish us with a picture painted in the colors of heaven. But in the brief and thrilling verses of the Evangelist we are not told that those angel songs were heard by any except the wakeful shepherds of an obscure village;—and those shepherds, amid the chill dews of a winter night, were guarding their flocks from the wolf and the rob-ber, in fields where Ruth, their Saviour's ancestress, had gleaned, sick at heart, amid the alien corn, and David, the despised and youngest son of a numerous family, had followed the ewes great with young. . . .

"Come now! let us go into Bethlehem, and see this thing which has come to pass, which the Lord made known to us," said the shepherds, when those angel songs had ceased to break the starry silence. Their way would lead them up the terraced hill, and through the moonlit gardens of Bethlehem, until they reached the summit of the grey ridge on which the little town is built. On that summit stood the village inn. The khan (or caravansary) of a Syrian village, at that day, was probably identical, in its appearance and accommodation, with those which still exist in modern Palestine. A khan is a low structure, built of rough stones, and generally only a single story in height. It consists for the most part of a square enclosure, in which the cattle can be tied up in safety for the night, and an arched recess for the accommodation of travellers. The *leewan,* or paved floor of the recess, is raised a foot or two above the level of the courtyard. A large khan—such, for instance, as that of which the ruins may still be seen at Khan Minyeh, on the shore of the Sea of Galilee—might contain a series of such recesses, which are, in fact, low small rooms with no front wall to them. They are, of course, perfectly public; everything that takes place in them is visible to every person in the khan. They are also totally devoid of even the most ordinary furniture. The traveller may bring his own carpet if he likes, may sit cross-legged upon it for his meals, and may lie upon it at night. As a rule, too, he must bring his own food, attend to his own cattle, and draw his own water from the neighboring spring. He would neither expect nor require attendance, and would pay only the merest trifle for the advantage of shelter, safety, and a floor on which to lie. But if he chanced to arrive late, and the *leewans* were all occupied by earlier guests, he would have no choice but to be content with such accommodation as he could find in the court-yard below, and secure for himself and his family such small amount of cleanliness and decency as are compatible with an unoccupied corner on the filthy area, which must be shared with horses, mules, and camels. The litter, the closeness, the unpleasant smell of the crowded animals, the unwelcome intrusion of the pariah dogs, the necessary society of the very lowest hangers-on of the caravansery, are adjuncts to such a position which can only be realized by any traveller in the East who happens to have been placed in similar circumstances.

In Palestine it not unfrequently happens that the entire khan, or at any rate the portion of it in which the animals are housed, is one of those innumerable caves which abound in the limestone rocks of its central hills. Such seems to have been the case at the little town of Bethlehem-Ephratah, in the land of Judah. Justin Martyr the Apologist, who, from his birth at Shechem, was familiar with Palestine, and who lived less than a century after the time of our Lord, places the scene of the nativity in a cave. This is, indeed, the ancient and constant tradition both of the Eastern and the Western Churches, and it is one of the few to which, though unrecorded in the Gospel history, we may attach a reasonable probability. . . .

From their northern home at Nazareth, in the mountains of Zabulon, Joseph, the village carpenter, had made his way . . . with Mary his espoused wife, being great with child. Fallen as were their fortunes, they were both of the house and lineage of David, and they were traversing a journey of eighty miles to the village which had been the home of their great ancestor while he was still a ruddy shepherd lad, tending his flocks upon the lonely hills. The object of that toilsome journey, which could not but be disagreeable to the settled habits of Oriental life, was to enroll their names as members of the house of David in a census which had been ordered by the Emperor Augustus. . . . In deference to Jewish prejudices, any infringement of which was the certain signal for violent tumults and insurrection, it was not carried out in the ordinary Roman manner, at each person's place of residence, but according to Jewish custom, at the town to which their family originally belonged. The Jews still clung to their genealogies and to the memory of long-extinct tribal relations; and though the journey was a weary and distasteful one, the mind of Joseph may well have been consoled by the remembrance of that heroic descent which would now be authoritatively recognized, and by the glow of those Messianic hopes to which the marvellous circumstances of which he was almost the sole depositary would give a tenfold intensity.

Travelling in the East is a very slow and leisurely affair, and was likely to be still more so if, as is probable, the country was at that time agitated by political animosities. Beeroth, which is fifteen miles distant from Bethlehem, or possibly even Jerusalem, which is only six miles off, may have been the resting-place of Mary and Joseph before this last stage of their journey. But the heavy languor, or even the commencing pangs of travail, must necessarily have retarded the progress of the maiden-mother. Others who were travelling on the same errand, would easily have passed them on the road, and when, after toiling up the steep hill-side, by David's well, they arrived at the khan—probably the very one which had been known for centuries as the House of Chimham, and if so, covering perhaps the very ground on which, one thousand years before, had stood the hereditary house of Boaz, of Jesse, and of David—every *leewan* was occupied. The enrolment had drawn so many strangers to the little town, that "there was no room for them in the inn." In the rude limestone grotto attached to it as a stable, among the hay and straw spread for the food and rest of the cattle, weary with their day's journey, far from home, in the midst of strangers . . . —in circumstances so devoid of all earthly comfort or splendor that it is impossible to imagine a humbler nativity—Christ was born.

SHEPHERDS WATCHED THEIR FLOCKS

ALFRED EDERSHEIM

That the Messiah was to be born in Bethlehem was a settled conviction. Equally so was the belief that He was to be revealed from *Migdal Eder*, 'the tower of the flock.' This *Migdal Eder* was *not* the watchtower for the ordinary flocks which pastured on the barren sheepground beyond Bethlehem, but lay close to the town, on the road to Jerusalem. A passage in the Mishnah (Shek. 7.4) leads to the conclusion, that the flocks, which pastured there, were destined for Temple-sacrifices, and, accordingly, that the shepherds, who watched over them, were not ordinary shepherds. The latter were under the ban of Rabbinism, on account of their necessary isolation from religious ordinances, and their manner of life, which rendered strict legal observance unlikely, if not absolutely impossible. The same Mishnic passage also leads us to infer that these flocks lay out *all the year round*. . . . Of the deep symbolic significance of such a coincidence, it is needless to speak.

It was, then, on that [special night], that shepherds watched the flocks destined for sacrificial services, in the very place consecrated by tradition as that where the Messiah was to be first revealed. Of a sudden came the long-delayed, unthought-of announcement. Heaven and earth seemed to mingle, as suddenly an Angel stood before their dazzled eyes, while the outstreaming glory of the Lord seemed to enwrap them, as in a mantle of light. Surprise, awe, fear would be hushed into calm and expectancy, as from the Angel they heard that what they saw boded not judgment, but ushered in to waiting Israel the great joy of those good tidings which he brought: that the long-promised Saviour, Messiah, Lord, was born in the City of David, and that they themselves might go and see, and recognize Him by the humbleness of the circumstances surrounding His Nativity.

It was, as if attendant angels had only waited the signal. . . . When the Herald-Angel had spoken, a multitude of heaven's host stood forth to hymn the good tidings he had brought. What they sang was but the reflex of what had been announced. It told in the language of praise the character, the meaning, the result, of what had taken place. Heaven took up the strain of 'glory'; earth echoed it as 'peace'; it fell on the ears and hearts of men as 'good pleasure':

Glory to God in the Highest—
And upon earth peace—
Among men good pleasure!

Only once before had the words of the Angels' hymn fallen upon mortal's ears, when, to Isaiah's rapt vision, Heaven's high Temple had opened, and the glory of Jehovah swept its courts, almost breaking down the trembling posts that bore its boundary gates. Now the same glory enwrapt the shepherds on Bethlehem's plains. Then the Angels' hymn had heralded the announcement of the Kingdom coming; now that of the King come. . . .

The hymn had ceased; the light faded out of the sky; and the shepherds were alone. But the Angelic message remained with them; and the sign, which was to guide them to the Infant Christ, lighted their rapid way up the terraced height to where, at the entering of Bethlehem, the lamp swinging over the hostelry directed them to the strangers of the house of David, who had come from Nazareth. Though it seems as if, in the hour of her utmost need, the Virgin-Mother had not been ministered to by loving hands, yet what had happened in the stable must soon have become known in the Khan. Perhaps friendly women were still passing to and fro on errands of mercy, when the shepherds reached the 'stable.' There they found, perhaps not what they had expected, but as they had been told. The holy group only consisted of the humble Virgin-Mother, the lowly carpenter of Nazareth, and the Babe laid in the manger. What further passed we know not, save that, having seen it for themselves, the shepherds told what had been spoken to them about this Child, to all around in the 'stable,' in the fields, probably also in the Temple, to which they would bring their flocks, thereby preparing the minds of a Simeon, of an Anna, and of all them that looked for salvation in Israel.

And now the hush of wondering expectancy fell once more on all who heard what was told by the shepherds—this time not only in the hill-country of Judæa, but within the wider circle that embraced Bethlehem and the Holy City. And yet it seemed all so sudden, so strange. That on such slender thread, as the feeble throb of an Infant-life, the salvation of the world should hang—and no special care watch over its safety, no better shelter be provided it than a 'stable,' no other cradle than a manger! And still it is ever so. On what slender thread has the continued life of the Church often seemed to hang; on what feeble throbbing that of every child of God—with no visible outward means to ward off danger, no home of comfort, no rest of ease. But, 'Lo, children are Jehovah's heritage!'—and: 'So giveth He to His beloved in *his* sleep!'

THE NATIVITY OF OUR LORD

CHARLES DICKENS

My dear children, I am very anxious that you should know something about the History of Jesus Christ. For everybody ought to know about Him. No one ever lived, who was so good, so kind, so gentle, and so sorry for all people who did wrong, or were in anyway ill or miserable, as he was. And as he is now in Heaven, where we hope to go, and all to meet each other after we are dead, and there be happy always together, you never can think what a good place Heaven is without knowing who he was and what he did.

He was born, a long long time ago—nearly Two Thousand years ago—at a place called Bethlehem. His father and mother lived in a city called Nazareth, but they were forced, by business to travel to Bethlehem. His father's name was Joseph, and his mother's name was Mary.

And the town being very full of people, also brought there by business, there was no room for Joseph and Mary in the Inn or any house; so they went into a Stable to lodge, and in this stable Jesus Christ was born. There was no cradle or anything of that kind there, so Mary laid her pretty little boy in what is called the Manger, which is the place the horses eat out of. And there he fell asleep.

While he was asleep, some Shepherds who were watching Sheep in the Fields, saw an Angel from God, all light and beautiful, come moving over the grass towards Them. At first they were afraid and fell down and hid their faces. But it said "There is a child born to-day in the City of Bethlehem near here, who will grow up to be so good that God will love him as his own son; and he will teach men to love one another, and not to quarrel and hurt one another; and his name will be Jesus Christ; and people will put that name in their prayers, because they will know God loves it, and will know that they should love it too." And then the Angel told the Shepherds to go to that Stable, and look at that little child in the Manger. Which they did; and they kneeled down by it in its sleep, and said "God bless this child!"

Now the great place of all that country was Jerusalem—just as London is the great place in England—and at Jerusalem the King lived, whose name was King Herod. Some wise men came one day, from a country a long way off in the East, and said to the King "We have seen a Star in the Sky, which teaches us to know that a child is born in Bethlehem who will live to be a man whom all people will love." When King Herod heard this, he was jealous, for he was a wicked man. But he pretended not to be, and said to the wise men, "Whereabouts is this child?" And the wise men said "We don't know. But we think the Star will show us; for the Star has been moving on before us, all the way here, and is now standing still in the sky." Then Herod asked them to see if the Star would show them where the child lived, and ordered them, if they found the child, to come back to him. So they went out, and the Star went on, over their heads a little way before them, until it stopped over the house where the child was. This was very wonderful, but God ordered it to be so.

When the Star stopped, the wise men went in, and saw the child with Mary his Mother. They loved him very much, and gave him some presents. Then they went away. But they did not go back to King Herod; for they thought he was jealous, though he had not said so. So they went away, by night, back into their own country. And an Angel came, and told Joseph and Mary to take the child into a Country called Egypt, or Herod would kill him. So they escaped too, in the night—the father, the mother, and the child—and arrived there, safely.

THE JOURNEY FROM NAZARETH TO JERUSALEM

J. REUBEN CLARK JR.

In this account, President Clark tells the story of the journey of Joseph, Mary, and Jesus to Jerusalem when Jesus was twelve years old. Though some of the circumstances were obviously different, in many ways this journey would have been very similar to that which Joseph and Mary took to Bethlehem at the time of Jesus' birth. Bethlehem is only five miles south of Jerusalem, and that first journey was also taken about the time of Passover. For this reason, this account adds much to our understanding of the journey at the time of the birth of Christ.

It was a spring day at the end of March (near the middle of the seventh Hebrew month, Nisan), the fields were yellowing with the ripening crops, the hills and valleys were covered with wild flowers, all nature was rejoicing, as Joseph and Mary and Jesus, with their kinsfolk and neighbors, left Nazareth with its white rocks and cliffs, splotched with green, and started down through the foothills to the valley floor of the plain of Jezreel, one thousand feet below. They were going to Jerusalem to observe the Passover, as had been their wont over the years, in obedience to the Rabbinical law, commending (and in certain instances requiring) the observance of the feast in Jerusalem by the Levitically clean males of Israel. The women were not legally bound to attend. The feast was a jubilee of great rejoicing, for it marked the anniversary of Israel's delivery from a grievous bondage to the Egyptians, and also her birth as a nation. . . .

So as these pilgrims wended downward over the foothills in the afternoon (in Palestine the first day of the journey was always a short one), they were a joyous group, chanting as they went, the "Psalms of Ascent" (Psalms 120–34), to the accompaniment of a flute. . . .

We do not know the details of their journey to Jerusalem, but they may well have stopped the first night at Nain, where later [Jesus] raised the son of the widow; or if the start were early enough they might have gone on to Jezreel, once the second capital of the northern kingdom. . . .

Journey of the Second Day

But wherever the first night was spent, the start the next morning was early. They now moved on Roman roads, as they passed on southwards toward the city of Samaria. Crossing the headwaters of the River Kishon (which both waters and drains the plains of Esdraelon), they would begin the ascent of the pass over the Carmelite range, the hill slopes probably covered with the yellow flowers of the broom. Villages dotted the high points along the way. They found rich orchards and vineyards on the summit and as they looked around them they could catch, here and there, glimpses of the Mediterranean (off to the west) and looking back to the north, they could see the snowy summit of Mount Hermon. Over to the left as they climbed up the pass, they had seen the rugged volcanic mountains of Gilboa, at the foot of which was fought the great battle between Saul and the Philistines, and where Saul killed himself. To the northeastward was Endor, the place where the witch lived whom Saul consulted, the Lord having failed to direct him, "neither by dreams, nor by Urim, nor by prophets." (1 Samuel 28:6.)

As they went forward over the undulating pass, they crossed a part of the plain of Dothan, where Joseph was sold to the Ishmaelites. Finally, passing the summit, they descended by easy grades to the city of Samaria, located on an isolated hill 300 feet above the surrounding country. Samaria was the next capital of the northern tribes after Shechem. It had been frequently destroyed but now, as [they] came to it, it was a great city, rebuilt by Herod the Great, with magnificent palaces, temples, and a stadium. The plain surrounding the city was exceedingly fertile, covered with orchards of figs and olives. Its beauty and its future provoked Isaiah to speak of its "glorious beauty, which is on the head of the fat valley, shall be a fading flower, and as the hasty fruit before the summer." (Isa. 28:4.) But here in the years long gone, before this visit, there had been planted a grove of Astarte (Venus), and Jezebel had erected a great temple to that same heathen goddess. Elisha had lived at the foot of the hill on which the city rested; and to this house came Naaman, the Syrian leper, to be healed. . . .

As the pilgrims went forward they were joined by others also going to the Passover in Jerusalem. On through the day, as newcomers flowed into the group, they renewed, time and time again, the chant of the "Psalms of the Ascent." They lived over again in thought and story, how the Lord had blessed them and delivered them from Egyptian bondage. . . .

Whether they stopped at Samaria or went on two hours further to Shechem, we do not know. But they were traveling over historic ground that reached in incident clear back to Abraham. They may, because of the prejudice against the Samaritans, have so planned their journey as to pass through Samaria in one day. But we cannot tell.

The Cradle of Israel

As they journeyed into the midst of Shechem itself, they came to the very spot where the waters divided, those flowing to the west into the Great Sea, those to the east into the Jordan.

The city lies where the two mountains, Ebal and Gerizim, falling away one from the other, leave a beautiful, fertile valley— the very cradle of Israel. To this valley, running out west and east from the city, came Abraham and Lot, forsaking at the Lord's command their own country under a promise that this land should be theirs. Here lived Jacob and his family; Jacob whose name was here changed to Israel. Here Joshua gathered the people and had them repeat the curses and blessings declared by Moses in the wilderness. . . .

Journey of the Third Day

But whether the pilgrims stopped at Samaria or at Shechem, or whether before they reached there or after, yet as they went on towards Jerusalem along the Roman road, they passed constantly the places where other great happenings in Israel's history took place.

About halfway, going southward, between Shechem and Bethel lies Shiloh. It was here that Joshua came with the Tabernacle and Ark after he left Gilgal, and it was here that he cast lots for the division of the Promised Land among the tribes. . . .

As the group moved southward from Shiloh towards Bethel, there would likely join them, increasingly as they neared

Jerusalem (for under the Rabbinical law every male Jew over twelve years living within fifteen miles of Jerusalem was obliged to attend the Passover), other pilgrims to the temple and the great feast. And ever as they marched forward over the Roman highway, they would be chanting the sacred Psalms.

On the right, to the westward, shortly after the group left Shiloh, lay the old Ephraimite Gilgal, whence went Elijah and Elisha on their way to the Jordan before Elijah was taken into heaven. From a hill at the side of a wild pass a little farther south, they could look back and still see Mount Hermon with its cap of snow. As they went down the other side of the pass, they traveled through great orchards of fig trees and olives. This was the rich territory of Ephraim.

Sanctuary of Bethel

And then came Bethel, a great sanctuary.

Abraham came to Bethel from Shechem, and again after his return from Egypt. On his first visit he built an altar, to which he returned after Egypt. . . .

To the east and slightly to the south of Bethel was Ai, and still further south, Ramah and Gibeon. Between these two latter Joshua fought the great battle against the Amorites, when, the day waning, without time to finish his victory, that great warrior cried out, "in the sight of Israel, Sun, stand thou still upon Gibeon; and thou, Moon, in the valley of Ajalon. . . . So the sun stood still in the midst of heaven, and hasted not to go down about a whole day." (Josh. 10:6 ff.)

The growing group was also now near Michmash. . . .

Still nearer to Jerusalem was Gibeah, . . . the home and headquarters of Saul while he was king.

40

Arrival in Environs of Jerusalem

The pilgrims were now in the environs of Jerusalem. If they reached there just before the Passover, they found the roads choked with the tens of thousands who were coming to the city of David to attend the feast, bringing with them their burnt and peace offerings, for none might appear empty. In Jesus' time as many as 256,000 lambs were slain for the Passover. The population of the city at Passover time varied from 2,500,000 to 3,000,000. Many who came camped outside the city; others found quarters within the city walls with friends or relatives who hospitably took them in, the guests leaving, as they took their departure, "the skins of the Passover lambs and the vessels which they had used in their sacred services" (Alfred Edersheim, *The Temple* [Fleming H. Revell Co., New York, 1874], p. 184); still others went to neighboring towns, Bethphage and Bethany being mentioned in the Talmud as especially hospitable. The shouts of greeting that passed between old friends again meeting; the chanting of the sacred Psalms by the coming worshipers keyed to a high pitch by their long journey of anticipation, their outbursts of joy over their approaching presence in the city of the fathers and their nearness to the Passover, and their reverent expressions of gratitude for their ancient deliverance, mingled with the lowing of the cattle brought for burnt offerings, the bleating of the sacrificial lambs, the cooing of the doves brought for peace offerings—all must have merged into a babel of sound never to be forgotten, and, heard from afar, must have been like the roar of a distant waterfall.

. . . One cannot escape the question whether they went on to Bethany, eastward of Jerusalem, for their lodgings, to the home where in the years to come Jesus spent so many happy hours in a home that loved and honored him. . . .

Or did they, in reverent commemoration, go back to Bethlehem, where twelve years before the Messiah was born in a manger?

CHRISTMAS AMONG THE NEPHITES

THE TESTIMONIES OF SAMUEL AND NEPHI*

And now it came to pass in the eighty and sixth year, . . . there was one Samuel, a Lamanite, came into the land of Zarahemla, and began to preach unto the people. And it came to pass that he did preach, many days, repentance unto the people, and they did cast him out, and he was about to return to his own land. But behold, the voice of the Lord came unto him, that he should return again, and prophesy unto the people whatsoever things should come into his heart.

And it came to pass that they would not suffer that he should enter into the city; therefore he went and got upon the wall thereof, and stretched forth his hand and cried with a loud voice, and prophesied unto the people whatsoever things the Lord put into his heart.

And he said unto them: Behold, I, Samuel, a Lamanite, do speak the words of the Lord which he doth put into my heart; and

*Helaman 13:1–7; 14:1–8, 13; 16:13–14; 3 Nephi 1:4–26.

behold he hath put it into my heart to say unto this people that the sword of justice hangeth over this people; . . . Yea, heavy destruction awaiteth this people, and it surely cometh unto this people, and nothing can save this people save it be repentance and faith on the Lord Jesus Christ, who surely shall come into the world, and shall suffer many things and shall be slain for his people.

And behold, an angel of the Lord hath declared it unto me, and he did bring glad tidings to my soul. And behold, I was sent unto you to declare it unto you also, that ye might have glad tidings; but behold ye would not receive me. . . .

And now it came to pass that Samuel, the Lamanite, did prophesy a great many more things which cannot be written.

And behold, he said unto them: Behold, I give unto you a sign; for five years more cometh, and behold, then cometh the Son of God to redeem all those who shall believe on his name. And behold, this will I give unto you for a sign at the time of his coming; for behold, there shall be great lights in heaven, insomuch that in the night before he cometh there shall be no darkness, insomuch that it shall appear unto man as if it was day. Therefore, there shall be one day and a night and a day, as if it were one day and there were no night; and this shall be unto you for a sign; for ye shall know of the rising of the sun and also of its setting; therefore they shall know of a surety that there shall be two days and a night; nevertheless the night shall not be darkened; and it shall be the night before he is born.

And behold, there shall a new star arise, such an one as ye never have beheld; and this also shall be a sign unto you. And behold this is not all, there shall be many signs and wonders in heaven. And it shall come to pass that ye shall all be amazed, and wonder, insomuch that ye shall fall to the earth.

And it shall come to pass that whosoever shall believe on the

Son of God, the same shall have everlasting life. . . . And if ye believe on his name ye will repent of all your sins, that thereby ye may have a remission of them through his merits. . . .

[And] it came to pass in the ninetieth year of the reign of the judges, there were great signs given unto the people, and wonders; and the words of the prophets began to be fulfilled. And angels did appear unto men, wise men, and did declare unto them glad tidings of great joy; thus in this year the scriptures began to be fulfilled. . . .

And it came to pass that in the commencement of the ninety and second year, behold, the prophecies of the prophets began to be fulfilled more fully; for there began to be greater signs and greater miracles wrought among the people.

But there were some who began to say that the time was past for the words to be fulfilled, which were spoken by Samuel, the Lamanite. And they began to rejoice over their brethren, saying: Behold the time is past, and the words of Samuel are not fulfilled; therefore, your joy and your faith concerning this thing hath been vain.

And it came to pass that they did make a great uproar throughout the land; and the people who believed began to be very sorrowful, lest by any means those things which had been spoken might not come to pass. But behold, they did watch steadfastly for that day and that night and that day which should be as one day as if there were no night, that they might know that their faith had not been vain.

Now it came to pass that there was a day set apart by the unbelievers, that all those who believed in those traditions should be put to death except the sign should come to pass, which had been given by Samuel the prophet.

Now it came to pass that when Nephi, the son of Nephi, saw this wickedness of his people, his heart was exceedingly sorrowful.

And it came to pass that he went out and bowed himself down upon the earth, and cried mightily to his God in behalf of his people, yea, those who were about to be destroyed because of their faith in the tradition of their fathers. And it came to pass that he cried mightily unto the Lord all that day; and behold, the voice of the Lord came unto him, saying:

Lift up your head and be of good cheer; for behold, the time is at hand, and on this night shall the sign be given, and on the morrow come I into the world, to show unto the world that I will fulfil all that which I have caused to be spoken by the mouth of my holy prophets. Behold, I come unto my own, to fulfil all things which I have made known unto the children of men from the foundation of the world, and to do the will, both of the Father and of the Son—of the Father because of me, and of the Son because of my flesh. And behold, the time is at hand, and this night shall the sign be given.

And it came to pass that the words which came unto Nephi were fulfilled, according as they had been spoken; for behold, at the going down of the sun there was no darkness; and the people began to be astonished because there was no darkness when the night came. And there were many, who had not believed the words of the prophets, who fell to the earth and became as if they were dead, for they knew that the great plan of destruction which they had laid for those who believed in the words of the prophets had been frustrated; for the sign which had been given was already at hand.

And they began to know that the Son of God must shortly appear; yea, in fine, all the people upon the face of the whole earth from the west to the east, both in the land north and in the land south, were so exceedingly astonished that they fell to the earth. For they knew that the prophets had testified of these things for many years, and that the sign which had been given was already at hand; and they began to fear because of their iniquity and their unbelief.

And it came to pass that there was no darkness in all that night, but it was as light as though it was mid-day. And it came to pass that the sun did rise in the morning again, according to its proper order; and they knew that it was the day that the Lord should be born, because of the sign which had been given.

And it had come to pass, yea, all things, every whit, according to the words of the prophets.

And it came to pass also that a new star did appear, according to the word.

And it came to pass that from this time forth there began to be lyings sent forth among the people, by Satan, to harden their hearts, to the intent that they might not believe in those signs and wonders which they had seen; but notwithstanding these lyings and deceivings the more part of the people did believe, and were converted unto the Lord.

And it came to pass that Nephi went forth among the people, and also many others, baptizing unto repentance, in the which there was a great remission of sins. And thus the people began again to have peace in the land. And there were no contentions, save it were a few that began to preach, endeavoring to prove by the scriptures that it was no more expedient to observe the law of Moses. Now in this thing they did err, having not understood the scriptures. But it came to pass that they soon became converted, and were convinced of the error which they were in, for it was made known unto them that the law was not yet fulfilled, and that it must be fulfilled in every whit; yea, the word came unto them that it must be fulfilled; yea, that one jot or tittle should not pass away till it should all be fulfilled; therefore in this same year were they brought to a knowledge of their error and did confess their faults.

And thus the ninety and second year did pass away, bringing glad tidings unto the people because of the signs which did come to pass, according to the words of the prophecy of all the holy prophets.

TRUE STORIES OF CHRISTMAS PAST

ARE YOU READY FOR CHRISTMAS?

HAROLD B. LEE

T he years have been full and plentiful since I was called as president of the old Pioneer Stake nearly forty years ago. It was a large stake by today's standards, a stake of nearly 7,500 members living in eleven wards. It was in the southwest part of Salt Lake City; the people there were feeling the economic depression, and times were hard.

One Christmas (I believe it was the first one during my presidency), our small daughters quickly opened their Christmas morning gifts and soon dashed over to show their little friends the new dolls and other gifts. Shortly they returned home, both in tears.

"What in the world is the matter?" we asked.

Sobbing, they said: "Our friends did not have any Christmas. Santa Claus did not come to their home."

All too late we remembered that just across the street was a family whose father was not a member of the Church, although the children were, and the mother passively so; he had been out of work, and we had forgotten. Our Christmas was spoiled.

We sent for those children and tried to divide what we had in an attempt to make up for our lack of thoughtfulness, but it was too late. Christmas dinner that day did not taste very good to me. I was unhappy. I realized that upon my shoulders rested the welfare of the people of the stake.

We made a survey and were startled to discover that 4,800 of our membership were either wholly or partially dependent—the heads of families did not have steady employment.

There were no government make-work projects in those days. We had only ourselves to look to. Church finances were declining. We were told that we couldn't expect much help from the general funds of the Church. Thus, it was in this same condition that we approached another Christmas season.

We knew that we had about one thousand children under ten years of age for whom, without someone to help them, there would be no Christmas.

We started to prepare. We found a second floor over an old store on Pierpont Street. We gathered toys, some of which were broken, and for a month or two before Christmas, fathers and mothers were there. Some arrived early or stayed late to make something special for their own little ones.

That was the spirit of Christmas giving—one only had to step inside the door of that workshop to see and feel it. Our goal was to see that none of the children would be without a Christmas.

There was to be Christmas dinner in all the homes of the 4,800 who, without help, wouldn't have Christmas dinner. Nuts, candy, oranges, a roast, and all that went with it would be their Christmas menu.

It so happened that I was then one of the city commissioners. On the day before Christmas that year we had had a heavy snowstorm, and I had been out all night with the crews getting the streets cleared, knowing that I would be blamed if any of my men fell down on the job. I had then gone home to change my clothes to go to the office.

As I started back to town, I saw a little boy on the roadside, hitchhiking. He stood in the biting cold, with no coat, no gloves, no overshoes. I stopped, and he climbed into the car beside me.

"Son," I asked, "are you ready for Christmas?"

"Oh, golly, mister, we aren't going to have any Christmas at our home. Daddy died three months ago and left Mamma and me and a little brother and sister."

Three children, each under ten!

"Where are you going, son?"

"I am going up to a free picture show."

I turned up the heat in my car and said, "Now, give me your name and address."

Further conversation revealed that they were not members of the Church.

"Somebody will come to your home; you won't be forgotten. Now, you have a good time today—it's Christmas Eve."

That night I asked each bishop to go with his delivery men and see that each family was cared for, and to report back to me.

While waiting for the last bishop to report, I painfully remembered something. In my haste to see that all my duties at work and my responsibilities in the Church were taken care of, I had forgotten the boy in my car and the promise that I had made.

When the last bishop reported, I asked, "Bishop, have you enough left to visit one more family?"

"Yes, we have," he replied.

I told him the story and gave him the address.

A little later he called to say that that family too had received some well-filled baskets. Christmas Eve was over at last, and I went to bed.

As I awoke that Christmas morning, I said in my heart, "God grant that I will never let another year pass, but that I, as a leader, will truly know my people. I will know their needs. I will be conscious of the ones who need my leadership most."

My carelessness had meant suffering the first year because I did not know my people. But now I had resolved never again to overlook the needs of those around me.

CHRISTMAS CAME LATE

ALICE MORGAN HANSEN

Christmas was near and my father, F. W. Morgan, was to leave on the morrow, Dec. 22nd, [from Teton Valley, Wyoming] for Market Lake, a distance of sixty miles, to bring back the sixty gallon barrel containing all our Christmas treasures. The barrel never failed to come in the four Christmases we had lived in the Basin.

Grandfather worked in the ZCMI in Salt Lake City and each year he and grandmother packed the barrel with apples, oranges, candy, nuts, raisins, currants, peel, toys for each of the children, and often clothing, and sent it to Market Lake where father went by team to get it. With money as scarce as it was and the stores as poorly stocked for Christmas as they were, the barrel was a veritable treasure chest.

The first two days father was gone passed rather slowly, but the third day actually dragged. From our low west window of our two-roomed log cabin, we could watch the winding road as it came up over the hill. Here, we spent most of the day with our noses pressed flat against the window-pane, watching for some sight of the sleigh.

As evening came, no sign of father, and mother became really worried. However, she put on a brave front, never letting us know how she felt.

Finally, unable to stay awake any longer, we hung up our stockings and went to bed. Mother made a few cookies with raisin faces and hung them on the tree. She covered walnut shells with a few bits of tinsel she found. She cut raisin boxes in half and covered them with bits of crepe paper and wall paper and hung them on the tree. In each stocking she put a cookie or two and some covered walnut shells. Towards morning, she went to bed but not to sleep.

In the meantime, father had reached Market Lake in good time and had gone directly to the depot for the barrel, but he was told nothing had come for him. He decided it would surely come the next day, but the train came, bringing no barrel. The following day being Christmas, father spent hours walking the floor and thinking of mother at home with five sadly disappointed little youngsters. The day after Christmas failed to bring the barrel, so he went over to the little branch store and there was the barrel. He learned that it had been in for four days. It had been sent to F. W. Morgan, in care of the ZCMI branch store. Needless to say, he was not long in getting started for home.

Santa made up to us children on New Year's morning what he had failed to do on Christmas, and while we will never forget that Christmas, it was much more indelibly stamped on the minds of our parents.

HONESTY'S REWARD

THOMAS J. GRIFFITHS

The year was 1916 and I was eight years old. While it happened long ago, it is still the Christmas I remember best.

Our family lived in a little village in Wales that went by the quaint name of Old Furnace. Our family consisted of Mam and Dad and eight children. The youngest was Ivor John, who was born two months early and was still a sickly child.

November that year was colder than usual. There was rain and snow with a cruel north wind that cut like a knife. One day while walking home from his work at the colliery, Dad found a woman's purse just outside the big iron gate of the Tredegar estate. He opened it and found that it belonged to Lady Tredegar. Beside her identification there was a roll of paper money that was more than Dad had ever seen at one time.

He took the money in his hand and thought of all the things it would buy, especially with Christmas approaching.

But he had been trained to be honest, so he returned the money to the purse and swung open the big iron gate. Lady Tredegar received him quite casually and after counting the money, and finding it all there, inquired of his name and where he lived.

"You are an honest man and it shall not be forgotten," she said, and then motioned to the butler to show him out.

As Dad continued homeward, he fumed that Lady Tredegar

56

had not given him a small reward. He was still angry when he entered our cottage and told mother of the incident.

In her Welsh dialect, she spoke to my father: "Indeed now, it's an honest man you are, and God will not forget."

As November came to a close, the bitter cold took its toll and Dad was stricken with pneumonia. In those days there were no antibiotics or other medication to fight this disease and one could only wait for the change that would decide life or death. For a while, it looked as if he would not live to see Christmas, but one night the change came.

We heard him call for Mam and we children crowded around his bed. The change had come. He was in a deep sweat and the fever was leaving. He would live to see Christmas.

Those were the days, too, when there was no such thing as sick pay or unemployment insurance, so before very long the family was in dire straits. Dad was still weak and it would be some time before he could return to work.

A few days before Christmas, Mam called the family together in the living room and explained that because of Dad's illness, there was no money for Christmas gifts, except for one. "Dad is still with us," she added.

Christmas Eve came and as we sat by the fireside we could hear the voices of the carolers in the distance, and over the cold frosty air came the chimes of the bells of Trevethin Church.

Dad was sitting in his big leather chair, his feet by the fire with Mam's shawl over his lap. He looked around at his family and with a voice touched by emotion, he said: "We have no gifts to give this year, but God has given us voices so let us sing of Bethlehem and the birth of Jesus."

So, as a family, we blended our voices and sang the songs of Christmas. As we were singing, there was the sound of horses' hooves on the road outside. They stopped in front of our house.

Then came a knock at the door. Mam answered and there, with a huge basket in his arms, was Lady Tredegar's butler. He put the basket on the kitchen table and returned to the waiting carriage. He came back with a second basket as full as the first.

As he turned to leave he said to Mam, "Lady Tredegar wishes an honest man a Merry Christmas."

Eagerly, the baskets were opened and an array of gifts was uncovered. There was a warm jacket for Dad and gloves in the pocket, a blue dress for Mam and gifts for the children. In the second basket was a huge goose surrounded by fruits from many lands.

This was the best Christmas I remember best and one that will never be forgotten.

HOW THE PIONEERS CELEBRATED CHRISTMAS

E. CECIL McGAVIN

Christmas always had a strong appeal to the pioneers and was observed by them no matter what their conditions were.

During the autumn of 1847, the harvest was so meager in Salt Lake Valley that no special Thanksgiving service was held, yet the pioneers did not fail to remember Christmas. Though food supplies were scarce, and their reasons for merriment were limited, Lorenzo D. Young wrote of that first Christmas the Pioneers spent in the Salt Lake Valley:

"I gave a Christmas dinner. Father John Smith, Brother John Young, Brother Pierce, and their wives, and also Brother Jedediah M. Grant, Sister Snow and Harriet and Martha took dinner with us. After dinner Father Smith blessed our little Lorenzo. The occasion was a most pleasant one and the day was spent in social chat, singing, etc. A prayer was offered up by Brother Grant. Brother Brigham and his quorum were remembered in particular. My house was dedicated to the Lord."

During the Christmastide in 1847, it was written in the *Journal History* concerning the Church members in Iowa:

"Friday, December 24. President Young and party proceeded to Miller's Hollow [now Council Bluffs, Iowa] where the brethren had built a log house, forty by sixty feet, capable of seating about one thousand persons. The house was dedicated by Elder Orson Pratt as a house of prayer and thanksgiving. The congregation was addressed by Elders Wilford Woodruff and Orson Pratt, and in the afternoon by Elders Amasa M. Lyman, Geo. A. Smith, and President Young. Elder Wm. I. Appleby preached during the evening service.

"Saturday, December 25. The Council went to the Log Tabernacle in Miller's Hollow, Iowa, and attended conference meeting. The congregation voted that the High Council on the east side of the Missouri River should have all municipal power given to them by the people, and that the Bishop's courts should have authority as civil magistrates among the people, until the laws of Iowa were extended over the Saints.

"December 26. Elder Orson Pratt met with the Saints in St. Louis, Mo., when they donated $705.84 to assist the Presidency of the Church to remove to Great Salt Lake Valley."

On Christmas Day, 1849, a gay party was held in President Brigham Young's home. One hundred and fifty persons had been invited for the occasion. "The tables were twice filled by the company," we read, "and all were feasted with the good things of the valley. When the tables were removed, dancing commenced, which was continued with energy and without interruption, except for supper, till a late hour."

At the same time in Kanesville, Iowa, a similar social was held. "In the evening we had a little sociable dance," we read, "the party being composed mostly of Philadelphians."

On December 25, 1851, Captain Pitt's band, consisting of twenty-six members, promenaded the streets of Salt Lake City "and played before the houses of the First Presidency, the Twelve Apostles and others, while riding on horseback."

The *Journal History* contains a complete and interesting account of the celebration at Christmastime in 1851, from which we quote:

"Christmas Day. Fine weather prevailed in Great Salt Lake City. All the hands engaged on the public works attended a picnic party in the Carpenters' Shop on the Temple Block which was cleared and decorated for the occasion. Several hundred persons attended and enjoyed themselves in both dance and song. President Brigham Young was also present. The enjoyments were varied with songs and addresses. The brethren of the band serenaded the inhabitants of the City from midnight till daylight which was quite a treat."

Elder George D. Watt gives the following account of these Christmas festivities:

"Early on Christmas morning, Thursday, December 25, several companies of serenaders, with brass instruments made the sleeping mountains echo with the sound of rejoicing. Our attention was drawn more particularly to the Governor's mansion, in the front of which was drawn up in military order a troop of horsemen. This was the brass band, giving his Excellency a good wish in sweet strains.

"At ten o'clock a.m., the committee of management was in respectful waiting to receive those who were invited to the party. The carpenters' hall, one hundred feet long and thirty-two feet wide, is admirably adapted for a mammoth party, which was comfortable, and suitably decorated for the occasion. Now the merry workmen, with their happy wives, and smiling daughters, clad in genteel apparel, came pouring in from every quarter, loaded with an abundance of luxuries of every description which were deposited in an adjoining hall, called the machine room, which is forty feet square, in which also was situated the ladies' dressing room.

"At 11 o'clock the house was called to order, and a suitable prayer and thanksgiving was offered up to the Donor of all good by Bishop N. H. Felt. The band then struck up a merry tune, and his Excellency, Governor Young, and Hon. H. C. Kimball, and other distinguished personages led off the first dance.

"The excellent order, the quick succession of dances do great honor to the managers. We counted from ninety-six persons to one hundred forty-four persons upon the floor at once. These were set in order to the same time that we have seen four cotillions in other parties. There was no confusion, no dissatisfied looks, no complaining, but the day passed in peace and happy merriment, with thanksgiving to the Father of all our mercies. . . .

"The atmosphere of our hall was not polluted with tobacco fumes, or the stench of the drunkard's breath. No! We breathed the pure mountain air, drank of the mountain stream, and ate of the produce of the mountains' valleys, we thought on the gloomy past, and the glorious present, and perspective future, every heart beat high with gratitude and gladness, and every countenance was lit up with the bright fire of enduring friendship.

"About seven p.m. a few songs were sung by sundry individuals; one in particular called up feelings not strange to us was sung by Phinehas H. Young, entitled 'Farewell to Nauvoo.' This song gave the company ample opportunity of comparing the present with the past.

"Governor Young arose to address the meeting, and congratulated the assembly on their present situation and blessings as a people."

On Friday evening, December 26, the "public hands" again met in the Carpenters' Shop where "dancing was kept up with great spirit until midnight when all separated highly delighted with their Christmas festivities. In the course of the evening Willard Richards spoke of the difference between this evening and the 27th of June, 1844, when the tragedy at Carthage, Illinois, took place."

Elder George D. Watt gives the following account of this festival:

"The seats in the Carpenters' Hall were filled by the not to be surpassed fair daughters of Zion, and the brave hearted sons of God.

"The company was called to order, and prayer was offered up by A. H. Raleigh. The dancing was conducted as on the previous day, and the same good order, joy and hilarity was manifested.

"After the Hall was illuminated, the company was treated to a feast in the shape of vocal and instrumental music by Mr. John Kay, his lady and two daughters, the one performed well on the Guitar, and the other on the Tambourine, at the same time accompanying their instruments with their voices, this with the sweet voice of Mrs. Kay, and the deep bass of Mr. Kay produced a species of harmony highly delightful to the ear. The performance was much applauded.

Brother Kay sang the Seer, in his usual pathos and sweetness, which drew from President Richards, a few touching remarks. Elder George A. Smith also addressed the meeting for a short time, after which the dance was resumed, and continued until 10 o'clock p.m. A vote of thanks was moved for the managers, which was responded to by 500 voices. After the benediction from Father Cahoon, the assembly retired, much gratified with their Christmas festival, which was the best they had ever witnessed."

In some of the communities of the Saints there were not enough food supplies to furnish the tables. Despite this shortage there was always a determined effort to celebrate Christmas in a suitable manner and make it the outstanding festival of the year. Such a spirit was manifest by the first settlers in Rockport Ward in Summit Stake.

The few families who moved to that region had taken but few cattle with them that season. At Christmastime they prepared a cooperative or community dinner. In the Church record we read that "the men jointly purchased a piece of beef for which they agreed to pay in grain after the following harvest."

Thus was the spirit of Christmas kept alive by the pioneers, no matter how limited their resources were.

MY FIRST CHRISTMAS TREE

HAMLIN GARLAND

I will begin by saying that we never had a Christmas tree in our house in the Wisconsin coulée; indeed, my father never saw one in a family circle till he saw that which I set up for my own children last year. But we celebrated Christmas in those days, always, and I cannot remember a time when we did not all hang up our stockings for "Sandy Claws" to fill. As I look back upon those days it seems as if the snows were always deep, the night skies crystal clear, and the stars especially lustrous with frosty sparkles of blue and yellow fire—and probably this was so, for we lived in a Northern land where winter was usually stern and always long.

I recall one Christmas when "Sandy" brought me a sled, and a horse that stood on rollers—a wonderful tin horse which I very shortly split in two in order to see what his insides were. Father traded a cord of wood for the sled, and the horse cost twenty cents—but they made the day wonderful.

Another notable Christmas Day, as I stood in our front yard, mid-leg deep in snow, a neighbor drove by closely muffled in furs, while behind his seat his son, a lad of twelve or fifteen, stood beside a barrel of apples, and as he passed he hurled a glorious big red one at me. It missed me, but bored a deep, round hole in the soft snow. I thrill yet with the remembered joy of burrowing for that delicious bomb. Nothing will ever smell quite as good as that Wine Sap or Northern Spy or whatever it was. It was a way-ward impulse on the part of the boy in the sleigh, but it warms my heart after more than forty years.

We had no chimney in our home, but stocking-hanging was a ceremony nevertheless. My parents, and especially my mother, entered into it with the best of humor. They always put up their own stockings or permitted us to do it for them—and they always laughed next morning when they found potatoes or ears of corn in them. I can see now that my mother's laugh had a tear in it, for she loved pretty things and seldom got any during the years that we lived in the coulée.

When I was ten years old we moved to Mitchell County, an Iowa prairie land, and there we prospered in such wise that our stockings always held toys of some sort, and even my mother's stocking occasionally sagged with a simple piece of jewelry or a new comb or brush. But the thought of a family tree remained the luxury of millionaire city dwellers; indeed it was not till my fifteenth or sixteenth year that our Sunday school rose to the extravagance of a tree, and it is of this wondrous festival that I write.

The land about us was only partly cultivated at this time, and our district schoolhouse, a bare little box, was set bleakly on the prairie; but the Burr Oak schoolhouse was not only larger but it stood beneath great oaks as well and possessed the charm of a forest background through which a stream ran silently. It was our chief social center. There of a Sunday a regular preacher held "Divine service" with Sunday school as a sequence. At night— usually on Friday nights—the young people let in "ly-ceums," as we called them, to debate great questions or to "speak pieces" and read essays; and here it was that I saw my first Christmas tree.

I walked to that tree across four miles of moonlit snow. Snow? No, it was a floor of diamonds, a magical world, so beautiful that my heart still aches with the wonder of it and with the regret that it has all gone—gone with the keen eyes and the bounding pulses of the boy.

Our home at this time was a small frame house on the prairie almost directly west of the Burr Oak grove, and as it was too cold to take the horses out my brother and I, with our tall boots, our visored caps and our long woolen mufflers, started forth afoot defiant of the cold. We left the gate on the trot, bound for a sight of the glittering unknown. The snow was deep and we moved side by side in the grooves made by the hoofs of the horses, setting our feet in the shine left by the broad shoes of the wood sleighs whose going had smoothed the way for us.

Our breaths rose like smoke in the still air. It must have been ten below zero, but that did not trouble us in those days, and at last we came in sight of the lights, in sound of the singing, the laughter, the bells of the feast.

It was a poor little building without tower or bell and its low walls had but three windows on a side, and yet it seemed very imposing to me that night as I crossed the threshold and faced the strange people who packed it to the door. I say "strange people," for though I had seen most of them many times they all seemed somehow alien to me that night. I was an irregular attendant at Sunday school and did not expect a present, therefore I stood against the wall and gazed with open-eyed marveling at the shining pine which stood where the pulpit was wont to be. I was made to feel the more embarrassed by reason of the remark of a boy who accused me of having forgotten to comb my hair.

This was not true, but the cap I wore always matted my hair down over my brow, and then, when I lifted it off invariably disarranged it completely. Nevertheless I felt guilty—and hot. I don't suppose my hair was artistically barbered that night—I rather guess Mother had used the shears—and I can believe that I looked the half-wild colt that I was; but there was no call for that youth to direct attention to my unavoidable shagginess.

I don't think the tree had many candles, and I don't remember that it glittered with golden apples. But it was loaded with presents, and the girls coming and going clothed in bright garments made me forget my own looks—I think they made me forget to remove my overcoat, which was a sodden thing of poor cut and worse quality. I think I must have stood agape for nearly two hours listening to the songs, noting every motion of Adoniram Burtch and Asa Walker as they directed the ceremonies and prepared the way for the great event—that is to say, for the coming of Santa Claus himself.

A furious jingling of bells, a loud voice outside, the lifting of a window, the nearer clash of bells, and the dear old Saint appeared (in the person of Stephen Bartle) clothed in a red robe, a belt of sleigh bells, and a long white beard. The children cried out, "Oh!" The girls tittered and shrieked with excitement, and the boys laughed and clapped their hands. Then "Sandy" made a little speech about being glad to see us all, but as he had many other places to visit, and as there were a great many presents to distribute, he guessed he'd have to ask some of the many pretty girls to help him. So he called upon Betty Burtch and Hattie Knapp—and I for one admired his taste, for they were the most popular maids of the school.

They came up blushing, and a little bewildered by the blaze of publicity thus blown upon them. But their native dignity asserted itself, and the distribution of the presents began. I have a notion now that the fruit upon the tree was mostly bags of popcorn and "corny copias" of candy, but as my brother and I stood there that night and saw everybody, even the rowdiest boy, getting something, we felt aggrieved and rebellious. We forgot that we had come from afar—we only knew that we were being left out.

But suddenly, in the midst of our gloom, my brother's name was called, and a lovely girl with a gentle smile handed him a bag of popcorn. My heart glowed with gratitude. Somebody had thought of us; and when she came to me, saying sweetly, "Here's something for you," I had not words to thank her. This happened nearly forty years ago, but her smile, her outstretched hand, her sympathetic eyes are vividly before me as I write. She was sorry for the shock-headed boy who stood against the wall, and her pity made the little box of candy a casket of pearls. The fact that I swallowed the jewels on the road home does not take from the reality of my adoration.

At last I had to take my final glimpse of that wondrous tree, and I well remember the walk home. My brother and I traveled in wordless companionship. The moon was sinking toward the west, and the snow crust gleamed with a million fairy lamps. The sentinel watchdogs barked from lonely farmhouses, and the wolves answered from the ridges. Now and then sleighs passed us with lovers sitting two and two, and the bells on their horses had the remote music of romance to us whose boots drummed like clogs of wood upon the icy road.

Our house was dark as we approached and entered it, but how deliciously warm it seemed after the pitiless wind! I confess we made straight for the cupboard for a mince pie, a doughnut and a bowl of milk!

As I write this there stands in my library a thick-branched, beautifully tapering fir tree covered with the gold and purple apples of Hesperides, together with crystal ice points, green and red and yellow candles, clusters of gilded grapes, wreaths of metallic frost, and glittering angels swinging in ecstasy; but I doubt if my children will ever know the keen pleasure (that is almost pain) which came to my brother and to me in those Christmas days when an orange was not a breakfast fruit, but a casket of incense and of spice, a message from the sunlands of the South.

That was our compensation—we brought to our Christmastime a keen appetite and empty hands. And the lesson of it all is, if we are seeking a lesson, that it is better to give to those who want than to those for whom "we ought to do something because they did something for us last year."

ONE MORE CAR

J. K. "TRAPPER" HATCH,
AS TOLD TO JO ANN HATCH

I grew up during the Great Depression in the little town of Taylor, Arizona. In those days there were no jobs around Taylor, so when I was seventeen years old, a couple of friends and I decided we would hitchhike the 250 miles to Phoenix to find some kind of work.

It was the first week in December of 1933, and we rode part of the way in the back of a cattle truck. We had to get down between the cows to keep warm.

When we arrived in Phoenix, we found out that there was no work to be had. Many men were standing in lines waiting for the free soup the government was giving out to those in need. You could buy hotcakes for ten cents, but we didn't have a dime; so after a while we joined the soup line.

We looked for work and somehow survived for two weeks; then Christmas drew near. One of my friends had a sister who lived not too far away, and he and my other friend decided to go to her house for Christmas. But I was determined to go home.

Early the next morning, the day before Christmas, I started hitchhiking.

I didn't get to Flagstaff until 5:00 in the afternoon. That was halfway home. The sky was steel gray and it was bitterly cold, with eight inches of snow on the ground. There were holes in both of my shoes, so I found some cardboard and cut pieces to fit inside to keep my feet a little drier. Then I started down the highway again, trying to get another ride.

Since it was Christmas Eve, there wasn't much traffic. It grew darker and colder, and I became more and more dejected as the few cars swished by in the snow and the chill of the night penetrated my thin coat.

By 10:00 I had become so cold and numb that I began to wonder what it would be like to freeze to death. I was so tired that I knew I'd never make it unless someone stopped soon. Several more cars passed me by, and I had to talk to myself to keep going. "One more car," I said. "If the next car doesn't stop, I'll lie down under a tree and let it happen. One more car."

In a short while I could hear an engine in the distance. "This is it," I told myself, taking a deep breath as I held out my thumb. Swish. The car went by me. I closed my eyes and sank to my knees in total despair.

In my misery, everything was shut out of my mind for several seconds; but then I heard a sound. The car had stopped and was backing up! I struggled to my feet, heart pounding. In the car were two men from my hometown of Taylor. They had recognized me as they passed.

At about 1:00 A.M. I was safely deposited at the front door of my home. I could see there was still a light on, and as I came quietly through the door, there sat Dad and Mom with their heads in their hands, praying. When I spoke I was greeted with joyful cries and tears. Mom told me they had been praying all evening and into the night for my well-being and safe return home.

There were no presents that Christmas. Dad killed an old rooster next morning, and that was our Christmas dinner. Yet I have never felt the spirit of Christmas more strongly than I did that day as I sat with Dad, Mom, and my brothers and sisters and felt the warmth and love of our family.

OUR GIVING CHRISTMASES

EMILY SMITH STEWART *

We believe in Christmas. To us, the George Albert Smith family, Christmas is one of the most blessed and precious days the years brings. We are striving to make each Christmas as loving and living as our parents made them for us. . . .

Preparations for Christmas at our home have always been very special. Our plans were extensive and carefully laid, the money budgeted, the gifts painstakingly chosen. Father and mother always insisted that whatever means we had to use for Christmas must be spread over a wide territory, for they planned that we should learn for ourselves that it's always "more blessed to give

*Emily Smith Stewart, born in 1895, was the second daughter of President George Albert Smith.

than to receive." We began with the wonderful box that mother always prepared for the Relief Society, and into which she put all of the goodies that we planned for ourselves, including mince pies and plum puddings with a wonderful buttery sauce. We assembled the contents of this Relief Society Christmas box for days. After everything was ready, it was loaded on the sled and dragged on top of the crisp, icy snow to the Relief Society room at the 17th Ward. Thus began our custom, one that has always been father's, of providing Christmas for those persons that others forgot. He has always considered the fact that where people were well remembered, they might do without his remembering them in a substantial way, other than to extend his sincere good wishes, while gifts and fancy holiday foods should be taken to those too frequently overlooked.

Christmas eve at our house began family festivities. We hung our stockings in front of the fireplace in the dining room. Father always hung a great, huge stocking, because he assured us that Santa never could get all the things he wanted in just a regular sock. And then, to add to the gaiety of the occasion, each year he brought his tall rubber boots up from the basement and stood one at either side of the fireplace in the dining room.

After stockings were hung, we spread a table for Santa Claus' supper . . . a bowl of rich milk and bread and a generous wedge of mince pie. We wrote a note to encourage him on his way and went to bed, but it seemed morning would never come. The length of Christmas eve night and the shortness of Christmas day was something we could never understand.

No matter how excited we children were, we never were permitted to go downstairs until we were washed, combed and fully dressed. Then we had morning prayers and sat down to breakfast, the worst breakfast of the year because it took so much time and seemed to hinder our getting to our stockings. Always there was something very unusual and very special down in the toe. First, we laughed and laughed over the things Santa Claus put in father's boots—coal and kindling and vegetables; and then we were offended because we thought Santa was not very kind to our father, who is always generous with everyone else. After this first experience with bootsful of jokes on Christmas, we bought something very special for father the next year to make up for the slight Santa Claus had made.

After we had enjoyed our toys and gifts in the stockings, the folding doors into the parlor were pushed aside and we beheld our twinkling candlelighted Christmas tree. Under the colorful, green tree were the packages for friends and the rest of the family. These were distributed and all had a very happy, festive time.

After our own mirth and merriment had partially subsided, father always took us with him to make the rounds of the forgotten friends that he habitually visited on Christmas. I was a very little girl when I went with father to see how the other half of the people lived. I remember going down a long alley in the middle of a city block where there were some very poor houses. We opened the door of one tiny home and there on the bed lay an old woman, very sad and alone. As we came in, tears ran down her cheeks, and she reached over to take hold of father's hand as we gave her our little remembrances. "I am grateful to you for coming," she said, "because if you hadn't come I would have had no Christmas at all. No one else has remembered me." We thoroughly enjoyed this part of our day.

Christmas dinner was another high spot in our Christmas celebration. We always had very wonderful Christmas dinners, usually turkey dinners served on our beautiful blue-lace plates.

One Christmas that I shall never forget is the one when father was very seriously ill. Expenses had been extremely high and it seemed that we were not going to be able to afford much of a

Christmas. Mother longed to provide our usual happy Christmas, but she knew she could not do so and still pay the tithing due before the end of the year, and which had accumulated as a result of father's illness. She felt that her children were entitled, as are all children, to a happy Christmas. If she bought the usual gifts and dinner for them, however, she couldn't possibly pay her tithing. If she paid her full tithing her children could have no Christmas. It was a difficult decision, but she finally decided that she must pay her tithing before she gave it further thought, as the desire of doing something for her children might tempt her too greatly. Hurriedly, she put on her wraps and went to the Bishop, where she paid her tithing in full.

On her way home her heart was very heavy. She was convinced that her children could have nothing for Christmas, and she dreaded our disappointment. She was walking through the snow, head down, when Mark Austin, her good neighbor, said, "Just a moment, Sister Smith. I have been thinking that your expenses have been exceedingly heavy during Brother Smith's long illness, so I should like very much to have you take this little gift and buy yourself something very special for Christmas. I am sure you haven't had anything for yourself in a long, long time." Mother, choking with tears, tried to thank him. She took the check, folded it, and went home, her heart fairly pounding with joy and thanks-giving. When she entered the house and turned the light on, she found he had given her one hundred dollars, the exact amount that she had paid in tithing.

When that Christmas morning arrived, mother said, "This is really your Tithing Christmas, children," and she told us the story as the day progressed. Bit by bit the blessing of tithing was thus deeply impressed upon us.

Since that Tithing Christmas, we have spent Christmases in many different lands. Some have been spent in England, some in the United States and in many states within the United States. We have had plentiful Christmases and meager Christmases, happy Christmases and Christmases that have not been so joyous. Irrespective of what our personal sorrows may have been, father has always seen to it that those who needed Christmas, who were not of our particular family, were not forgotten. All of our holiday celebrations at Christmas time have been motivated by the thought impressed upon us in early childhood . . . "It is more blessed to give than to receive." In fact, not only Christmas, but every day of our father's life has stressed this philosophy, the practicing of which has made a lifelong impression upon our minds. We believe in Christmas!

THE WIDOW'S MIGHT

ELAINE S. McKAY

Bessie watched the wind hurl snow as it howled through Huntsville. It's a cold Christmas Eve, she thought . . . colder than those of the Depression . . . colder now that her husband was dead.

Before the fire had flickered out, Bessie had heated the iron and made her way up the winding stairs of the stone home to iron the sheets before her eight children climbed into their beds. "Warmmm," purred the baby as she snuggled in her crib. Even

Bessie's sixteen-year-old son chuckled and sighed as his feet found where the iron had been. The children were noisily unaware that the iron was heated by bits of slack coal from a supply that wouldn't last the winter. Nor had they ever noticed that the smiling woman who pressed the sheets wore patched dresses and was somehow never hungry.

The next morning Bessie would build the fire while the four boys went out to feed and milk old Sally, the only animal not sold to pay debts. The little girls would wait in the kitchen until chores were done. Then all would line up—smallest to tallest—and, at the sound of Bessie's first notes on the piano, would march and sing their way in to the tree. . . . "O come, all ye faithful, joyful and triumphant. . . ."

They had cut the tree themselves and trimmed it with paper chains and popcorn. But there was nothing under it, and Bessie had little to put there. She had bought oranges and nuts. That was enough, she knew, to cause shouts of delight. But, as she sat looking out at the half-buried village the old question returned, "What can I give my children for Christmas?" After a moment, she saw the answer.

In the morning when songs were sung and oranges eaten, Bessie said, "Today, because it's Christmas Day, we're going to do something special. We are going to take gifts to a family who is poor." The house grew quiet. *Poor* was a word they shunned.

Then Bessie, her eyes shining, explained that many people in the world had very little and since they themselves had so much it was only right that they share. They could look through their possessions and find a gift—a hair ribbon, a book, some clothes. . . . "And I'll make apple pies," she beamed.

When the pies were cooled, Bessie placed two in a basket where the children had put their gifts. She covered all with a bright cloth. At last everything was ready. Then above the excited chatter, a boy's voice demanded, "Mother, why are we doing this when we don't have enough for ourselves?"

There. Someone had said it. The smiles vanished. Even the baby was silent.

"What we have is enough," Bessie said softly, "and what we are giving is small. We are keeping and sharing the precious things . . . our testimonies of the gospel, this great stone house built by your grandfather, our love for each other, happy memories of what has been, hope for good things that are to come. . . . All this is ours to keep. These few gifts we have gathered are ours to share. . . . Come, my son, you may carry the basket."

Christmas night was cold, and Bessie again ironed the sheets. Amid the clamor of getting ready for bed, she felt a sense of peace and assurance. She could not know that [one of] her sons would become a United States Congressman, that all of them would fill missions and serve their country in foreign lands. She could not visualize the twelve college degrees, the scholarships, trophies, and awards that would accumulate. Nor could she know for sure that each would marry in a temple. She could not foresee the shared planning, pennies, and prayers that would cause it all to happen. And later that evening as she watched the last embers die in the old stove and felt the house grow cold, she little knew that in twenty-seven years she would be named Utah's Mother of the Year.

Bessie knew only that she had given her children something for Christmas that they could never lose. Years from now on a cold winter night when they were far from home, they would find it, small and sacred, in their hearts. And there would be other things she could give to them as days and months went by—little things—like warmed sheets.

THE YEAR OF THE
FLEXIBLE FLYERS

ANEY B. CHATTERTON

The year was 1932 and the nation's economy was at an all-time low. The disastrous crash of '29 had left its mark, and we were experiencing a time that was to become known as the Great Depression.

I was in the eighth grade, and we all started school that fall with few clothes and school supplies. There was no lunch program, and for many students there was no food to bring. So those of us who could bring something to eat shared whatever we had.

I remember that whenever any of us had an extra penny, we would put it in an envelope and hide it; when we had twenty pennies saved, we would take them to the store and buy two cans of Vienna sausages, a treat far better than candy. Then we would find a secluded area, put all our lunches together, open the cans of sausage, and divide everything equally. Those were special days.

As Christmastime approached that year, we didn't feel the excitement that usually comes with the holiday season. We understood about the Depression and knew there would be very little for any of us.

But there was one desire we all had, though none of us would have mentioned it to our parents. A new sled had appeared on the market called the Flexible Flyer. With its sleek finish, sharp runners, and smooth handlebars that steered it easily and gracefully, it was the Rolls-Royce of all sleds.

We all marched to the hardware store one day after school to see the new wonder sled. "How much are the sleighs, Mr. Evans?" one of the boys asked.

"Well," he replied, "I think I can sell them for $4.98."

Our hearts sank. But that didn't stop us from dreaming the impossible dream.

School was finally dismissed for the holidays, and when Christmas Eve came we had our usual Christmas play and party. We returned to our homes, happy, yet sad, feeling keenly the weight of those depressed times.

I awoke early Christmas morning but was not anxious to get up. My mother finally called, so I dressed and we all went to the living room where the tree was. I was surprised to see that the tree had been redecorated and was more beautiful than ever. But the biggest surprise was still in store. There underneath the tree, with a big red ribbon tied around it, was a shiny new sled—a Flexible Flyer!

I let out a startled cry and dropped to the floor, sliding my fingers along the satiny finish, moving the handlebars back and forth, and finally cradling the precious sled in my arms. Tears rolled down my cheeks as I looked up at my parents and asked, "Where did you get the money for it?"

My mother wiped away a tear with the corner of her apron and replied, "Surely you believe in Santa Claus. Open your other present."

I opened another box and there was a beautiful dress, and though I loved it, my eyes were on the sled. I could only stand and gaze in awe. I was now the owner of a Flexible Flyer.

After our midday Christmas dinner, Mother announced, "Put on your boots and bundle up warm. We're going to town. We have another surprise for you." I didn't think anything could compare with the surprise I already had.

Dad hitched up the team to our big sleigh, I loaded in my new sled, and we went to town. As soon as we crossed the bridge I saw what the surprise was. Kids were everywhere, and so were Flexible Flyers. Main Street had been roped off so that we could start at the top of the hill and glide all the way down across the bridge without danger from cars. The entire community had turned out. Boys and girls were all jumping up and down, some were crying, most were throwing their arms around each other and shouting, "You got one too!"

Our parents finally got us calmed down long enough to listen to instructions. Three farmers with their horses and sleighs would take turns pulling us to the top of the hill where we would start. The older boys went first, running and then flopping "belly first," as we called it, onto their sleds. We watched as they glided effortlessly over the crusted snow. Faster and faster they went, crossing the bridge and coming to rest amid the cheers and clapping of parents. We all took turns, and as the day wore on we got braver and wilder. The boys discovered they could do tricks by dragging their feet in a certain way, causing their sleds to turn around and tip over. We all got caught up in this adventure, tumbling in a tangle of arms and legs, laughing helplessly as we slipped around, ending up in a pile of bundled bodies.

As night drew near, our parents called for us to stop—it was time to return home for chores. "No, no," we cried. "Please let us stay." Reluctantly they agreed, releasing us from chores for this one time only. When they returned it was dark, but the moon shone brightly, lighting the hill. The cold wind blew over our bodies; the stars seemed so brilliant and close, the hill dark and shadowy as we made our last run for the day. Cold and hungry, but happy, we loaded our Flexible Flyers and returned home with memories that would last a lifetime.

Everywhere I went in the days that followed, my Flexible Flyer went with me. One night I decided to go to the barn, as I often did, just to watch Dad at work. I noticed that one of the stalls was empty, and I asked, "Where's Rosie? She isn't in her stall."

There was an awkward silence, and my dad finally replied, "We had to sell her. She cut her foot in the fence."

Sell Rosie? I thought. *Gentle, friendly Rosie?*

"But the cut would have healed," I said. "Why didn't you sell Meanie? She never does anything we want, but Rosie always leads the herd into the barn."

Dad didn't say anything, and suddenly I knew. Rosie had been sold to buy my Flexible Flyer. She was the best and would bring more money; and my parents had given the best they had—for me. I had always understood that my parents treasured me dearly, but until that moment I had never known a love so great. I ran from the barn in tears and hid myself behind the haystack.

I returned to the hill the next day and told my best friend about Rosie. "Yes, I know," she said. "My dad took ten bushels of apples from our cellar and took them to Pocatello and sold them door to door. He's never had to do that before. That's how I got my Flexible Flyer."

A growing amazement overtook me. "But how did they know?" I asked. "I didn't ask for a sled, so how did all the parents know we all wanted Flexible Flyers?"

Little by little we began to put the pieces together like a jigsaw puzzle. Everyone had a similar story to tell. Then we began to realize how the entire community had united in one monumental effort of sharing, trading, peddling, extra working, and, most of all, caring, to buy the Flexible Flyers. None of us ever had the slightest hint of what was going on right under our noses. That had to be the best-kept secret of all time in so small a community.

When school resumed and we marched into our classroom and stood by our desks waiting for the teacher to say those familiar words, "You may be seated," it seemed we all stood just a bit taller. Not that we had grown in stature, but we had grown in a different way. Nothing had really changed, yet everything had changed. The economy was still the same and we still shared our lunches and saved our pennies for the sausages, but inside we had all changed. We were happier, we played harder, and we studied more diligently. It was as if we had all committed ourselves to be the best we could be, to make our parents and community proud of us. It was the only way we knew to say "thanks."

When the snow finally melted and it was time to store the sleds, we were reluctant to part with them. We clung to them as a child clings to a favorite blanket. They had given meaning to our lives and provided us with a sense of identity. That terrible monster, the Great Depression, no longer seemed such a threat to us. Somehow we knew there would be better times, a brighter tomorrow, and a more prosperous future.

Many years later, long after I married, I asked my mother how they had pulled that secret off, and who started it. Her eyes twinkled. She gave me one of those warm, loving smiles that only a mother can give and replied, "My dear daughter, you must never stop believing in Santa Claus."

"Again It Was Christmas Eve":
A Letter to Thomas E. McKay

DAVID O. McKAY

Christmas experiences in the Old Home were always joyous occasions. Perhaps the finest description of these days is contained in a letter written in 1938 by President McKay to his brother, Thomas E., who was at that time presiding in the Swiss–German Mission of The Church of Jesus Christ of Latter-day Saints.

Salt Lake City, Utah
December 12, 1938
My dear brother and playmate, Thomas E.,

I went to Huntsville the other day and visited the Old Home. It was a typical wintery day, so you can easily imagine how cold the rooms were in which no fires were burning, and in which none had been for weeks. The house was just like a large refrigerator.

There were a few things which I wanted to do so I threw your old coonskin coat over my shoulders and soon felt warm and comfortable. For a few moments I strolled leisurely from room to room, and, being in a reminiscent mood, I let my mind wander at will down the lanes of memory. I saw "Tommy" and "Dadie" go upstairs to bed, and felt the tender touch of the dearest, sweetest mother that ever lived as she tenderly tucked the bed-clothes around her two roguish boys and gave them good-night kisses.

Again it was Christmas Eve. Our stockings having been hung where Santa couldn't help but see them, we lay half expecting to hear the jingle of the sleigh bells announcing the approach of

83

good old St. Nick to the chimney top—sleep came tardily, but finally the sandman succeeded in closing our eyes.

Christmas morning. I can see those boys creeping down the stairs before daybreak—no electric switch to press and flood the room with light; no flashlight at hand. They didn't even light the old kerosene lamp. Step by step they groped their way in the dark, and sought the nail (or chair) on which each had hung respectively his empty stocking. Who can ever forget the thrill of that first touch of the stocking filled with Santa's treasures! Apple in the toe, sticks of red and white candy protruding from the top, and trinkets and presents hidden in between! Perhaps a trumpet stuck out with the candies; but the drum and sled were standing near by.

The air in the room was cold even though the last embers in the kitchen were still smouldering—evidence, if the boys had stopped to think, that father and mother had sat up late enough to welcome St. Nick to our house.

Soon the girls were awake also, and the lamp was lit—then the "oh's" and the "ah's," and the medley of sounds of drums, Jew's harp, harmonica, and music box!

As the sun came smiling over those snow-capped mountains, he turned the frost into diamonds that sparkled from the leafless trees and seemed to dance on the twelve-inch blanket of pure white snow.

Then came the playmates with their merry cry, "Christmas gift."

In the afternoon the children's dance! (One of those boys danced with a sweet little girl eleven successive times!) Oh, the romance of childhood!

Chores—evening shadows, supper and bed, and another Christmas was gone. Why, to childhood, is Christmas Day so short, and the next far away?

Christmas again, anticipated by the trip up South Fork to get our own Christmas tree from the hillside. They were older then, those boys, but their stockings still were hung, and good old Santa never failed to fill them.

Summertime and the swimming hole in Spring Creek; baseball on the "square." Boys and girls strolling "across the creek," over on the knoll plucking flowers—daisies, bluebells, and the modest forget-me-nots, then leisurely back to town where we played croquet—parlor games in the evening where we had to redeem the forfeits!

Later came school and missions, yet still the tender ties that radiated from a devoted father and loving mother ever pulled us back to the Old Home, the dearest, sweetest spot on earth.

It is only an old country home, but no palace was ever filled with truer love and devotion on the part of parents, brothers, and sisters, than those which pervaded the hearts of the loved ones in that family circle.

Hanging your coat in its accustomed place, I walked out of the front door; as the night-latch clicked, I thought it might have been the click of the lid of a treasure chest that held the wealth of memories that no money could buy.

Well, my brother and pal of youthful days, I just wanted you to share with me this glimpse of happy memories, and to say, as the yuletide now approaches, my heart is full of loving wishes to you, that you and yours may enjoy the happiest Christmas ever, and that the New Year may come laden with happiness and joy supreme.

"My First Ball Dress Was Stunning"

SUSAN WELLS

I well remember Brother Brigham's Christmas party of 1849. Like the girls of today, on receiving my invitation the first thought was "nothing to wear." This was literally true, as all our clothing was shabby and patched.

Necessity is the mother of invention, so, after careful consideration, the wagon cover that had done such faithful service during our journey across the plains, was brought out. We couldn't afford canvas and our cover consisted of several thicknesses of unbleached factory cloth. This was carefully dyed and as good luck would have it, it turned out a very pretty brown.

We made this into dresses for myself and sister, trimmed with silk from an old cape of mother's. This cape, black, lined with light brown, not only furnished trimming for our dresses, but I made poke bonnets from the black with quilted lining of the light brown. I had embroidered buckskin moccasins with ravellings from a piece of silk, but I believe for this occasion father, who was a shoemaker, made me a pair of slippers from his old boot legs. I tell you my first ball dress was stunning!

"This Is Christ's Birthday"

SHAUNA STEWART LARSEN

My grandfather, George Albert Smith, had heard my brother, sister and me talk about what we wanted for Christmas for weeks. We described, in detail, what we would get, what color, what size, and on and on.

Christmas Eve finally arrived and we all hung up our stockings on the fireplace mantel, still hoping aloud for LOTS of gifts.

Just before we went to bed, Grandfather said, "Wait a minute, I have to get my stocking." Pretty soon he came back with his blue eyes twinkling. He carried a great big scout sock in his hand. What's more, he had taken a pair of scissors and cut off the toe of the stocking. He hung up his stocking with great glee and then went over and got the empty coal bucket and put it right beneath the stocking.

Well, I was very impressed with how smart Grandfather was. Not only would Santa have to fill his stocking, but he'd have to fill the coal bucket too. What a smart idea!

Christmas morning, after breakfast, we opened the doors to the living room and raced in to where the tree was. I was especially anxious to see what Santa had left Grandfather.

But when I saw his stocking, my heart sank, and my eyes filled with tears, because Santa had left my very SPECIAL Grandfather a switch and coal and onions.

Grandfather saw the tears in my eyes and he pulled me towards him and said, "Now Shauna, you must remember that this is Christ's birthday we are celebrating and even Santa doesn't like to see anyone be greedy."

I learned a great lesson, one I've never forgotten, and one I've always been grateful for.

A HINT FOR NEXT CHRISTMAS*

A. A. MILNE

Obviously there should be a standard value for a certain type of Christmas present. One may give what one will to one's family or particular friends; that is all right. But in a Christmas house-party there is a pleasant interchange of parcels, of which the string and the brown paper and the kindly thought are the really important ingredients, and the gift inside is nothing more than an excuse for those things. It is embarrassing for you if Jones has apologized for his brown paper with a nice shirt and you have only excused yourself with a pair of socks; perhaps still more embarrassing if it is you who have lost so heavily on the exchange. An understanding that the contents were to be worth five shillings exactly would avoid this embarrassment.

And now I am reminded of the ingenuity of a friend of mine, William by name, who arrived at a large country house for

---

*Adapted from an essay by the same name.

Christmas without any present in his bag. He had expected neither to give nor to receive anything but to his horror he discovered on the 24th that everybody was preparing a Christmas present for him, and that it was taken for granted that he would require a little privacy and brown paper on Christmas Eve for the purpose of addressing his own offerings to others. He had wild thoughts of telegraphing to London for something to be sent down, and spoke to other members of the house party in order to discover what sort of presents would be suitable.

"What are you giving our host?" he asked one of them.

"Mary and I are giving him a book," said John, referring to his wife.

William then approached the youngest son of the house, and discovered that he and his next brother Dick were sharing in this, that, and the other. When he had heard this, William retired to his room and thought profoundly.

He was the first down to breakfast on Christmas morning. All the places at the table were piled high with presents. He looked at John's place. The top parcel said, "To John and Mary from Charles." William took out his fountain-pen and added a couple of words to the inscription. It then read, "To John and Mary from Charles and William," and in William's opinion looked just as effective as before. He moved on to the next place. "To Angela from Father," said the top parcel. "And William," wrote William. At his hostess' place he hesitated for a moment. The first present there was for "Darling Mother, from her loving children." It did not seem that an "and William" was quite suitable. But his hostess was not to be deprived of William's kindly thought; twenty seconds later the handkerchiefs "from John and Mary and William" expressed all the nice things which he was feeling for her. He passed on to the next place. . . .

It is of course impossible to thank every donor of a joint gift;

one simply thanks the first person whose eyes one happens to catch. Sometimes William's eye was caught, sometimes not. But he was spared all embarrassment; and I can recommend his solution of the problem with perfect confidence to those who may be in a similar predicament next Christmas.

A SURPRISE VISIT FROM SANTA

FRANKLIN BADGER

A schoolmistress had prepared a wonderful holiday program for her students. Everyone in town [Elko, Nevada, in about 1885] had contributed something to the event. There was a large Christmas tree decorated with popcorn, apples, doughnuts, and also a pack for Santa Claus to distribute among the schoolchildren.

The crowd had all gathered but the duly appointed Santa Claus had not put in his appearance. Just at this crucial moment sleighbells were heard in the distance—they grew louder and louder. The teacher, looking out of the back door, saw a sleigh drawn by a beautiful span of horses, covered with snow and icicles, coming toward her. Around the girth of each horse was a string of shining silver bells. When the sleigh came to a halt, a man dressed for this sub-zero climate in cap, coat and long woolen chaps arose from the covers. It was George Badger, a kindly man who was foreman of the McIntyre Ranch in Elko, traveling to his home in Holden, Utah, after the last cattle roundup of the season.

George was immediately drafted into service. It took no persuasion on his part, and but little make-up for him to enter wholeheartedly into the spirit of the occasion. In seconds he turned his cap and coat wool side out and draped a string of bells around him. The entire school of youngsters arose with shouts of glee as this new Santa entered the door with his pack. How their faces glowed when their names were called and presents were handed to them by this strange and jovial Santa Claus. After the children had gone, the profuse thanks of the little teacher was sufficient reward for the help he had so willingly given. Then out into the cold night, with stars gleaming on the glistening snow, he continued his course to his ranch where he found the ranch boys snugly asleep in their warm beds.

ALL QUIET FOR CHRISTMAS

PIERS COMPTON

It was going to be a bitter Christmas. Weather experts predicted a spell of hard frosty weather. . . . It was the first Christmas of the Great War, 1914. Half the nations of Europe were engaged in a life-or-death struggle. Thousands of men faced each other in trenches spread like an elongated maze across Belgium and France.

Force, not wisdom, was the order of the day. The pleas for a Christmas truce made by Pope Benedict XV had been disregarded by both sides. . . .

But although the leaders in London and Berlin could remain impervious to the Christmas appeal, there were signs that the men in the firing zone were ready to respond.

On Christmas Eve a party from the Medical Corps wandered into the ruined town of Ypres. The cathedral was shattered but the organ had not been touched, and one of the party settled himself at the keyboard.

How far the notes penetrated we shall never know, but with devastation all about them, and with guns booming in the near distance, he played some verses of *Adeste Fideles*.

It was, as predicted, a day of hard frost. With the coming of darkness, when things quieted down, fires were lighted in the trenches where strange rumours were being circulated. The rumours had no official sanction. No one knew exactly how or where they came into being. There was no definite arrangement, and conditions differed all down the line. But it soon became generally known that German and British had promised to cease fire throughout Christmas Day.

In some sectors the British could see coloured lights and candles burning along the top of the German trenches.

Here and there a Christmas tree was set up on the parapet. And something of the holiness, the magic of Christmas, entered into the suddenly quiet world of war.

Rifles were kept near at hand. . . . But no one fired. Instead groups of British and Germans clambered out of their trenches, worked round the barbed wire, and met together in the snowy desolation of No Man's Land. The cry of no shooting became general. It seems that the British, at the start, were more suspicious than the Germans, for the latter were heard calling: "Come out, you British!" At one point they hoisted a placard wishing their enemies "A happy Christmas." At another, in front of the trenches held by the Scots Guards, they revealed the efficiency of their intelligence service by displaying a board with the message: "A merry Christmas, Scottie Guardie."

A line was drawn half-way between the trenches, and here the fighting men met, regarding each other curiously at first, the officers saluting each other and shaking hands, the Germans, very polite and clicking their heels with a bow. Conversation was sometimes difficult, but an interpreter could always be found before long.

Both sides agreed not to take advantage of the lull by improving or repairing their barbed wire defences. It was also agreed that if a shot was accidentally fired it would not be regarded as an act of war, and that an apology would be accepted.

They exchanged the chocolate [and other small items] received in their Christmas parcels. Cap badges and buttons were given as souvenirs. One German produced a bottle of wine and asked the British to drink their king's health. . . .

Those Germans who knew London indulged in reminiscences of Marble Arch and "Peecadeely." A British battalion played a Saxon team at football and the Saxons won 3–2.

The only serious business of the day was the burying of the dead. Both sides dug graves for those who had fallen in front of the trenches, and the British supplied some wooden crosses. One party of Germans came forward bareheaded, and bearing the body of a British officer who had fallen behind their lines. Another gathering took place in a turnip field where some Germans, to mouth-organ accompaniment, did a queer sort of hopping dance that caused amusement.

There were sectors where the British were invited to visit the German trenches. Those who did so stayed for some time, and reported afterwards that they had been very well entertained. And so the day passed. The early darkness of a cold frosty night came on, and the strangely mixed company gathered for a sing-song. They entertained each other by singing in turn, and here the Germans were, of course, more competent and knowledgeable than the British, whose repertoire was usually restricted to popular songs or snatches of a carol.

The German contributions varied from "Tipperary" and "Home Sweet Home" to a fine Saxon rendering of "God Save the King." An excellent baritone overcame the narrow sense of nationality that divided his audience with Schuman's "Two Grenadiers." A cornet player (he must be professional, thought the British) warmed their hearts with sentimental airs.

The two sides applauded each other. Sometimes a flare went up, and the now superfluous light was greeted with new bursts of cheering and waving of caps.

But all too soon it was midnight. The men said goodbye to each other with more handshakes and the clicking of heels; and the next flare illumined a deserted No Man's Land and the wraiths of barbed wire overlooking the imminence of death.

CHRISTMAS IN ORDERVILLE

AUTHOR UNKNOWN

One December evening some of the sisters of Orderville met to plan a Christmas treat for the children. The Order had no luxuries and the necessities were strictly rationed. About the only sweets the people had was molasses, so, the sisters decided to make molasses candy and cookies for the youngsters.

But on Christmas Eve, they came to "Grandmother Spencer," wife of Howard Orson Spencer, bishop and leader in Orderville, with the news that the brother in charge of the molasses "won't let us have any. He says our allowance for the month is already used." Grandmother's lips tightened. "The children are going to have something for Christmas. I'll speak to my husband after dinner—he'll give us permission."

When her husband came in tired and hungry, Sister Spencer hovered over him and after dinner urged him to rest by the fire. As he sat looking drowsily into the flames, she said in a low voice, "You do think the children should have some candy and cookies for Christmas, don't you Howard?" "Ummhmm," was the sleepy response, and grandmother went away smiling. She reported to the ladies that everything was all right, "My husband has given us permission." "Did he say we could have the molasses?" asked one doubting Thomas. "He didn't say 'No,'" replied Sister Spencer truthfully. "Now we won't wake up the brother in charge of the molasses. We'll just slip out and take what we need."

The man in charge of the molasses barrel was very conscious

of his responsibility. On the lid of the barrel he had placed a section of heavy logging chain and a large boulder. Only a thin wooden partition at the head of the bed separated him from the barrel outside, and he was a light sleeper. Shivering from the cold the women crunched through the snow toward the barrel. It was beginning to snow again and the night was very dark.

With infinite caution they removed the heavy chain without so much as one betraying clank. It took the combined efforts of all the women to lower the boulder noiselessly to the ground. There was a breathless pause as Sister Spencer raised the lid and dipped into the barrel with a saucepan. She emptied its contents into a bucket and dipped again, and again. "We have enough now," whispered one of the women. "Let's go back."

With the same caution the chain and boulder were replaced and the women filed back to the warm kitchen to make the Christmas goodies. But, there was a dismayed gasp when they looked into the pail. "Oh dear, we haven't enough molasses. We'll have to get some more." "Oh no, Sister Spencer. It's cold and dark. It's too risky." "Well, just the same, we must unless we want the children to be disappointed."

There could only be one answer to such a statement and the little band of mothers went again to the molasses barrel. They returned safely and set to work. When morning came, every child in Orderville had two molasses cookies and one big slightly sticky lump of candy in his stocking. Santa Claus had not forgotten them. Grandfather insisted all his life that he could not remember ever having given the women permission to get the molasses.

CHRISTMAS REMINISCENCES

JOSEPH F. SMITH

From 1846 to 1848 and 9 I knew no Christmas, and no holiday; and, indeed, if we had a Christmas or a New Year celebration at all before 1846 —or until after I was married, for the life of me, at this moment, I cannot remember it. I was teamster, herd-boy, plow-boy, irrigator, harvester, with scythe or cradle, wood-hauler, thresher, winnower (by the half-bushel measure or fanning-mill, later) general roustabout, and a fatherless, motherless, and almost friendless missionary, and withal, always penniless.

I say *almost friendless*. I had one true friend, a widow, frail, aged—but oh! so true! She was my never-to-be-forgotten and ever-to-be-loved and remembered Aunt Mercy R. Thompson. She, like my own precious mother, never forgot me while they lived. But in their time, they had very little, and it was a continuous struggle just to live!

Then when, after these dreary experiences, my own precious cherubs began to come along, we were existing on $3 per day for each working day employed, and that in tithing products at high prices. Well, I cannot tell you how we managed to live at all, but we did! God must have helped us, for I did not *steal* nor defraud my neighbor. I did not owe any man, woman or child one cent, except it was my gracious Aunt Mercy who, as often as she could, slipped a favor in my way. I owed no man through all those days, and I *had* to work—I could not be idle.

Now again to the Christmas holidays: There [was] . . . not a dollar in cash, with which to buy one thing for Christmas. I could draw a few pounds of flour, or meat, a little molasses, or something of that kind, ahead, at the general Tithing Office and pay up at the end of the month with tithing scrip, received in payment of my labor which more than often began at 6 A.M. and ended at 11 P.M., at $3 per day in tithing pay, which was not cash.

I saw many reveling in luxuries, with means to lavish on their every *want,* which were far more than their needs—riding in buggies, on prancing horses, enjoying their leisure, while *I—we all!* were on foot and of necessity tugging away with all our mights to keep soul and body together. Under these spiritless conditions, one day just before Christmas, I left the old home with feelings I cannot describe. I wanted to do something for my chicks. I wanted something to please them, and to mark the Christmas day from all other days—but not a cent to do it with! I walked up and down Main Street, looking into the shop windows—into Amussen's jewelry store, into every store—everywhere—and then slunk out of sight of humanity and sat down and wept like a child, until my poured-out grief relieved my aching heart; and after awhile returned home, as empty as when I left, and played with my children, grateful and happy . . . for them. . . .

After these trials, my pathway became more smooth. I began to pick up; by hard work, rigid economy, self-denial, and the love of God, I prospered. Little openings were presented, and I improved them. . . . Oh! let God be praised.

FIRST CHRISTMAS IN UTAH

ELIZABETH   HUFFAKER

I remember our first Christmas in the Valley. We all worked as usual. The men gathered sagebrush, and some plowed; for though it had snowed, the ground was still soft, and the plows were used nearly the entire day.

We celebrated the day on the Sabbath, (Christmas was on Saturday), when all gathered around the flagpole in the center of the Fort, and there we held a meeting. And what a meeting it was! We sang praises to God, we all joined in the evening prayer, and the speaking that day has always been remembered. There were words of thanksgiving and cheer. Not a despairing word was uttered. The people were hopeful and buoyant because of their faith in the great work they were undertaking. After the meeting there was handshaking all around. Some wept with joy. The children played in the inclosure, and around a sagebrush fire that night. We gathered and sang "Come, Come Ye Saints."

We had boiled rabbit and a little bread for our dinner. Many who were there for that first Christmas in the Valley later remarked that in the sense of perfect peace and good will, they never had a happier Christmas in all their lives.

GINGERBREAD TOYS

HANNAH CORNABY

The recent famine experience had taught me economy, and the little I could procure from the sale of some clothing enabled us to live. I could have made our condition known and have received help, but delicacy forbade; so I made the best of the situation, exerting myself unceasingly for the helpless little ones.

Christmas Eve came, and my darlings, with childish faith, hung up their stockings, wondering if Santa Claus would fill them. With aching heart, which I concealed from them, I assured them they would not be forgotten; and they fell asleep with joyful anticipation for the morrow.

Not having a particle of sweetening, I knew not what to do. They must not, however, be disappointed. I then thought of some squashes in the house, which I boiled, then strained off the liquid; that, when simmered a few hours, made a sweet syrup. With this and a little spice, I made gingerbread dough which, when cut into every conceivable variety of design and baked in a skillet (I had no stove) filled their stockings and pleased them as much as would the most fancy confectionaries.

I sometimes wonder if the children of today enjoy the costly Christmas presents of toys and rich candies with which they are surfeited any more than my little ones did their gingerbread toys.

OLD CHRISTMAS IN ENGLAND

WASHINGTON IRVING

Christmas Eve

It was a brilliant moonlight night, but extremely cold; our chaise whirled rapidly over the frozen ground; the post-boy smacked his whip incessantly, and a part of the time his horses were on a gallop. . . .

As we approached the house, we heard the sound of music, and now and then a burst of laughter from one end of the building. This, Bracebridge said, must proceed from the servants' hall, where a great deal of revelry was permitted, and even encouraged, by the Squire throughout the twelve days of Christmas, provided everything was done conformably to ancient usage. Here were kept up the old games of hoodman blind, shoe the wild mare, hot cockles, steal the white loaf, bob apple and snapdragon: the Yule log and Christmas candle were regularly burnt, and the mistletoe, with its white berries, hung up to the imminent peril of all the pretty housemaids.

So intent were the servants upon their sports, that we had to ring repeatedly before we could make ourselves heard. On our arrival being announced, the Squire came out to receive us, accompanied by his two other sons; one a young officer in the army, home on leave of absence; the other an Oxonian, just from the University. The Squire was a fine, healthy-looking old gentleman, with silver hair curling lightly round an open, florid countenance. . . .

The family meeting was warm and affectionate; as the evening was far advanced, the Squire would not permit us to change our travelling dresses, but ushered us at once to the company, which was assembled in a large old-fashioned hall. It was composed of different branches of a numerous family connection, where there were the usual proportion of old uncles and aunts, comfortably married dames, superannuated spinsters, blooming country cousins, half-fledged striplings, and bright-eyed boarding-school hoydens. They were variously occupied; some at a round game of cards; others conversing around the fireplace; at one end of the hall was a group of the young folks, some nearly grown up, others of a more tender and budding age, fully engrossed by a merry game; and a profusion of wooden horses, penny trumpets, and tattered dolls, about the floor, showed traces of a troop of little fairy beings, who, having frolicked through a happy day, had been carried off to slumber through a peaceful night. . . .

Supper was announced shortly after our arrival. It was served up in a spacious oaken chamber, the panels of which shone with wax, and around which were several family portraits decorated with holly and ivy. Beside the accustomed lights, two great wax tapers, called Christmas candles, wreathed with greens, were placed on a highly-polished buffet among the family plate. The table was abundantly spread with substantial fare; but the Squire made his supper of frumenty, a dish made of wheat cakes boiled in milk with rich spices, being a standing dish in old times for Christmas eve. I was happy to find my old friend, minced-pie, in the retinue of the feast; and finding him to be perfectly orthodox, and that I need not be ashamed of my predilection, I greeted him with all the warmth wherewith we usually greet an old and very genteel acquaintance. . . .

The dance, like most dances after supper, was a merry one; some of the older folks joined in it, and the Squire himself figured down several couples with a partner with whom he affirmed he had danced at every Christmas for nearly half a century. . . .

The party now broke up for the night with the kind-hearted old custom of shaking hands. As I passed through the hall, on the way to my chamber, the dying embers of the Yule-log still sent forth a dusky glow; and had it not been the season when "no spirit dares stir abroad," I should have been half tempted to steal from my room at midnight, and peep whether the fairies might not be at their revels about the hearth. . . .

I had scarcely got into bed when a strain of music seemed to break forth in the air just below the window. I listened, and found it proceeded from a band, which I concluded to be the waits from some neighbouring village. They went round the house, playing under the windows.

I drew aside the curtains, to hear them more distinctly. The moonbeams fell through the upper part of the casement, partially lighting up the antiquated apartment. The sounds, as they receded, became more soft and aerial, and seemed to accord with quiet and moonlight. I listened and listened—they became more and more tender and remote, and, as they gradually died away, my head sank upon the pillow and I fell asleep.

Christmas Day

. . . When I awoke the next morning, it seemed as if all the events of the preceding evening had been a dream, and nothing but the identity of the ancient chamber convinced me of their reality. While I lay musing on my pillow, I heard the sound of little feet pattering outside of the door, and a whispering consultation. Presently a choir of small voices chanted forth an old Christmas carol, the burden of which was:

> "Rejoice, our Saviour he was born
> On Christmas Day in the morning."

I rose softly, slipped on my clothes, opened the door suddenly, and beheld one of the most beautiful little fairy groups that a painter could imagine.

It consisted of a boy and two girls, the eldest not more than six, and lovely as seraphs. They were going the rounds of the house, and singing at every chamber-door; but my sudden appearance frightened them into mute bashfulness. They remained for a moment playing on their lips with their fingers, and now and then stealing a shy glance, from under their eyebrows, until, as if by one impulse, they scampered away, and as they turned an angle of the gallery, I heard them laughing in triumph at their escape. . . .

I had scarcely dressed myself, when a servant appeared to invite me to family prayers. He showed me the way to a small chapel in the old wing of the house, where I found the principal part of the family already assembled in a kind of gallery, furnished with cushions, hassocks, and large prayer-books; the servants were seated on benches below. The old gentleman read prayers from a desk in front of the gallery, and Master Simon acted as clerk, and made the responses; and I must do him the justice to say that he acquitted himself with great gravity and decorum.

The service was followed by a Christmas carol, which Mr. Bracebridge himself had constructed from a poem of his favourite author, Herrick; and it had been adapted to an old church melody by Master Simon. As there were several good voices among the household, the effect was extremely pleasing; but I was particularly gratified by the exaltation of heart, and sudden sally of grateful feeling, with which the worthy Squire delivered one stanza: his eyes glistening, and his voice rambling out of all the bounds of time and tune:

> "'Tis thou that crown'st my glittering hearth
> With guiltlesse mirth,
> And giv'st me wassaile bowles to drink,

Spiced to the brink:
Lord, 'tis Thy plenty-dropping hand,
That soiles my land;
And giv'st me for my bushell sowne,
Twice ten for one."

. . . Our breakfast consisted of what the Squire denominated true old English fare. He indulged in some bitter lamentations over modern breakfasts of tea-and-toast, which he censured as among the causes of modern effeminacy and weak nerves, and the decline of old English heartiness; and though he admitted them to his table to suit the palates of his guests, yet there was a brave display of cold meats, wine, and ale, on the sideboard.

After breakfast I walked about the grounds with Frank Bracebridge and Master Simon, or Mr. Simon as he was called by everybody but the Squire. We were escorted by a number of gentleman-like dogs, that seemed loungers about the establishment; from the frisking spaniel to the steady old staghound; the last of which was of a race that had been in the family time out of mind: they were all obedient to a dog-whistle which hung to Master Simon's buttonhole, and in the midst of their gambols would glance an eye occasionally upon a small switch he carried in his hand. . . .

While we were talking we heard the distant toll of the village bell, and I was told that the Squire was a little particular in having his household at church on a Christmas morning; considering it a day of pouring out of thanks and rejoicing; for, as old Tusser observed:

"At Christmas be merry, and thankful withal,
And feast thy poor neighbours, the great and the small."

. . . As the morning, though frosty, was remarkably fine and clear, the most of the family walked to the church, which was a very old building of gray stone, and stood near a village, about half

105

a mile from the park gate. Adjoining it was a low snug parsonage, which seemed coeval with the church. The front of it was perfectly matted with a yew-tree that had been trained against its walls, through the dense foliage of which apertures had been formed to admit light into the small antique lattices. As we passed this sheltered nest, the parson issued forth and preceded us.

I had expected to see a sleek, well-conditioned pastor, such as is often found in a snug living in the vicinity of a rich patron's table; but I was disappointed. The parson was a little, meagre, black-looking man, with a grizzled wig that was too wide, and stood off from each ear; so that his head seemed to have shrunk away within it, like a dried filbert in its shell. He wore a rusty coat, with great skirts, and pockets that would have held the church Bible and prayer-book; and his small legs seemed still smaller, from being planted in large shoes decorated with enormous buckles. . . .

The usual services of the choir were managed tolerably well, the vocal parts generally lagging a little behind the instrumental, and some loitering fiddler now and then making up for lost time by travelling over a passage with prodigious celerity, and clearing more bars than the keenest fox-hunter to be in at the death. But the great trial was an anthem that had been prepared and arranged by Master Simon, and on which he had founded great expectation. Unluckily there was a blunder at the very outset; the musicians became flurried; Master Simon was in a fever; everything went on lamely and irregularly until they came to a chorus beginning "Now let us sing with one accord," which seemed to be a signal for parting company: all became discord and confusion; each shifted for himself, and got to the end as well, or rather as soon, as he could, excepting one old chorister in a pair of horn spectacles bestriding and pinching a long sonorous nose; who, happening to stand a little apart, and being wrapped up in his own melody, kept on a quavering course, wriggling his head, ogling his book, and winding all up by a nasal solo of at least three bars' duration.

The parson gave us a most erudite sermon on the rites and ceremonies of Christmas, and the propriety of observing it not merely as a day of thanksgiving, but of rejoicing; supporting the correctness of his opinions by the earliest usages of the Church, and enforcing them by the authorities of Theophilus of Cesarea, St. Cyprian, St. Chrysostom, St. Augustine, and a cloud more of Saints and Fathers, from whom he made copious quotations. I was a little at a loss to perceive the necessity of such a mighty array of forces to maintain a point which no one present seemed inclined to dispute; but I soon found that the good man had a legion of ideal adversaries to contend with; having, in the course of his researches on the subject of Christmas, got completely embroiled in the sectarian controversies of the Revolution, when the Puritans made such a fierce assault upon the ceremonies of the Church, and poor old Christmas was driven out of the land by proclamation of Parliament. The worthy parson lived but with times past, and knew but a little of the present. . . .

We had not been long home when the sound of music was heard from a distance. A band of country lads, without coats, their shirt-sleeves fancifully tied with ribands, their hats decorated with greens, and clubs in their hands, were seen advancing up the avenue, followed by a large number of villagers and peasantry. They stopped before the hall door, where the music struck up a peculiar air, and the lads performed a curious and intricate dance, advancing, retreating, and striking their clubs together, keeping exact time to the music; while one, whimsically crowned with a fox's skin, the tail of which flaunted down his back, kept capering around the skirts of the dance, and rattling a Christmas-box with many antic gesticulations. . . .

The Christmas Dinner

. . . I had finished my toilet, and was loitering with Frank Bracebridge in the library, when we heard a distant thwacking sound, which he informed me was a signal for the serving up of the dinner. The Squire kept up old customs in kitchen as well as hall; and the rolling-pin, struck upon the dresser by the cook, summoned the servants to carry in the meats. . . .

The dinner was served up in the great hall, where the Squire always held his Christmas banquet. A blazing, crackling fire of logs had been heaped on to warm the spacious apartment, and the flame went sparkling and wreathing up the wide-mouthed chimney. The great picture of the crusader and his white horse had been profusely decorated with greens for the occasion; and holly and ivy had likewise been wreathed around the helmet and weapons on the opposite wall. . . .

We were ushered into this banqueting scene with the sound of minstrelsy, the old harper being seated on a stool beside the fireplace, and twanging his instrument with a vast deal more power than melody. Never did Christmas board display a more goodly and gracious assemblage of countenances; those who were not handsome were, at least, happy; and happiness is a rare improver of your hard-favoured visage. . . .

The parson said grace, which was not a short, familiar one, such as is commonly addressed to the Deity, in these unceremonious days; but a long, courtly, well-worded one of the ancient school.

There was now a pause, as if something was expected; when suddenly the butler entered the hall with some degree of bustle; he was attended by a servant on each side with a large wax-light, and bore a silver dish, on which was an enormous pig's head, decorated with rosemary, with a lemon in its mouth, which was placed with great formality at the head of the table. . . .

The table was literally loaded with good cheer, and presented an epitome of country abundance, in this season of overflowing larders. . . . There were several dishes quaintly decorated, and which had evidently something traditionary in their embellishments; but about which, as I did not like to appear over curious, I asked no questions. I could not, however, but notice a pie, magnificently decorated with peacocks' feathers, in imitation of the tail of that bird, which overshadowed a considerable tract of the table. This, the Squire confessed, with some little hesitation, was a pheasant-pie, though a peacock-pie was certainly the most authentical; but there had been such a mortality among the peacocks this season, that he could not prevail upon himself to have one killed. . . .

When the cloth was removed, the butler brought in a huge silver vessel of rare and curious workmanship, which he placed before the Squire. Its appearance was hailed with acclamation; being the Wassail Bowl, so renowned in Christmas festivity. The contents had been prepared by the Squire himself; for it was a beverage in the skillful mixture of which he particularly prided himself, alleging that it was too abstruse and complex for the comprehension of an ordinary servant. It was a fine potation, indeed, . . . with roasted apples bobbing about the surface. . . .

When the ladies had retired, the conversation, as usual, became still more animated; many good things were broached which had been thought of during dinner, but which would not exactly do for a lady's ear; and though I cannot positively affirm that there was much wit uttered, yet I have certainly heard many contests of rare wit produce much less laughter. . . .

But enough of Christmas and its gambols; it is time for me to pause in this garrulity. Methinks I hear the questions asked by my grave readers, "To what purpose is all this?—how is the world to be made wiser by this talk?" Alas! is there not wisdom enough extant for the instruction of the world? And if not, are there not thousands of abler pens labouring for its improvement?—It is so much pleasanter to please than to instruct—to play the companion rather than the preceptor.

What, after all, is the mite of wisdom that I could throw into the mass of knowledge? or how am I sure that my sagest deductions may be safe guides for the opinions of others? But in writing to amuse, if I fail, the only evil is my own disappointment. If, however, I can by any lucky chance, in these days of evil, rub out one wrinkle from the brow of care, or beguile the heavy heart of one moment of sorrow; if I can now and then penetrate through the gathering film of misanthropy, prompt a benevolent view of human nature, and make my reader more in good humour with his fellow beings and himself, surely, surely, I shall not then have written entirely in vain.

WHEN LORENZO YOUNG PLAYED SANTA CLAUS

MATILDA Y. STOLWORTHY STAKER

In order that you may understand what a few gifts at Christmas time meant to a group of pioneer children, I will have to describe the community and the conditions under which the people lived.

My father was foreman over the "United Order" cattle for

12 years, and when the Order was discontinued there was nothing for the young people to do but branch out and make homes for themselves. So my father, Thomas Stolworthy, and seven or eight young cowboys rode away to find a new home.

They found a valley lying in the shape of a horse shoe almost surrounded by high mountains. It had a wonderful climate, there was plenty of land and water, with only a few families living on the banks of the mountain stream. The men took up a homestead right on the vacant land and built three log houses. Then they returned for their families.

In the spring of 1886, Father and several others loaded up wagons for pioneering again. All farm implements were put on one wagon; extra food and provisions on another. They had planned to take provisions for a year. The wagons were loaded with flour, dried fruit, molasses, jerked meats, beans, corn and all kinds of seeds. There were also several kegs of butter they had saved while they were at the dairy. The butter was put in the kegs while fresh, then the kegs were filled with a salty brine, then a tight lid was put on. When the butter was used it would have to be in water over night and worked good to get the salt out of it. It seemed the best butter ever eaten.

Then with Father, Mother, my sister four years old, myself, and Father's other wife, Hannah, we started out. After a long journey we arrived at Huntington, Emery County.

When the "Order" was going, Mother had put three cows in the Order, but when it broke up, she was allowed only one cow. Mother did not think it was fair and told Brigham Young so. He said, "Don't worry, Lydia, you did your part and I promise you in the name of the Lord that your one cow will do you more good than any three cows." And she surely did. About a week before Christmas a man came to Huntington with six head of oxen. He tried to buy feed for them; but there was no feed to be found. One morning Father found all six head of oxen in our corn fodder; they had destroyed it all. Father was very angry; Mother cried. The man did not have any money to pay for the feed. He said he was leaving but he had a forty gallon barrel of molasses that we could have. When he had left the molasses I heard Father and Mother talking. Father said, "Don't give up. I will go to Emery and buy a load of straw and the Lord can bless the straw as well as corn." When he got back, the cow ate the straw as though it were the best of hay.

Can you imagine a Christmas under such conditions and Mother listening to the children's prattle about Christmas? Every one had prayed to the Heavenly Father for Santa to find them. The men were busy making chairs out of willows, and cradles for dolls. The women made big rag dolls with eyes made of buttons and yarn for hair. The day before Christmas, we kiddies were told to go play and not come in the house and bother. We all ganged up and played steal sticks, run sheep run, or anything to keep moving and warm. When we were running we would have a chance to smell something real good as some of the mothers would come out and run home with something very nice in their aprons. The mothers had mixed, rolled, cut and baked ginger bread dolls, all sizes. There were dogs, cats and horses with raisins for eyes. They were made out of bran ginger bread with just enough precious flour to hold it together.

On that Christmas morning, there were rag dolls in cradles made from willows, ginger bread dolls, and great big sticks of molasses candy. Father went outdoors and there in the doorway sat a great big new rocking chair with a big bundle in it. Father brought the bundle in, then the chair. He picked mother up and sat her in it. In the bundle was 40 yards of gray linsey, a bundle of floss, 40 yards of factory, 10 pounds of sugar, a lot of dried fruit, a lot of nuts, 10 pounds of store candy! Just think, lumps of clear candy with flowers through it, striped candy, pretty lumps that looked like little cakes; two white candy bird nests with little eggs and a little blue bird. It was the most beautiful thing we had ever seen.

Then there were two boxes with our names on them. When we opened them there were two dolls all dressed, one with dark hair and a pink dress, and the other with light hair and a blue dress. They would open and shut their eyes. It was the first dolls we had ever seen. A letter was in the bottom from Great Grandfather Lorenzo Young saying:

"Dear Lydia: I cannot help worrying about you away off there, wondering if you are cold and hungry. When Bro. Aliphant was going through Huntington to his home I hired him to take a few things for you for Christmas. Hoping you a Merry Christmas, and a Happy New Year."

Now I will tell you how we enjoyed that Christmas. I will begin with the gray linsey, as of course the factory was used later for undergarments, sheets and pillow cases. Grandfather got a new suit of gray linsey and we could not understand why mother cried as she cut a pattern from Grandfather's velvet coat and vest and then sewed on Father's suit. Father put his arm around her and said, "Never mind, it will be so much better and warmer. I can hardly wait to try it on." Mother and Aunt Hannah made them each a dress, cut princess style. My sister and I each had two slips to wear under our aprons, also two new Sunday dresses. Mother embroidered them and we were so proud of our new dresses. All the women and children were barefoot, so Sister Marshall cut and sewed the tops for shoes, Bro. Marshall tanned a horse hide and put soles on the slippers. Everyone had new shoes.

But you will say, "Did you eat all that candy alone?" We did not. Inside of an hour on that Christmas morning a cup of white sugar, some dried fruit, some nuts, two pieces of candy for each child was in every home in the valley. The candy was so pretty and too precious to eat, so the children just sat and looked at it and tried to see who could keep it the longest.

After we had been to each home, mother called my sister and myself and said, "How would you like to take your bird nests to John and Delight?" They were two children who had been badly burned and were still in bed. She said, "You have your dolls and you can run and play." You will never know how bad we wanted to keep the bird nests. We looked at them and then at Mother, so sweet and sad, and away we went. Never will I forget as long as I live the look of joy in those children's eyes as we put the nests in their hands and how the weeping mother hugged and kissed us, although she could not speak. That was the happiest Christmas of our lives. Surely God had heard our prayers and whispered to Great-grandfather of our needs. Lorenzo D. Young was "Great-grandfather" to every child in that little town ever after.

THE CHRISTMAS
OUR PARENTS WEPT

LILLIE BUHLER DAY

The year was 1931 and I was fourteen, the oldest of eleven children in our family in Highland, Utah. One day my father and mother and a neighbor were in a car accident.

Dad, a very strong man, managed to lift the car up enough to release mother and the neighbor. He himself suffered a broken arm and several broken ribs.

Because of the accident, dad was unable to work his 160-acre farm, and the bank foreclosed the mortgage on our home. The depression had hit us in all its force. Dad was given a short time to move out.

The meaning of that foreclosure became clear to me just a few weeks later when we had to build a house across the street on a small piece of land dad had just bought. Because dad was still recovering from his accident, mother did much of the work. It was a small, one-room shack with no floor, no windows, a bad roof, and wooden walls. We took hot rocks to bed with us that winter to keep warm. When the snow began to melt on the roof it would leak down into our beds. At night we would often find ice in the covers, and in the morning we could not make the beds because the edges of the blanket were frozen together. We knew for the first time in our lives how it felt to go to bed without any supper. We had to save hard pieces of bread for the younger children, and we lived on dry beans cooked without salt.

Dad finally got a few days' work on a dry farm, and when the owner found dad didn't bring any lunch because we had no food, he came to our house with a sack of flour and other groceries. I remember that we were so hungry we tried eating the flour uncooked.

Christmas came that year with a lot of snow, but no gifts. My brother Reuben told young Fred to save the candy and nuts they received at the American Fork firemen's Christmas party, because that was all they would get from Santa.

Dad was able to make a payment on our home and install a wooden floor and two windows, and we knew that would be our Christmas.

But that was a Christmas we all remembered. Dad joked and tried to play family games with us. Finally he said, "Well, children, perhaps Santa did forget us this year. I'll bet there won't be one of you that will forget this Christmas."

He was right, for we learned that Christ's spirit lived in our hearts. That day we learned the true value of love and found that one could be happy in its single embrace.

But one other wonderful thing happened that Christmas. It happened just after we had a late dinner and dad had to go out to do his nightly chores. He looked out at the blizzard, watched that snow hurdle through the air, hating to go outside. Suddenly a knock sounded at the door. We all looked at one another half believing what we heard. We couldn't imagine anyone coming to our door at this time of night.

The knock came again, and quickly one of us opened the door to find—Santa! Santa was actually standing in the storm, holding a large bag across his shoulder. He stepped into our living room saying, "Merry Christmas, Merry Christmas to you all!" He put the bag down in the center of the room and started shaking hands with the boys. Finally, he ended up with us girls. When he shook hands with Reuben he said, "This is the boy that made my trip possible. I overheard him say to his younger brother at the firemen's Christmas gathering to be sure to save his candy, for that would be all he'd get for Christmas."

Then he said, "I've been trying to get here since early this afternoon, but the blizzard was too severe." After getting warmed by our old heater, he opened the bag. There were dolls, plenty of candy for everyone, nuts and oranges, food and toys! I saw tears on the cheeks of mother and dad. To know someone had not forgotten us! Mr. Irving Pratt, the elderly American Fork fire chief, had risked his life in the worst blizzard anyone in Highland could remember to come to a little farm shack miles out from town.

After visiting with us and taking a rest, Mr. Pratt asked dad if he would get his team of horses and help him get his car out of a huge snowdrift about a mile and a half away. Dad, of course, was happy to do it, and I saw them both disappear into the stormy night. After hours of anxious waiting, we received dad safely home again.

We all knelt and thanked our Father in Heaven for Mr. Pratt and the love it took him to think of us in such trying circumstances.

THE KING OF HEARTS

MAX B. RICHARDSON

The front door of the Calico Cat Saloon burst open and in a flurry of snowflakes a small boy darted in. It was Christmas Eve and the Calico Cat Saloon was hardly the place you would expect to find such a small lad; but there he was, wet and shivering cold. He was a skinny tow-headed kid, only nine or ten years old, and there was a wistful, almost sad look in his eyes. In place of a coat he wore a threadbare sweater over his patched pair of striped bib overalls; and his feet were clad only in worn-out canvas gym shoes that were soaking wet and made a squishing sound with each step he took.

The boy's eyes scanned the smoke-filled room. Then he ran squishing past the bar toward the rear of the room where men sat huddled around a large round table that was covered with green felt.

"Daddy, mama sent me to get you!" the boy exclaimed, smiling with delight in having found his father.

"I'm not ready to go home yet, boy," his father said, without looking up from his cards.

My father, Lewis Hillman Richardson, sat in the dealer's chair that snowy Christmas Eve. Compared to Pa most card sharks were little more than toothless minnows. There were not laws out west in those days to restrict such things; and I guess he figured that for a man with only a fifth grade education, dealing cards was a lot easier than digging ditches or most other things he might have done for a living.

I had only stopped in to wish Dad a Merry Christmas, but with the appearance of this tiny waif, I couldn't resist staying longer. Would he get his father home before he lost all of his paycheck? How would my dad react to this little stranger? I knew he thought amateurs who gambled with professionals were fools. Losing their money was a just reward for their stupidity, but what about the tiny boy and his brothers and sisters? What was their reward to be?

Dad was a large rugged man who looked the part of the gambler he was; but I knew something about the tough old gambler that others didn't know—underneath that rough, calloused exterior beat the tender heart of a sentimental old softie.

"Come on, daddy," pleaded the boy, after his father lost again. "We won't have grocery money."

"You'd better take that boy home before he catches pneumonia," said my father.

"I'll worry about him," snapped the man. "You worry about your dealing!" The boy's father continued to lose heavily.

"Please come home, daddy," sobbed the boy.

"Just one more hand," the man said, still never looking at his son; a phrase he was to repeat again and again as long as his money would last. Finally he had lost it all. He hadn't had much money to start with, only forty or fifty dollars. But forty or fifty dollars is a lot of money when it's all you've got, and it was all he had.

"I told you you'd lose it all, daddy!" the boy sobbed. The boy's father got up without a word and walked toward the door, the boy at his heels, still sobbing.

"That's all for tonight," Dad said, as he got up from the table. Some of the men who wanted to gamble longer grumbled. "It's Christmas Eve and I'm going to spend what's left of it with my family," Dad snapped. He scooped up the night's winnings and gave the money to old Vick, the owner of the saloon. "Here, count this and give me what I've got coming," he said.

My father hurried after the man and his little boy, and caught them just before they reached the door. The money the boy's father had lost belonged to the saloon. It was not my father's to give back; but he felt so bad about what had happened that he took forty dollars of his own money out of his pocket and kneeling on one knee, he tucked it into the little boy's pocket.

"Merry Christmas, lad," Pa said with an affectionate smile. "Now take your daddy home."

"Big night, Lewie," said Vick, handing Dad his pay.

"Yes, the suckers were really biting tonight, Vick; but that was the last game I'll ever deal."

"You make joke, Lewie," said Vick. "You can't mean that."

"I mean it all right—I'm through," Dad said, as we walked toward the door. "Seeing that ragged half-starved little boy tonight made me realize just how bad gambling really is and I'll have no more of it."

"You'll be back, Lewie," old Vick taunted. "You don't know anything but gambling."

"Maybe not, but there's one thing I do know—I don't have to steal food from children to get my daily bread," said Dad as the door closed behind us.

All my life I had lived in the shadow of the town gambler. A stigma seemed to follow my sister and me wherever we went. At school or even at Sunday School it was always the same—we were the town gambler's kids. Nothing could ever change that. But that snowy Christmas Eve at the Calico Cat Saloon, I wouldn't have traded that tough old gambler for the fanciest bank president in town. Nor would I have traded him in the years that followed, for he kept his word. Even though it often meant working dirty knuckle-busting, backbreaking jobs that paid him but a fraction of what he could have earned as a gambler, to the day he died he never touched another card.

They Called Him Mordecai

ATWELL J. PARRY

From the time I was old enough to know anything, I can remember Christmas. It was during the Great Depression of the 1920s and 1930s, and times were hard for almost everyone. By today's standard we were very poor. But because we had a happy home with a loving mother and father, we didn't know we were poor.

At one point my father could find no work of any kind. I would catch my mother weeping and in my childish way would ask, "What's the matter, Mom? Did you hurt yourself? Are you sick? Why are you crying?" She would dab at her eyes, wipe the tears from her cheeks, draw my brother Del and me close to her, and say, "Don't worry, I'll be okay."

Little did I understand—I was about six at the time—that Christmas was drawing near, we didn't have much food in the house, and the prospects of us having anything for Christmas at all looked impossible. We had no Christmas tree, and it was explained to us that we would not be able to get one.

The day before Christmas my dad was out looking for work, and mother had left us alone for a few minutes. Two men came to the house and each of them placed a box on our kitchen table. They sternly cautioned us to stay out of the boxes and not to snoop. They might just as well have said, "Boys, we want you to stop breathing until your folks get home." No sooner were they out the door than we were into the boxes. To our disappointment there was only flour and sugar and canned goods—things of absolutely no interest at all to little boys. There were also small packages wrapped in brown paper that we didn't dare open. Before we could get much deeper into the boxes mother came through the door. When we told her that two men had brought the boxes, she did a strange thing. She looked into the boxes, moved some of the items around in them, then sat down and sobbed. We were sure she was crying because we had disobeyed and gotten into the boxes.

On Christmas morning we each found an orange in the sock we had hung by our stove. Beside each sock was a small brown package. My package contained a serpentine thing that made a terrible noise when I blew on it. My brother's package had a metal noise-maker with a clapper on each side that made a loud clanging noise. My dad usually did not hold us on his lap or show much affection to us. But on this Christmas morning he picked us both up and put us on his lap. He was sitting in a large, old-fashioned rocking chair. I sat there blowing my serpentine and Del clanged his clapper. We made a racket that must have sounded like the demons of hell had broken loose. Dad rocked us back and forth and said nothing.

With the oranges (the only orange we had all year), the noise-makers, the closeness in the rocking chair—all in all it turned out to be a very special Christmas.

There were other special Christmases, such as the year Del and I received a two-wheeled bike to share. I don't know what sacrifices Mom and Dad made to get us that bike, but we thought we were the luckiest boys on earth. But none of these Christmases compared to the Christmas we had when I was thirteen years old, the Christmas with Mordecai.

At the beginning of the school year that September we had moved to a new neighborhood and a new school. That's when we met Mordecai. The kids called him Mordi. He was a tall, gangly, skinny kid whose hands were always dirty with grime that had worn into his hands because they hadn't been properly washed for years. Mordi had strange mannerisms. He was always getting into trouble with the teacher. It seemed like her day was not complete until she had smacked him a couple of times. He wore clothes that were hand-me-downs, that didn't fit too well. He never wore socks, even in the winter. His shoes were too big for his feet. His pants were too short. All in all he was quite a sight to see.

I used to wonder how he could keep from freezing when the snow was deep in winter. He had no coat or gloves. Some days he would wear two shirts—one much bigger than the other. I think he went to school because it was a warm place to be.

Mordi didn't fit in with the other kids. He was lonely and an outcast. He sometimes tried to join in with their play, but the kids didn't seem to want him. He was always the last to be chosen in the schoolyard games—if he was chosen at all. Surprisingly, in spite of the way the kids treated him, Mordi was always cheerful and took the treatment handed out to him in stride.

One evening our dad overheard my brother and me talking and laughing about the strange boy at school. We were making fun of him and saying some very unkind things about the way he looked and acted. My father was a very kind man. He didn't speak evil of anyone, and he didn't like to hear his sons mocking others. He sat us down and said, "Why do you make fun of this boy?"

We said, "Because he is strange and dresses funny."

"Why does he dress funny and act so strange?" Dad asked us.

"We don't know; he just does," we answered.

"Then find out. There may be some good reason he acts and dresses like he does. And I don't want to ever hear you talk about him or anyone else like you were doing tonight. Do you understand?" When Dad used that tone in asking if we understood, you can be sure that we understood.

Del and I had a good friend named Pete, who was just our age. We told Pete what our dad had said and enlisted Pete's help in playing detective with us to see what we could find out about Mordi. The next several days we became friendly with Mordi. We asked him a lot of questions and would get him to talk to us when we could. We tried to get as much information as we could without letting him think we were being snoopy. Sometimes he would answer us and sometimes he would act like he didn't hear us. He always kept some distance from us. It was like he wasn't used to having someone his age he could talk to.

About this time an incident happened during a noon hour that began to change things. We didn't have hot lunch in those days; we didn't even have a lunch room. We had a multi-purpose room where most of us would gather to eat our lunches, which we had brought in brown paper sacks. We would put some desks in a circle and use the top of the desks for a table. We would sit and eat our lunch and tease the girls and generally have a good time.

Mordi wouldn't join us in the circle, but he would go to a corner of the room and eat alone. He seemed to prefer it that way; so we didn't spend much time trying to get him to join us. This particular day, one of the older boys grabbed Mordi's lunch bag saying, "Let's see what ol' Mordi has to eat today." He tossed the sack to another one of the boys and for a few minutes they tossed it back and forth, laughing and pushing Mordi aside as he tried to get his lunch. Finally the boys grew tired of the game. One of them sat on a desk and opened up Mordi's sack and pulled out a sandwich. It was two slices of a coarse homemade bread with a little lard—or pig fat—holding the two slices together. No lunch meat, no peanut butter and jelly like most of us had, no cookies or milk, nothing but two slices of bread with a little lard for the filling. The sandwich wasn't even wrapped to keep it from drying out. The room became very quiet. The boy holding the sandwich put it back in the brown bag and handed the bag to Mordi. He didn't say a word; in fact, no one said a word. Mordi had tears in his eyes. He took the sack and went back to his corner; with his back turned to us he ate his lunch in silence.

That day as Pete and Del and I walked home we decided that never again would we sit by and let the older boys pick on Mordi— or any other boy for that matter. We also decided that we would take a little extra in our lunches for Mordi and do what we could to get him to join us at lunch.

That night as Mom was fixing our lunches, Del and I told her what had happened that day. We asked her to put in something extra in our bags for Mordi. Mom would always have homemade chocolate cake or cookies for our lunches. She said that she would put some extra food in one of our sacks, but that we would have to be careful on how we offered it to Mordi. She could tell from what we told her that Mordi ate his lunch alone because he was probably a proud young man and didn't want any handouts or for anyone to feel sorry for him. She said, "Be careful that you don't hurt him anymore."

The next day at lunch, we put the chairs in a circle as usual. We sat down at the desks and proceeded to take our lunches out of our bags. As Del put his lunch in front of him he said, "Atwell, did mom give you a piece of cake?"

I checked and said, "She sure did."

Del said, "I can't believe this, mom gave me two pieces of cake. I can't eat that much. Does anyone want this extra cake?"

Del held it up, but no one said a word. Mordi finally said, "I'll take it if no one else wants it." Del tossed the cake to Mordi in a kind of don't-care attitude, secretly rejoicing that our plan had worked.

And so it went for the next several days. Del or Pete or I always had an extra sandwich, or cake, or cookies. Each day one of us would say, "Mom did it again. I have more lunch than I can eat. Who wants it?" If anyone besides Mordi had reached for it, we would have broken his arm. It didn't take too many days before we had Mordi joining us in our lunch circle. I'm sure that it didn't take Mordi too long to figure out what was going on, but by then we were pals, and pals always look out for each other and share what they have.

During those days we began to find out a lot about Mordi. He was the youngest of ten children. His father was very old and had been unable to work for several years. His mother was also in poor health. He had a brother who was in prison, which was a source of shame to Mordi and his family. He felt that people judged the whole family because of his brother's bad choices. The family had no money and very little of the world's possessions.

As Christmas drew near and the four of us boys would talk about what we would like for Christmas, we found out that Mordi had never had a Christmas tree. The family just couldn't afford one. Mordi had never received a Christmas gift, or Christmas candy, or any little thing that would make Christmas day any different from other days. To Mordi, Christmas day was just like any other day. He said that if you don't expect anything you don't feel bad when you don't get anything.

Then school was out for Christmas vacation, and Pete, Del, and I spent our time on the hill close to our place, on our sleds. We didn't see Mordi because he lived several blocks from us. I don't know who had the idea or when we begin to think about it, but the idea began to slowly grow that we should get a Christmas tree for Mordi. The more we thought about, it the more excited about the idea we became. Two days before Christmas, we pooled our money together and went down to Mr. Green's grocery store to buy a tree. We told Mr. Green what we had in mind, and he got into the spirit of the idea and gave us a good deal on a little tree. Then it occurred to us that if a family had never had a tree they probably didn't have any decorations to put on a tree. So we bought a few icicles and decided we would see if we couldn't take some ornaments from our own trees, and maybe our neighbors could help us out a little. We remembered that we had never seen Mordi wear any socks, so we dug a little deeper into our pockets and bought two pair of boys' socks. We wrapped the socks in Christmas wrap and put a note on the package that the socks were from Santa Claus.

I remember that night as if it were yesterday. We gathered the ornaments, the Christmas package, and the tree, and the three of us headed for Mordi's house. A light snow was falling, adding to the considerable snow already on the ground. We talked continuously in our excitement.

"Boy, will Mordi ever be surprised!"

"I want to hide where I can see Mordi open the door; then I can see the look on his face."

"I wonder if he will wear the socks to school."

"I wonder if he even knows how to put them on."

And so it went: three young boys carrying a tree down the street through the snow, chattering and laughing and scuffling as we went.

We were soon in front of Mordi's house. We quietly made our way across the yard and onto the front porch. We had to be careful because the front window had no curtains or blinds. As we peeked into the window we saw an old lady sitting at the table. An old man was sitting in a rocking chair. We couldn't see Mordi anywhere. The only furniture in the room was the table, a chair, and the rocking chair. Two wooden apple boxes were standing next to the table; it appeared that they also were used for chairs.

We put the tree in front of the door with the ornaments and the package of socks under it. When we had everything set as we wanted it, I knocked really hard on the front door. The three of us took off like scared cats. We ran to the edge of the yard and lay down behind the small hedge that run along the edge of the yard. In a few moments the little old lady answered the door. When she saw the tree she let out a sort of a scream. Mordi came to the door. The three of us lying in the snow were not prepared for what happened next. Mordi dropped to his knees. He had the most surprised look on his face. He picked up an ornament, then another one, then the package of socks. While still on his knees he opened the package, held the socks up to his face, and began to cry. We were not used to seeing a boy our age cry—boys just didn't cry. Finally Mordi took the tree, the ornaments, and the socks into the house. He set up the tree in the middle of the room and then just stood looking at it.

We sat in the snow and silently watched. When we finally thought we wouldn't get caught, we got on our feet and started home. On the way to Mordi's house we had been loudly talking and laughing. On the way back we hardly said a word.

That night I learned lessons about the true Christmas spirit that have never left me: It really does feel better to give than receive. You can't judge others by how they dress or how they act. And, no matter what your circumstances, you are surely blessed with what you have because there is doubtless someone who has a lot less than you.

I've had more than sixty Christmases since that year. I've often wondered what became of my friend Mordecai. But I will never forget the image of him kneeling on that porch next to a small tree, holding two pair of inexpensive socks, and weeping without shame.

The Story of "Far, Far Away on Judea's Plains"

ADAPTED FROM
GEORGE D. PYPER

Far, Far Away on Judea's Plains" (*Hymns*, no. 212) is the only Christmas carol in our hymnbook written by a Latter-day Saint—and it is one of the few American Christmas carols in existence.

The words and tune of the song were the work of John Menzies Macfarlane, son of John and Annabella Sinclair Macfarlane, born October 11, 1833, at Sterling, near the city of Glasgow, Scotland. His father was a duke's coachman and when the Queen of England visited Scotland, he was assigned as her coachman.

The father died when John was quite young. John came to America with the family and settled in Cedar City, Utah, in 1851 or 1852, where he married Ann Chatterley. He organized a choir and when St. George was settled he took his choir there and gave a concert to cheer up the people. After the concert Elder Erastus Snow told him, "We need a choir in St. George. You go home, sell out, and come down here to live." This he did. In the meantime he helped settle Toquerville and built the first house there.

When Bishop Scanlan of the Catholic Church visited Silver Reef, a flourishing mining camp in those days, he expressed a desire to hold mass in St. George. The Latter-day Saint authorities liberally consented, and Brother Macfarlane trained his choir for six weeks learning the Latin mass. It was given in the St. George Tabernacle.

As involved as he was in music, John Macfarlane even dreamed music, and more than once he sprang from his bed in the middle of the night to jot down a melody, lest the light of morning should erase it from his memory. In 1869 he decided his choir needed a new carol for their Christmas program. At his request, his friend Charles L. Walker provided a suitable text. But John Macfarlane labored in vain for a suitable melody. Then one night it came, suddenly, in a dream. John was awake instantly. He shook his wife into wakefulness, crying out, "Ann, Ann, I have the words for a song, and I think I have the music, too!"

He found the next morning that the words he had written were in fact quite different from Charles L. Walker's text. Even so, he urged Charles Walker to put his name down as author. But Walker replied, "These are not my words, John. I have never seen them before. These are your words. You have written both the words and music yourself, and you must take the full credit."

"Far, Far Away on Judea's Plains" was first published in the *Juvenile Instructor* on December 15, 1889, twenty years after it was written. Brother Macfarlane died in 1892.

> Far, far away on Judea's plains,
> Shepherds of old heard the joyous strains:
> Glory to God, Glory to God,
> Glory to God in the highest;
> Peace on earth, goodwill to men,
> Peace on earth, good-will to men!
>
> Sweet are these strains of redeeming love,
> Message of mercy from heav'n above:
> Glory to God, Glory to God,
> Glory to God in the highest;
> Peace on earth, goodwill to men,
> Peace on earth, good-will to men!

Lord, with the angels we too would rejoice,
Help us to sing with the heart and voice:
Glory to God, Glory to God,
Glory to God in the highest;
Peace on earth, goodwill to men,
Peace on earth, good-will to men!

Hasten the time when, from ev'ry clime,
Men shall unite in the strains sublime:
Glory to God, Glory to God,
Glory to God in the highest;
Peace on earth, goodwill to men,
Peace on earth, good-will to men!

THE STORY OF "SILENT NIGHT"

ADAPTED FROM
GEORGE D. PYPER

On the morning of Christmas Eve, 1818, Joseph Mohr, an assistant pastor at Oberdorf, near Arnsdorf, Germany, was attending a celebration in the schoolhouse at Arnsdorf with his dear friend Franz Gruber, a village schoolmaster, song writer, and church organist. These two friends talked earnestly and regretfully over the fact that there was no really great Christmas song. Pondering the thought later in the day, young Mohr in his church study saw the picture—"*and there were shepherds in the same*

country, abiding in the fields, and keeping watch over their flocks by night"
(Luke 2:8). At that moment, a flash and the inspiration came, and
so on the peaks of the Tyrolian Alps were framed the words of the
carol that was to be heard around the world.

When the words were finished, Mohr rushed to the home of
Franz Gruber and presented him with a folded copy of his carol.
Franz opened it, read it and exultingly exclaimed, "You have
found it!—the right song!—God be praised!" He then repaired to
his own room and, inspired by the words, composed the tune as
we now have it. Franz hurried back to his friend saying: "Your
song—it sings itself: the tune came to me at once and while you
were gone I played to the Strasser sisters and we have together
composed it."

Mohr and Gruber sang it as a duet at the Christmas service
that very evening, the author singing the melody, the composer
the bass. Gruber accompanied them on his guitar since the
church organ was broken. In 1854, thirty-six years after it was written, the Berlin Church Choir sang it before Emperor Frederick
Wilhelm IV. The Emperor was so delighted with the beautiful song
that he ordered it given first place in all Christmas programs. It
has since been translated into more than a hundred languages
and is sung around the world.

> Silent Night, Holy Night!
> All is calm, all is bright,
> Round yon Virgin Mother and Child!
> Holy Infant so tender and mild.
> Sleep in heavenly peace!
>
> Silent Night, Holy Night!
> Shepherds quake at the sight.
> Glories stream from heaven afar,
> Heavenly hosts sing Alleluia;
> Christ, the Savior is born!

Silent Night, Holy Night!
Son of God, Love's pure light
Radiant beams from Thy holy face,
With the dawn of redeeming grace,
Jesus, Lord at Thy birth!

Silent Night, Holy Night!
Guiding star, lend thy light,
See the eastern Wise Men bring
Gifts and homage to our King
Jesus, the Savior is Born.

Silent Night! Holy Night!
Brought the world gracious light,
Down from heaven's golden height
Comes to us the glorious sight:
Jesus, as one of mankind.

Silent Night! Holy Night!
By his love, by his might
Christ our Savior us has graced,
As a brother gently embraced
Jesus, all nations on earth.

Silent Night! Holy Night!
Long ago, minding our plight
God the world from misery freed,
In the dark age of our fathers decreed:
All the humble redeemed.

WISE YOUNG SANTA CLAUS

HARRISON R. MERRILL

White whiskers and white hair are usually a part of the makeup of Santa Claus, but in reality he is of all ages and—strange to say—of both sexes. I sometimes wonder why Mrs. Santa Claus is not found more frequently in our lore. The only reason I can find for her omission is that she—wonderful mothers of the world—*made* Santa Claus for us, and with the adroit manipulations for which she is famous, made us love him with all our hearts.

A mother recently told me an interesting story of a youthful Santa Claus.

Vern was a boy of eleven, but he became Santa to a spinster lady of fifty-five—and a mighty wise Santa, too; much wiser than many a one of the white-whiskered type.

He said to his mother one day last year: "Mother, Miss Lander is all alone. She hasn't a soul to make fires for her, or carry in her coal, or do anything at all, and, Mother, I think she needs a good warm wrap when she gets up in the morning."

Now this mother was of the Santa Claus–making variety. She smiled sweetly at the little Santa-Claus-in-the-making, but she said never a word.

"Well," Vern went on, "I've decided to get her a Christmas present."

The mother listened. It is good sometimes just to listen to these men—growing-up.

"I am going to get her a bath robe—one like yours that's good

134

and warm, so when she gets up in the morning in her cold house, she can slip into it and stay in it 'til she gets her fire started."

"And how will you get this bath robe?" the mother asked.

"I'll sell papers from now 'til Christmas—that ought a do it."

It did.

He hoarded his money like a young Midas.

Then one day some carpenters came into Vern's vicinity to build a house. He saw the pieces of boards, the broken shingles and lath—odds and ends of lumber—and they gave him another idea. He went to the builder and asked if he might gather some of the smaller pieces to take over to Miss Lander to be used as kindling. The builder was willing, and soon Miss Lander had the finest pile of wood that had been stacked in her coal house in years.

On Christmas Eve, Vern—beautiful, warm bath robe under his arm—went over to Miss Lander's. The good lady was overjoyed.

"I'll treasure it," said she, the tears streaming down her cheeks and falling upon the robe which was pressed against her face.

"You're to wear it, not treasure it," said the Santa Claus-growing-up, stoutly. "I'll come over every morning to see if you have it on."

"Yes, Virginia, There Is a Santa Claus"

NEW YORK SUN EDITORIAL, 1897

We take pleasure in answering thus prominently the communication below, expressing at the same time our great gratification that its faithful author is numbered among the friends of *The Sun:*

> *I am 8 years old. Some of my little friends say there is no Santa Claus. Papa says, "If you see it in* The Sun, *it's so." Please tell me the truth, is there a Santa Claus?*
>
> *Virginia O'Hanlon*

Virginia, your little friends are wrong. They have been affected by the skepticism of a skeptical age. They do not believe except they see. They think that nothing can be which is not comprehensible by their little minds. All minds, Virginia, whether they be men's or children's, are little. In this great universe of ours, man is a mere insect, an ant, in his intellect as compared with the boundless world about him, as measured by the intelligence capable of grasping the whole of truth and knowledge.

Yes, Virginia, there is a Santa Claus.

He exists as certainly as love and generosity and devotion exist, and you know that they abound and give to your life its highest beauty and joy. Alas! How dreary would be the world if there were no Santa Claus! It would be as dreary as if there were no Virginias. There would be no childlike faith then, no poetry, no romance to

TRUE STORIES OF CHRISTMAS PAST

make tolerable this existence. We should have no enjoyment, except in sense and sight. The external light with which childhood fills the world would be extinguished.

Not believe in Santa Claus! You might as well not believe in fairies. You might get your papa to hire men to watch in all the chimneys on Christmas eve to catch Santa Claus, but even if you did not see Santa Claus coming down, what would that prove? Nobody sees Santa Claus, but that is no sign that there is no Santa Claus. The most real things in the world are those that neither children nor men can see. Did you ever see fairies dancing on the lawn? Of course not, but that's no proof that they are not there. Nobody can conceive or imagine all the wonders there are unseen and unseeable in the world.

You tear apart the baby's rattle and see what makes the noise inside, but there is a veil covering the unseen world which not the strongest man, nor even the united strength of all the strongest men that ever lived could tear apart. Only faith, poetry, love, romance, can push aside that curtain and view and picture the supernal beauty and glory beyond. Is it all real? Ah, Virginia, in all this world there is nothing else real and abiding.

No Santa Claus? Thank God he lives and lives forever. A thousand years from now, Virginia, nay ten times ten thousand years from now, he will continue to make glad the heart of childhood.

Merry Christmas and a Happy New Year!

CLASSIC CHRISTMAS TALES

THE MAN WHO MISSED CHRISTMAS

J . E D G A R P A R K

It was Christmas Eve; and, as usual, George Mason was the last
to leave the office. He walked over to a massive safe, spun the
dials, swung the heavy door open. Making sure the door
would not close behind him, he stepped inside.

A square of white cardboard was taped just above the topmost
row of strongboxes. On the card a few words were written. George
Mason stared at those words, remembering . . .

Exactly one year ago he had entered this self-same vault. And
then, behind his back, slowly, noiselessly, the ponderous door
swung shut. He was trapped—entombed in the sudden and terri-
fying dark.

He hurled himself at the unyielding door, his hoarse cry
sounding like an explosion. Through his mind flashed all the stories he had heard of men found suffocated in time vaults. No time
clock controlled this mechanism; the safe would remain locked
until it was opened from the outside. Tomorrow morning.

Then the realization hit him. No one would come tomorrow—
tomorrow was Christmas.

Once more he flung himself at the door, shouting wildly, until
he sank on his knees exhausted. Silence came, high-pitched,
singing silence that seemed deafening. More than thirty-six hours
would pass before anyone came—thirty-six hours in a steel box
three feet wide, eight feet long, seven feet high. Would the oxygen
last? Perspiring and breathing heavily, he felt his way around the
floor. Then, in the far right-hand corner, just above the floor, he

found a small, circular opening. Quickly he thrust his finger into it and felt, faint but unmistakable, a cool current of air.

The tension release was so sudden that he burst into tears. But at last he sat up. Surely he would not have to stay trapped for the full thirty-six hours. Somebody would miss him. But who? He was unmarried and lived alone. The maid who cleaned his apartment was just a servant; he had always treated her as such. He had been invited to spend Christmas Eve with his brother's family; but children got on his nerves and expected presents.

A friend had asked him to go to a home for elderly people on Christmas Day and play the piano—George Mason was a good musician. But he had made some excuse or other; he had intended to sit at home, listening to some new recordings he was giving himself.

George Mason dug his nails into the palms of his hands until the pain balanced the misery in his mind. Nobody would come and let him out. Nobody, nobody . . .

Miserably the whole of Christmas Day went by, and the succeeding night.

On the morning after Christmas the head clerk came into the office at the usual time, opened the safe, then went on into his private office.

No one saw George Mason stagger out into the corridor, run to the water cooler, and drink great gulps of water. No one paid any attention to him as he left and took a taxi home.

There he shaved, changed his wrinkled clothes, ate breakfast and returned to his office where his employees greeted him casually.

That day he met several acquaintances and talked to his own brother. Grimly, inexorably, the truth closed in on George Mason. He had vanished from human society during the great festival of brotherhood; no one had missed him at all.

Reluctantly, George Mason began to think about the true meaning of Christmas. Was it possible that he had been blind all these years with selfishness, indifference, pride? Was not giving, after all, the essence of Christmas because it marked the time God gave His own Son to the world?

All through the year that followed, with little hesitant deeds of kindness, with small, unnoticed acts of unselfishness, George Mason tried to prepare himself . . .

Now, once more, it was Christmas Eve.

Slowly he backed out of the safe, closed it. He touched its grim steel face lightly, almost affectionately, and left the office.

There he goes now in his black overcoat and hat, the same George Mason as a year ago. Or is it? He walks a few blocks, then flags a taxi, anxious not to be late. His nephews are expecting him to help them trim the tree. Afterwards, he is taking his brother and his sister-in-law to a Christmas play. Why is he so happy? Why does this jostling against others, laden as he is with bundles, exhilarate and delight him?

Perhaps the card has something to do with it, the card he taped inside his office safe last New Year's Day. On the card is written, in George Mason's own hand:

"To love people, to be indispensable somewhere, that is the purpose of life. That is the secret of happiness."

Mama and the Magic Bag

LILA L. SMITH

The howling wind made the tall old house rock and creak. It came down the stovepipe blowing puffs of smoke into the room from the big pot-bellied stove.

The windows were rattling, and Mama was stuffing rags into the cracks to hold back the snow. I ran to her and held onto her skirt. Sternly she told me to let go so she could move around.

She stopped for a minute, scraped frost from the glass pane, looked out, then started to cry. Mama cried a lot these cold winter days. Papa said she was just homesick, but I knew better, for I heard them talking after they put me to bed.

"There's no use our staying in this God-forsaken place," Mama said. "Now that you have sold the cattle, we can go back to Southern Utah, and live like other people!"

"I am not leaving the land I took in as part payment on the cattle," Papa said. "Besides, Canada is a coming country; already the land is fast being taken by homesteaders."

I did not know what a God-forsaken place was, or what homesteaders were, but I thought it must have something to do with all the snow and ice piling up outside, and something terrible would happen to us as it did to the people in the Bible when God did not like them.

It was dark when Papa and the boys came in, stomping snow from their boots and clothes. Mama lit the lamp and started supper.

"Is it time to put the nails in the wall for the stockings?" I asked Mama.

"Yes, get your brothers to put them in behind the kitchen stove, so the things Santa puts in them won't freeze," Mama said, looking at Papa.

"Do you think Santa Claus can get through the deep snow?" I whispered to my big brother.

"Sure," he said. "Mr. Taylor at the post office says he always gets through. Sometimes the mailman brings things for him."

I ran to get the stockings and started hanging them on the nails, but as I reached far over to the last nail my hand slipped and I touched the back of the hot stove. I let out a scream. Papa picked me up and started soothing me.

Mama did not say a word. She just reached for the magic bag from the top of the cupboard, took me from Papa, put salve that smelled of camphor on my burned arm, and wrapped a clean white cloth around it.

She dried my eyes, kissed my cheek, and put me in the big rocker. "You'll be all right now," she said with a smile. "Just think about it being Christmas Eve and Santa coming."

Somehow it did not hurt any longer, and I almost fell asleep as I smelled the loaves of brown bread Mama was taking from the oven and watched her dish up hot stew for our supper.

The house did not creak any longer, and after supper my brothers rubbed the frost off the window so we could see the deep snow glistening in the moonlight.

Papa said the storm was over, and Mama said, "After three days it is about time, or we will all be buried alive!"

We had just settled down to story reading when the knock came at the door.

Papa opened it, and a big man in a fur coat and hat came in.

He was covered with snow, and icicles hung from his eyebrows and mustache.

"I am Mr. Armstrong," he said. "My wife needs help, and I can't get through those drifts to Kimball to get Mrs. Talbot in time. I heard that your wife has had training with the sick, so I came to ask her to help us."

Mr. Armstrong was all out of breath when he had finished. Papa tried to take his coat and hat, but Mr. Armstrong said, "No, there is not time. I must get back."

Mama took down the magic bag and opened it to check the medicine inside, and then I followed her into the bedroom and watched while she combed her long black hair. She whirled it round and round, then pinned it in a big bob on top of her head. She put on a clean white apron and let me kneel beside her while she said her prayers.

Papa helped her into his big fur coat; he put Lorin's overshoes on her feet. She put a wool fascinator scarf around her head and then followed Mr. Armstrong into the cold, frosty night.

I cried myself to sleep when Papa put me to bed. It was sad not to have Mama home when Santa Claus was coming.

The room was still dark when I woke up and saw the light shining through the curtain over the doorway. I jumped out of bed and ran into the big room that was kitchen, boys' bedroom, and living room for our family.

A blast of cold air came in the door with Mama and Mr. Armstrong. They were both covered with snow. Mama said the horse could not pull them and the buggy through the deep drifts and they had to get out and walk. She looked tired and pale. Papa helped her off with the big coat.

In my excitement at seeing Mama I had forgotten about Santa and the stockings. Then the boys jumped out of bed, and we went to look behind the stove. Santa had got through. The boys had skates, and standing beneath my stocking was a pretty Red-Riding-Hood doll.

But I lost interest in the doll when I heard Mr. Armstrong say that Mama had given them a beautiful baby boy for Christmas!

The rest of the day I played with my doll, but kept looking at the magic bag on top of the cupboard in hopes another Christmas baby would come out.

We ate our dinner of roast beef, mashed potatoes, and creamed carrots, topped off with Mama's suet pudding and sauce, which we could hardly choke down after Mama told us there would be no Christmas dinner at the Armstrongs, just potatoes, cabbage, and an egg if the hens laid enough. The early snow and freezing had covered their crop before it could be cut and threshed.

After the boys had washed the dishes for Mama, Papa brought around the horses and sleigh to take Mama to see how Mrs. Armstrong and the baby were getting along, and we all went with them.

The horses lunged through the deep snow, sending snowballs from their hooves back into the sleigh. We laughed when the drifts were so high the sleigh bounced over the top, jarring us when it hit bottom.

We arrived at the Armstrong house that looked like two boxes put together with a lean-to porch in between. Papa tied the horses, and we followed Mama into one of the boxes. I looked at the other door, and just knew it must be the stable. The side we went in was a kitchen where four children sat with their coats on, huddled around the stove.

"You better keep your coats on," the oldest boy said. "There's not enough wood to keep both stoves going, and Mama and the baby must be kept warm. Papa has gone over to an old shed to find more wood."

Mama told me to take off my hood and mittens. But when I pulled off my mittens out came the two red apples I had carried clenched in my fists, and they rolled on the floor. I was afraid Mama would scold—but she just smiled as I picked them up and gave them to the two little girls.

Mama took the kettle from the stove and the magic bag and left for the stable. I helped the two girls cut out paper dolls from a catalog, and my two brothers played marbles with the two Armstrong boys.

Papa came carrying a big box. He took out Mama's big roaster and put it in the oven and then piled wood and a few chunks of coal in the stove.

Soon Mama came to the door and told us we could come see the baby.

When we went through the other door it wasn't a stable, but a big bedroom. The baby was in a cradle made of a wooden box, not a manger. He had a red face, but no halo on his head as it shows the Christmas Baby in the Bible stories!

Then we left for home, and the setting sun made the white world and clouds look pink.

Mama said, "This has been a beautiful Christmas day."

And we sang "Jingle Bells" to the sound of the squeaking sleigh runners cutting the crisp snow.

When we arrived home Mama and I took off our wraps, my brother Ray brought in the coal, and Papa built up a warm fire.

"What's for supper, Mama?" Lorin asked.

"Oh, we can make sandwiches from the roast beef left from dinner," she said.

"I don't think we can," Papa said. "I took it and the gravy to the Armstrongs. But we can have the rest of the suet pudding and sauce."

"No, we can't," Mama said. "I took that to Mrs. Armstrong."

"Well, boys, let's have some of the nuts and candy from your stockings," Papa said, "because it won't matter if they do spoil our appetites now."

"We can't give you any from our stockings, Papa, we took them to the Armstrong children," Ray said.

Everyone laughed, and we made jokes and riddles while we ate our supper of bread and milk.

From then on if anything was lost, we would ask, "Did you take it to the Armstrongs?"

Mama never cried by the window any longer; she was too busy making carbolic salve, camphorated oil, liniment, and canker medicine from the recipes Grandpa Pugh had brought across the plains with him in the magic black bag. They had been given to him by his Welsh ancestors and given to Mama when she left for Canada.

Mama always said she found a magic recipe for happiness in the magic bag that Christmas Eve, and she often told it to us: A lot of faith, with a lot of work, will make everything turn out right. And never feel sorry for yourself—there is always someone in the world with more miseries than your own.

All winter she went through blizzards, rain, winds, and floods to help children with croup, pneumonia, and broken bones. She left babies for ranch women, women on lonely homesteads, and women across the boundary line on the Indian reservation.

Through it all she had a smile, time to tell us stories, and time to sing.

MISTLETOE

DOUGLAS W. EVANS

I stood under the mistletoe. The green, leafy clusters speckled with waxy-white berries hung from the branches of every apple tree.

That's the same stuff they sell in the stores for Christmas decorations, I said to myself. *Why can't I sell mistletoe, too?* Christmas was three weeks away. Selling mistletoe would be a perfect way to earn money to buy a gift for my brother, Derek.

I took a few steps back, ran, leaped, and reached as high as I could. But the lowest mistletoe cluster was too high. I missed it by a mile. So that was that.

I had started for home, when something strange caught my eye. At the edge of the apple orchard, one tree stood bare. Of course I knew the leaves and apples fell off months ago. But all the mistletoe, every sprig of it, had fallen off the branches also. It lay in a neat pile at the foot of the tree, as if put there just for me.

Delighted, I carefully picked out the best sprigs and put them in my lunch box. When it was jam-packed, I sprinted across the flattened cornfield to the mobile home where I lived.

I entered the side door, listening. Yes, a guitar was playing. I walked down the narrow hall to my bedroom and pounded on the door. "Derek, are you in there?"

The guitar stopped. "One sec," came a grumpy reply. A moment later the door was flung open. My brother stood there wearing his brown leather jacket.

"Where are you going?" I asked.

"None of your business," he muttered, sailing past me.

It wasn't easy sharing that cramped bedroom with my older brother. We got on each other's nerves a lot. That whole trailer was far too small for our family.

With Derek out of the room, I emptied the contents of my lunch box onto my bed. I split the sprigs of mistletoe into smaller ones and carefully picked off every dead leaf and berry. In my mom's sewing box, I found a roll of red ribbon. I used it to tie bows around the sprigs, then put each one into a little plastic bag.

As I looked for something to put the mistletoe in, I saw Derek's guitar on his bed, wrapped in an old towel. That guitar was the only beautiful thing Derek owned, and I knew what to buy with the mistletoe money: a case for that guitar. Even if Derek was grumpy sometimes, he was still my brother, and I loved him.

The next day I took my mistletoe packages—ten in all—to school. During lunchtime I sold every one. My pockets jingled with change as I walked home that day. But it was hardly enough money to buy a guitar case.

After school, I cut through the apple orchard again. A surprise awaited me—two more trees were bare, and under each one lay a pile of mistletoe! I loaded my lunch box, filled my pockets, then raced for home.

Derek was striding across the cornfield as I approached the trailer. His head was lowered. His hands were jammed into the pockets of his leather jacket.

"Derek! Derek!" I hollered as friendly as I could. But when he looked up and saw me, he stopped and turned in another direction.

That night I made twice as many mistletoe packages. After school the next day, I walked to the shopping center office and got permission to sell my mistletoe there. Then I found a wooden

box to use as a sales stand. I thumb-tacked a sign on it that read:
Christmas Mistletoe, 25¢.

Within an hour the mistletoe was sold out.

I hurried over to the music store. In the front display window, on cotton snow, lay a row of wooden recorders. I had learned to play a plastic one at school, and more than anything, I wanted one of those wooden ones, which sounded so much better. Each year that was at the top of my Christmas list. But each year there wasn't enough money.

I was calculating how much more money I'd need to buy a recorder when I saw the towers of guitar cases in the back of the store. As much as I wanted a recorder, I wanted to buy Derek a guitar case more. Even if he had been a grouch lately, he was a pretty neat brother. Going inside the store, I found the perfect case for Derek, a brown one with gold buttons. It cost a bundle, though. Much more than I had. I hoped that there would be lots more mistletoe in the orchard when I got there.

I reached the orchard after the sun had just set, and the air was icy. The shadowy crooked branches of the apple trees appeared as grabbing fingers against the purple sky. Something rustled in a distant tree. Rotten apples squished under my feet as I tried to creep closer to see what it was.

Then I tripped. My knees sunk into a pile of something scratchy. Mistletoe! Another big heap of it. It was a miracle!

I was filling my lunch box, when a voice right behind me softly said, "Chilly night to be out, young man."

I spun around. "I'm collecting m-m-mistletoe," I stuttered, half from cold, half from fright.

"Sorry I scared you," the man said with a friendly smile. "The fact is, I'm paying a guy to cut all that mistletoe out of my trees."

"What!" I exclaimed, puzzled.

"My apple trees are loaded with mistletoe. That very plant

people kiss under can do these old trees harm. It attaches itself to their branches and sucks out a lot of food and water. Eventually it could kill these trees. Anyway, you're welcome to take all you want."

The man wished me a merry Christmas, then walked on across the orchard. He stopped under a tree about thirty yards away and looked up. Out of that tree tumbled a big clump of mistletoe. Then another and another. An instant later two legs dangled down from the lowest branch. All of a sudden someone dropped down next to the man. It was Derek! He didn't see me in the shadows.

"A few more nights ought to do it," the man said.

"Yeah," Derek replied, brushing off his jeans.

"So what are you doing with all the money I'm paying you?" asked the man. "Are you going out and having a good time?"

"Nah," said Derek, shuffling his feet. "I'm saving up to buy my kid brother something for Christmas."

"Is that right?" said the man.

"Yeah, he's been wanting a wooden recorder for ages. He can play pretty well. And you know how it is—he's my brother."

MORNING AT BETHLEHEM

LEW WALLACE

It was now the beginning of the third watch, and at Bethlehem the morning was breaking over the mountains in the east, but so feebly that it was yet night in the valley. The watchman on the roof of the old khan, shivering in the chilly air, was listening for the first distinguishable sounds with which life, awakening, greets the dawn, when a light came moving up the hill towards the house.

He thought it a torch in someone's hand; next moment he thought it a meteor; the brilliance grew, however, until it became a star. Sore afraid, he cried out, and brought everybody within the walls to the roof. The phenomenon, in eccentric motion, continued to approach; the rocks, trees, and roadway under it shone as in a glare of lightning; directly its brightness became blinding.

The more timid of the beholders fell upon their knees, and prayed, with their faces hidden; the boldest covering their eyes, crouched, and now and then snatched glances fearfully. Afterwhile the khan and everything thereabout lay under the intolerable radiance. Such as dared look beheld the star standing still directly over the house in front of the cave where the Child had been born.

In the height of this scene, the wise men came up, and at the gate dismounted from their camels, and shouted for admission. When the steward so far mastered his terror as to give them heed, he drew the bars and opened to them. The camels looked spectral in the unnatural light, and, besides their outlandishness, there were in the faces and manner of the three visitors an eagerness and exaltation which still further excited the keeper's fears and fancy; he fell back, and for a time could not answer the question they put to him.

"Is not this Bethlehem of Judea?"

But others came, and by their presence gave him assurance.

"No, this is but the khan; the town lies farther on."

"Is there not here a child newly born?"

The bystanders turned to each other marvelling, though some of them answered, "Yes, yes."

"Show us to him!" said the Greek, impatiently.

"Show us to him!" cried Balthasar, breaking through his gravity; "for we have seen his star, even that which ye behold over the house, and are come to worship him."

The Hindoo clasped his hands, exclaiming, "God indeed lives! Make haste, make haste! The Saviour is found. Blessed, blessed are we above men!"

The people from the roof came down and followed the strangers as they were taken through the court and out into the enclosure; at sight of the star yet above the cave, though less candescent than before, some turned back afraid; the greater part went on. As the strangers neared the house, the orb arose; when they were at the door, it was high up overhead vanishing; when they entered, it went out, lost to sight. And to the witnesses of what then took place came a conviction that there was a divine relation between the star and the strangers, which extended also to at least some of the occupants of the cave. When the door was opened, they crowded in.

The apartment was lighted by a lantern enough to enable the strangers to find the mother, and the child awake in her lap.

"Is the child thine?" asked Balthasar of Mary.

And she who had kept all the things in the least affecting the little one, and pondered them in her heart, held it up in the light, saying,

"He is my son!"

And they fell down and worshipped him.

They saw the child was as other children: about its head was neither nimbus nor material crown; its lips opened not in speech; if it heard their expressions of joy, their invocations, their prayers, it made no sign whatever, but, baby-like, looked longer at the flame in the lantern than at them.

In a little while they arose, and, returning to the camels, brought gifts of gold, frankincense, and myrrh, and laid them before the child, abating nothing of their worshipful speeches; of which no part is given, for the thoughtful know that the pure worship of the pure heart was then what it is now, and has always been, an inspired song.

And this was the Savior they had come so far to find!

Yet they worshipped without a doubt.

Why?

Their faith rested upon the signs sent them by him whom we have since come to know as the Father; and they were of the kind to whom his promises were so all-sufficient that they asked nothing about his ways. Few there were who had seen the signs and heard the promises—the Mother and Joseph, the shepherds, and the Three—yet they all believed alike; that is to say, in this period of the plan of salvation, God was all and the Child nothing. But look forward, O reader! A time will come when the signs will all proceed from the Son. Happy they who then believe in him!

Let us wait that period.

THE GIFT OF THE MAGI

O . H E N R Y

One dollar and eighty-seven cents. That was all. And sixty cents of it was in pennies. Pennies saved one and two at a time by bulldozing the grocer and the vegetable man and the butcher until one's cheeks burned with the silent imputation of parsimony that such close dealing implied. Three times Della counted it. One dollar and eighty-seven cents. And the next day would be Christmas.

There was clearly nothing to do but flop down on the shabby little couch and howl. So Della did it. Which instigates the moral reflection that life is made up of sobs, sniffles, and smiles, with sniffles predominating.

While the mistress of the home is gradually subsiding from the first stage to the second, take a look at the home. A furnished flat at $8 per week. It did not exactly beggar description, but it certainly had that word on the lookout for the mendicancy squad.

In the vestibule below was a letter-box into which no letter would go, and an electric button from which no mortal finger could coax a ring. Also appertaining thereunto was a card bearing the name "Mr. James Dillingham Young."

The "Dillingham" had been flung to the breeze during a former period of prosperity when its possessor was being paid $30 per week. Now, when the income was shrunk to $20, though, they were thinking seriously of contracting to a modest and unassuming D. But whenever Mr. James Dillingham Young came home and reached his flat above he was called "Jim" and greatly hugged by

Mrs. James Dillingham Young, already introduced to you as Della. Which is all very good.

Della finished her cry and attended to her cheeks with the powder rag. She stood by the window and looked out dully at a gray cat walking a gray fence in a gray backyard. Tomorrow would be Christmas Day, and she had only $1.87 with which to buy Jim a present. She had been saving every penny she could for months, with this result. Twenty dollars a week doesn't go far. Expenses had been greater than she had calculated. They always are. Only $1.87 to buy a present for Jim. Her Jim. Many a happy hour she had spent planning for something nice for him. Something fine and rare and sterling—something just a little bit near to being worthy of the honor of being owned by Jim.

There was a pier-glass between the windows of the room. Perhaps you have seen a pier-glass in an $8 flat. A very thin and very agile person may, by observing his reflection in a rapid sequence of longitudinal strips, obtain a fairly accurate conception of his looks. Della, being slender, had mastered the art.

Suddenly she whirled from the window and stood before the glass. Her eyes were shining brilliantly, but her face had lost its color within twenty seconds. Rapidly she pulled down her hair and let it fall to its full length.

Now, there were two possessions of the James Dillingham Youngs in which they both took a mighty pride. One was Jim's gold watch that had been his father's and his grandfather's. The other was Della's hair. Had the queen of Sheba lived in the flat across the airshaft, Della would have let her hair hang out the window some day to dry just to depreciate Her Majesty's jewels and gifts. Had King Solomon been the janitor, with all his treasures piled up in the basement, Jim would have pulled out his watch every time he passed, just to see him pluck at his beard from envy.

So now Della's beautiful hair fell about her, rippling and

shining like a cascade of brown waters. It reached below her knee and made itself almost a garment for her. And then she did it up again nervously and quickly. Once she faltered for a minute and stood still while a tear or two splashed on the worn red carpet.

On went her old brown jacket; on went her old brown hat. With a whirl of skirts and with the brilliant sparkle still in her eyes, she fluttered out the door and down the stairs to the street.

Where she stopped the sign read: "Mme. Sofronie. Hair Goods of All Kinds." One flight up Della ran, and collected herself, panting. Madame, large, too white, chilly, hardly looked the "Sofronie."

"Will you buy my hair?" asked Della.

"I buy hair," said Madame. "Take yer hat off and let's have a sight at the looks of it."

Down rippled the brown cascade.

"Twenty dollars," said Madame, lifting the mass with a practiced hand.

"Give it to me quick," said Della.

Oh, and the next two hours tripped by on rosy wings. Forget the hashed metaphor. She was ransacking the stores for Jim's present.

She found it at last. It surely had been made for Jim and no one else. There was no other like it in any of the stores, and she had turned all of them inside out. It was a platinum fob chain simple and chaste in design, properly proclaiming its value by substance alone and not by meretricious ornamentation—as all good things should do. It was even worthy of The Watch. As soon as she saw it she knew that it must be Jim's. It was like him. Quietness and value—the description applied to both. Twenty-one dollars they took from her for it, and she hurried home with the 87 cents. With that chain on his watch Jim might be properly anxious about the time in any company. Grand as the watch was, he sometimes looked at it on the sly on account of the old leather strap that he used in place of a chain.

When Della reached home her intoxication gave way a little to prudence and reason. She got out her curling irons and lighted the gas and went to work repairing the ravages made by generosity added to love. Which is always a tremendous task, dear friends—a mammoth task.

Within forty minutes her head was covered with tiny close-lying curls that made her look wonderfully like a truant schoolboy. She looked at her reflection in the mirror long, carefully, and critically.

"If Jim doesn't kill me," she said to herself, "before he takes a second look at me, he'll say I look like a Coney Island chorus girl. But what could I do—oh! what could I do with a dollar and eighty-seven cents?"

At seven o'clock the coffee was made and the frying-pan was on the back of the stove hot and ready to cook the chops.

Jim was never late. Della doubled the fob chain in her hand and sat on the corner of the table near the door that he always entered. Then she heard his step on the stair away down on the first flight, and she turned white for just a moment. She had a habit of saying little silent prayers about the simplest everyday things, and now she whispered: "Please God, make him think I am still pretty."

The door opened and Jim stepped in and closed it. He looked thin and very serious. Poor fellow, he was only twenty-two—and to be burdened with a family! He needed a new overcoat and he was without gloves.

Jim stopped inside the door, as immovable as a setter at the scent of quail. His eyes were fixed upon Della, and there was an expression in them that she could not read, and it terrified her. It was not anger, nor surprise, nor disapproval, nor horror, nor any of the sentiments that she had been prepared for. He simply stared at her fixedly with that peculiar expression on his face.

Della wriggled off the table and went for him.

"Jim, darling," she cried, "don't look at me that way. I had my hair cut off and sold it because I couldn't have lived through Christmas without giving you a present. It'll grow out again—you won't mind, will you? I just had to do it. My hair grows awfully fast. Say 'Merry Christmas!' Jim, and let's be happy. You don't know what a nice—what a beautiful, nice gift I've got for you."

"You've cut off your hair?" asked Jim, laboriously, as if he had not arrived at that patent fact yet even after the hardest mental labor.

"Cut it off and sold it," said Della. "Don't you like me just as well, anyhow? I'm me without my hair, ain't I?"

Jim looked about the room curiously.

"You say your hair is gone?" he said, with an air almost of idiocy.

"You needn't look for it," said Della. "It's sold, I tell you—sold and gone, too. It's Christmas Eve, boy. Be good to me, for it went for you. Maybe the hairs of my head were numbered," she went on with a sudden serious sweetness, "but nobody could ever count my love for you. Shall I put the chops on, Jim?"

Out of his trance Jim seemed quickly to wake. He enfolded his Della. For ten seconds let us regard with discreet scrutiny some inconsequential object in the other direction. Eight dollars a week or a million a year—what is the difference? A mathematician or a wit would give you the wrong answer. The magi brought valuable gifts, but that was not among them. This dark assertion will be illuminated later on.

Jim drew a package from his overcoat pocket and threw it upon the table.

"Don't make any mistake, Dell," he said, "about me. I don't

think there's anything in the way of a haircut or a shave or a shampoo that could make me like my girl any less. But if you'll unwrap that package you may see why you had me going a while at first."

White fingers and nimble tore at the string and paper. And then an ecstatic scream of joy; and then, alas! a quick feminine change to hysterical tears and wails, necessitating the immediate employment of all the comforting powers of the lord of the flat.

For there lay The Combs—the set of combs, side and back, that Della had worshiped long in a Broadway window. Beautiful combs, pure tortoise shell, with jeweled rims—just the shade to wear in the beautiful vanished hair. They were expensive combs, she knew, and her heart had simply craved and yearned over them without the least hope of possession. And now, they were hers, but the tresses that should have adorned the coveted adornments were gone.

But she hugged them to her bosom, and at length she was able to look up with dim eyes and a smile and say: "My hair grows so fast, Jim!"

And then Della leaped up like a little singed cat and cried, "Oh, oh!"

Jim had not yet seen his beautiful present. She held it out to him eagerly upon her open palm. The dull precious metal seemed to flash with a reflection of her bright and ardent spirit.

"Isn't it a dandy, Jim? I hunted all over town to find it. You'll have to look at the time a hundred times a day now. Give me your watch. I want to see how it looks on it."

Instead of obeying, Jim tumbled down on the couch and put his hands under the back of his head and smiled.

"Dell," said he, "let's put our Christmas presents away and keep 'em a while. They're too nice to use just at present. I sold the watch to get the money to buy your combs. And now suppose you put the chops on."

The magi, as you know, were wise men—wonderfully wise men—who brought gifts to the Babe in the manger. They invented the art of giving Christmas presents. Being wise, their gifts were no doubt wise ones, possibly bearing the privilege of exchange in case of duplication. And here I have lamely related to you the uneventful chronicle of two foolish children in a flat who most unwisely sacrificed for each other the greatest treasures of their house. But in a last word to the wise of these days let it be said that of all who give gifts these two were the wisest. Of all who give and receive gifts, such as they are wisest. Everywhere they are wisest. They are the magi.

THE LITTLE BLUE DISHES

AUTHOR UNKNOWN

Once upon a time there was a poor woodcutter who lived with his wife and three children in a forest in Germany. There was a big boy called Hans and a little boy named Peterkin and a little sister named Gretchen, just five years old. When Christmas was getting near, the children went to the toy shop to look at all of the toys.

"Gretchen," said Peterkin, "what do you like best?"

"Oh! That little box of blue dishes," said Gretchen. "That is the very best of all."

On Christmas Eve the children hung up their stockings, although their mother had said that they were so poor they could not have much this Christmas. Hans ran out after supper to play with the big boys. Gretchen and Peterkin sat talking before the fire about the Christmas toys and especially about the box of blue dishes. By and by Gretchen ran off to bed and was soon asleep. Peterkin ran to look in his bank. There was only one penny, but he took it and ran quickly to the toy shop.

"What have you for a penny?" he said to the toy man.

"Only a small candy heart with a picture on it," said the man.

"But I want that set of blue dishes," said Peterkin.

"Oh, they cost ten cents," said the man.

So Peterkin bought the candy heart and put it in Gretchen's stocking, and then he ran off to bed.

Pretty soon Hans came home. He was cold and hungry. When he saw Gretchen's stocking he peeked in, then put his hand in and drew out the candy heart. "Oh," said Hans, "how good this smells," and before you could say a word he had eaten the candy heart. "Oh, dear," he said, "that was for Gretchen for Christmas. I'll run and buy something else for her." So he ran to his bank and he had ten pennies. Quickly he ran to the toy store.

"What have you got for ten pennies?" he asked the store-keeper.

"Well, I'm almost sold out," said the toy man, "but here in this little box is a set of blue dishes."

"I will take them," said Hans, and home he ran and dropped the dishes into Gretchen's stocking. Then he went to bed.

Early in the morning the children came running downstairs.

"Oh!" said Gretchen. "Look at my stocking!" And when she saw the blue dishes, she was as happy as could be. But Peterkin could never understand how his candy heart had changed into a box of blue dishes.

THE LITTLE MATCH GIRL

HANS CHRISTIAN ANDERSEN

Once upon a time . . . a little girl tried to make a living by selling matches in the street. It was New Year's Eve and the snowclad streets were deserted. From brightly lit windows came the tinkle of laughter and the sound of singing. People were getting ready to bring in the New Year. But the poor little matchseller sat sadly beside the fountain. Her ragged dress and worn shawl did not keep out the cold and she tried to keep her bare feet from touching the frozen ground. She hadn't sold one box of matches all day and she was frightened to go home, for her father would certainly be angry. It wouldn't be much warmer anyway, in the draughty attic that was her home. The little girl's fingers were stiff with cold. If only she could light a match! But what would her father say at such a waste! Falteringly she took out a match and lit it. What a nice warm flame! The little matchseller cupped her hand over it, and as she did so, she magically saw in its light a big brightly burning stove.

She held out her hands to the heat, but just then the match went out and the vision faded. The night seemed blacker than before and it was getting colder. A shiver ran through the little girl's thin body.

After hesitating for a long time, she struck another match on the wall, and this time, the glimmer turned the wall into a great sheet of crystal. Beyond that stood a fine table laden with food and lit by a candlestick. Holding out her arms towards the plates, the little matchseller seemed to pass through the glass, but then the match went out and the magic faded. Poor thing: in just a few seconds she had caught a glimpse of everything that life had denied her: warmth and good things to eat. Her eyes filled with tears and she lifted her gaze to the lit windows, praying that she too might know a little of such happiness.

She lit the third match and an even more wonderful thing happened. There stood a Christmas tree hung with hundreds of candles, glittering with tinsel and coloured balls. "Oh, how lovely!" exclaimed the little matchseller, holding up the match. Then, the match burned her finger and flickered out. The light from the Christmas candles rose higher and higher, then one of the lights fell, leaving a trail behind it. "Someone is dying," murmured the little girl, as she remembered her beloved Granny who used to say: "When a star falls, a heart stops beating!"

Scarcely aware of what she was doing, the little matchseller lit another match. This time, she saw her grandmother.

"Granny, stay with me!" she pleaded, as she lit one match after the other, so that her grandmother could not disappear like all the other visions. However, Granny did not vanish, but gazed smilingly at her. Then she opened her arms and the little girl hugged her crying: "Granny, take me away with you!"

A cold day dawned and a pale sun shone on the fountain and the icy road. Close by lay the lifeless body of a little girl surrounded by spent matches. "Poor little thing!" exclaimed the passersby. "She was trying to keep warm!"

But by that time, the little matchseller was far away where there is neither cold, hunger nor pain.

THE STORY OF THE OTHER
WISE MAN

HENRY VAN DYKE

You know the story of the Three Wise Men of the East, and how they traveled from far away to offer their gifts at the manger-cradle in Bethlehem. But have you ever heard the story of the Other Wise Man, who also saw the star in its rising, and set out to follow it, yet did not arrive with his brethren in the presence of the young child Jesus? Of the great desire of this fourth pilgrim, and how it was denied, yet accomplished in the denial; of his many wanderings and the probations of his soul; of the long way of his seeking, and the strange way of his finding, the One whom he sought—I would tell the tale as I have heard fragments of it in the Hall of Dreams, in the palace of the Heart of Man.

The Sign in the Sky

In the days when Augustus Caesar was master of many kings and Herod reigned in Jerusalem, there lived in the city of Ecbatana, among the mountains of Persia, a certain man named Artaban, the Median. His house stood close to the outermost of the seven walls which encircled the royal treasury. From his roof he could look over the rising battlements of black and white and crimson and blue and red and silver and gold, to the hill where the summer palace of the Parthian emperors glittered like a jewel in a sevenfold crown.

Around the dwelling of Artaban spread a fair garden, a tangle of flowers and fruit trees, watered by a score of streams descending from the slopes of Mount Orontes, and made musical by innumerable birds. But all color was lost in the soft and odorous darkness of the late September night, and all sounds were hushed in the deep charm of its silence, save the plashing of the water, like a voice half sobbing and half laughing under the shadows. High above the trees a dim glow of light shone through the curtained arches of the upper chamber, where the master of the house was holding council with his friends.

He stood by the doorway to greet his guests—a tall, dark man of about forty years, with brilliant eyes set near together under his broad brow, and firm lines graven around his fine, thin lips; the brow of a dreamer and the mouth of a soldier, a man of sensitive feeling by inflexible will—one of those who, in whatever age they may live, are born for inward conflict and a life of quest. . . .

"Welcome!" he said, in his low, pleasant voice, as one after another entered the room. . . .

"You have come to-night," said [Artaban], looking around the circle, "at my call, as the faithful scholars of Zoroaster. . . .

"Hear me, then, . . . while I tell you of the new light and truth that have come to me through the most ancient of all signs. We have searched the secrets of nature together, and studied the healing virtues of water and fire and the plants. We have read also the books of prophecy in which the future is dimly foretold in words that are hard to understand. But the highest of all learning is the knowledge of the stars. To trace their courses is to untangle the threads of the mystery of life from the beginning to the end. If we could follow them perfectly, nothing would be hidden from us. But is not our knowledge of them still incomplete? Are there not many stars still beyond our horizon—lights that are known only to the dwellers in the far southland, among the spice trees of Punt and the gold mines of Ophir?"

There was a murmur of assent among the listeners.

"The stars," said Tigranes, "are the thoughts of the Eternal. They are numberless. But the thoughts of man can be counted, like the years of his life. The wisdom of the Magi is the greatest of all wisdoms on earth, because it knows its own ignorance. And that is the secret of power. We keep men always looking and waiting for a new sunrise. But we ourselves know that the darkness is equal to the light, and that the conflict between them will never be ended."

"That does not satisfy me," answered Artaban, "for, if the waiting must be endless, if there could be no fulfilment of it, then it would not be wisdom to look and wait. We should become like those new teachers of the Greeks, who say that there is no truth, and that the only wise men are those who spend their lives in discovering and exposing the lies that have been believed in the world. But the new sunrise will certainly dawn in the appointed time. Do not our own books tell us that this will come to pass, and that men will see the brightness of a great light?"

"That is true," said the voice of Abgarus; "every faithful disciple of Zoroaster knows the prophecy of the Avesta and carries the word in his heart. 'In that day Sosiosh the Victorious shall arise out of the number of the prophets in the east country. Around him shall shine a mighty brightness, and he shall make life everlasting, incorruptible, and immortal, and the dead shall rise again.'"

"This is a dark saying," said Tigranes, "and it may be that we shall never understand it. It is better to consider the things that are near at hand, and to increase the influence of the Magi in their own country, rather than to look for one who may be a stranger, and to whom we must resign our power."

The others seemed to approve these words. There was a silent feeling of agreement manifest among them; their looks responded with that indefinable expression which always follows when a speaker has uttered the thought that has been slumbering in the hearts of his listeners. But Artaban turned to Abgarus with a glow on his face, and said:

"My father, I have kept this prophecy in the secret place of my soul. Religion without a great hope would be like an altar without a living fire. And now the flame has burned more brightly, and by the light of it I have read other words which also have come from the fountain of Truth, and speak yet more clearly of the rising of the Victorious One in his brightness."

He drew from the breast of his tunic two small rolls of fine linen, with writing upon them, and unfolded them carefully upon his knee.

"In the years that are lost in the past, long before our fathers came into the land of Babylon, there were wise men in Chaldea, from whom the first of the Magi learned the secret of the heavens. And of these Balaam, the son of Beor, was one of the mightiest. Hear the words of his prophecy: 'There shall come a star out of Jacob, and a sceptre shall arise out of Israel.'"

The lips of Tigranes drew downward with contempt, as he said:

"Judah was a captive by the waters of Babylon, and the sons of Jacob were in bondage to our kings. The tribes of Israel are scattered through the mountains like lost sheep, and from the remnant that dwells in Judea under the yoke of Rome neither star nor sceptre shall arise."

"And yet," answered Artaban, "it was the Hebrew Daniel, the mighty searcher of dreams, the counsellor of kings, the wise Belteshazzar, who was most honored and beloved of our great King Cyrus. A prophet of sure things and a reader of the thoughts of God, Daniel proved himself to our people. And these are the words that he wrote." (Artaban read from the second roll:) "'Know, therefore, and understand that from the going forth of the commandment to restore Jerusalem, unto the Anointed One, the Prince, the time shall be seven and three-score and two weeks.'"

"But, my son," said Abgarus, doubtfully, "these are mystical numbers. Who can interpret them, or who can find the key that shall unlock their meaning?"

Artaban answered: "It has been shown to me and to my three companions among the Magi—Caspar, Melchior, and Balthazar. We have searched the ancient tablets of Chaldea and computed the time. It falls in this year. We have studied the sky, and in the spring of the year we saw two of the greatest stars draw near together in the sign of the Fish, which is the house of the Hebrews. We also saw a new star there, which shone for one night and then vanished. Now again the two great planets are meeting. This night is their conjunction. My three brothers are watching at the ancient Temple of the Seven Spheres, at Borsippa, in Babylonia, and I am watching here. If the star shines again, they will wait ten days for me at the temple, and then we will set out together for Jerusalem, to see and worship the promised one who shall be born King of Israel. I believe the sign will come. I have made ready for the journey. I have sold my house and my possessions, and bought these three jewels—a sapphire, ruby, and a pearl—to carry them as tribute to the King. And I ask you to go with me on the pilgrimage, that we may have joy together in finding the Prince who is worthy to be served."

While he was speaking he thrust his hand into the inmost fold of his girdle and drew out three great gems—one blue as a fragment of the night sky, one redder than a ray of sunrise, and one as pure as the peak of a snow-mountain at twilight—and laid them on the outspread linen scrolls before him.

But his friends looked on with strange and alien eyes. A veil of doubt and mistrust came over their faces, like a fog creeping up from the marshes to hide the hills. They glanced at each other with looks of wonder and pity, as those who have listened to incredible sayings, the story of a wild vision, or the proposal of an impossible enterprise.

At last Tigranes said: "Artaban, this is a vain dream. It comes from too much looking upon the stars and the cherishing of lofty thoughts. It would be wiser to spend the time in gathering money for the new fire-temple at Chala. No king will ever rise from the broken race of Israel, and no end will ever come to the eternal strife of light and darkness. He who looks for it is a chaser of shadows. Farewell."

And another said: "Artaban, I have no knowledge of these things, and my office as guardian of the royal treasure binds me here. The quest is not for me. But if thou must follow it, fare thee well."

And another said: "In my house there sleeps a new bride, and I cannot leave her nor take her with me on this strange journey. This quest is not for me. But may thy steps be prospered wherever thou goest. So, farewell."

And another said: "I am ill and unfit for hardship, but there is a man among my servants whom I will send with thee when thou goest, to bring me word how thou farest."

But Abgarus, the oldest and the one who loved Artaban the best, lingered after the others had gone, and said, gravely: "My son, it may be that the light of truth is in this sign that has appeared in the skies, and then it will surely lead to the Prince and the mighty brightness. Or it may be that it is only a shadow of the light, as Tigranes has said, and then he who follows it will have only a long pilgrimage and an empty search. But it is better to follow even the shadow of the best than to remain content with the worst. And those who would see wonderful things must often be ready to travel alone. I am too old for this journey, but my heart shall be a companion of the pilgrimage day and night, and I shall know the end of thy quest. Go in peace."

So one by one they went out of the azure chamber with its silver stars, and Artaban was left in solitude.

He gathered up the jewels and replaced them in his girdle. For a long time he stood and watched the flame that flickered and sank upon the altar. Then he crossed the hall, lifted the heavy curtain, and passed out between the dull red pillars of porphyry to the terrace on the roof.

The shiver that thrills through the earth ere she rouses from her night sleep had already begun, and the cool wind that heralds the daybreak was drawing downward from the lofty, snow-traced ravines of Mount Orontes. Birds, half awakened, crept and chirped among the rustling leaves, and the smell of ripened grapes came in brief wafts from the arbors.

Far over the eastern plain a white mist stretched like a lake. But where the distant peak of Zagros serrated the western horizon, the sky was clear. Jupiter and Saturn rolled together like drops of lambent flame about to blend in one.

As Artaban watched them, behold, an azure spark was born out of the darkness beneath, rounding itself with purple splendors to a crimson sphere, and spiring upward through rays of saffron and orange into a point of white radiance. Tiny and infinitely remote, yet perfect in every part, it pulsated in the enormous vault as if the three jewels in the Magian's breast had mingled and been transformed into a living heart of light.

He bowed his head. He covered his brow with his hands.

"It is the sign," he said. "The King is coming, and I will go to meet him."

By the Waters of Babylon

All night long Vasda, the swiftest of Artaban's horses, had been waiting, saddled and bridled, in her stall, pawing the ground impatiently, and shaking her bit as if she shared the eagerness of her master's purpose, though she knew not its meaning.

Before the birds had fully roused to their strong, high, joyful chant of morning song, before the white mist had begun to lift lazily from the plain, the other wise man was in the saddle, riding swiftly along the highroad, which skirted the base of Mount Orontes, westward. . . .

Artaban must indeed ride wisely and well if he would keep the appointed hour with the other Magi; for the route was a hundred and fifty parasangs, and fifteen was the utmost that he could travel in a day. But he knew Vasda's strength, and pushed forward without anxiety, making the fixed distance every day, though he must travel late into the night, and in the morning long before sunrise.

He passed along the brown slopes of Mount Orontes, furrowed by the rocky courses of a hundred torrents.

He crossed the level plains of the Nisaeans, where the famous herds of horses, feeding in the wide pastures, tossed their heads at Vasda's approach, and galloped away with a thunder of many hoofs, and flocks of wild birds rose suddenly from the swampy meadows, wheeling in great circles with a shining flutter of innumerable wings and shrill cries of surprise.

He traversed the fertile fields of Concabar, where the dust from the threshing-floors filled the air with a golden mist, half hiding the huge temple of Astarte with its four-hundred pillars.

At Baghistan, among the rich gardens watered by fountains from the rock, he looked up at the mountain thrusting its immense rugged brow out over the road, and saw the figure of King Darius trampling upon his fallen foes, and the proud list of his wars and conquests graven high upon the face of the eternal cliff.

Over many a cold and desolate pass, crawling painfully across the wind-swept shoulders of the hills; down many a black mountain-gorge, where the river roared and raced before him like a savage guide; across many a smiling vale, with terraces of yellow limestone full of vines and fruit trees; through the oak groves of Carine and the dark Gates of Zagros, walled in by precipices; into the ancient city of Chala, where the people of Samaria had been kept in captivity long ago; and out again by the mighty portal, riven through the encircling hills, where he saw the image of the High Priest of the Magi sculptured on the wall of rock, with hand uplifted as if to bless the centuries of pilgrims; past the entrance of the narrow defile, filled from end to end with orchards of peaches and figs, through which the river Gyndes foamed down to meet him; over the broad rice fields, where the autumnal vapors spread their deathly mists; following along the course of the river, under tremulous shadows of poplar and tamarind, among the lower hills; and out upon the flat plain, where the road ran straight as an arrow through the stubble-fields and parched meadows; past the city of Ctesiphon, where the Parthian emperors reigned, and the vast metropolis of Seleucia which Alexander built; across the swirling floods of Tigris and the many channels of Euphrates, flowing yellow through the corn-lands—Artaban pressed onward until he arrived at nightfall on the tenth day, beneath the shattered walls of populous Babylon.

Vasda was almost spent, and he would gladly have turned into the city to find rest and refreshment for himself and for her. But he knew that it was three hours' journey yet to the Temple of the Seven Spheres, and he must reach the place by midnight if he would find his comrades waiting. So he did not halt, but rode steadily across the stubble-fields.

A grove of date-palms made an island of gloom in the pale yellow sea. As she passed into the shadow Vasda slackened her pace, and began to pick her way more carefully.

Near the farther end of the darkness an access of caution seemed to fall upon her. She scented some danger or difficulty; it was not in her heart to fly from it—only to be prepared for it, and to meet it wisely, as a good horse should do. The grove was close and silent as the tomb; not a leaf rustled, not a bird sang.

She felt her steps before her delicately, carrying her head low, and sighing now and then with apprehension. At last she gave a quick breath of anxiety and dismay, and stood stock-still, quivering in every muscle, before a dark object in the shadow of the last palm tree.

Artaban dismounted. The dim starlight revealed the form of a man lying across the road. His humble dress and the outline of his haggard face showed that he was probably one of the poor Hebrew exiles who still dwelt in great numbers in the vicinity. His pallid skin, dry and yellow as parchment, bore the mark of the deadly fever which ravaged the marshlands in autumn. The chill of death was in his lean hand, and as Artaban released it the arm fell back inertly upon the motionless breast.

He turned away with a thought of pity, consigning the body to that strange burial which the Magians deemed most fitting—the funeral of the desert, from which the kites and vultures rise on dark wings, and the beasts of prey slink furtively away, leaving only a heap of white bones in the sand.

But, as he turned, a long, faint, ghostly sigh came from the man's lips. The brown, bony fingers closed convulsively on the hem of the Magian's robe and held him fast.

Artaban's heart leaped to his throat, not with fear, but with a dumb resentment at the importunity of this blind delay.

How could he stay here in the darkness to minister to a dying stranger? What claim had this unknown fragment of human life upon his compassion or his service? If he lingered but for an hour he could hardly reach Borsippa at the appointed time. His companions would think he had given up the journey. They would go without him. He would lose his quest.

But if he went on now, the man would surely die. If he stayed, life might be restored. His spirit throbbed and fluttered with the urgency of the crisis. Should he risk the great reward of his divine faith for the sake of a single deed of human love? Should he turn aside, if only for a moment, from the following of the star, to give a cup of cold water to a poor, perishing Hebrew?

"God of truth and purity," he prayed, "direct me in the holy path, the way of wisdom which Thou only knowest."

Then he turned back to the sick man. Loosening the grasp on his hand, he carried him to a little mound at the foot of the - palm tree.

He unbound the thick folds of the turban and opened the garment above the sunken breast. He brought water from one of the small canals near by, and moistened the sufferer's brow and mouth. He mingled a draught of one of those simple but potent remedies which he carried always in his girdle—for the Magians were physicians as well as astrologers—and poured it slowly between the colorless lips. Hour after hour he labored as only a skilful healer of disease can do; and at last the man's strength returned; he sat up and looked about him.

"Who art thou?" he said in the rude dialect of the country, "and why hast thou sought me here to bring back my life?"

"I am Artaban the Magian, of the city of Ecbatana, and I am going to Jerusalem in search of one who is to be born King of the Jews, a great Prince and Deliverer of all men. I dare not delay any longer upon my journey, for the caravan that has waited for me may depart without me. But see, here is all that I have left of bread and wine, and here is a potion of healing herbs. When thy strength is restored thou canst find the dwellings of the Hebrews among the houses of Babylon."

The Jew raised his trembling hand solemnly to heaven.

"Now may the God of Abraham and Isaac and Jacob bless and prosper the journey of the merciful, and bring him in peace to his desired haven. But stay; I have nothing to give thee in return— only this: that I can tell thee where the Messiah much be sought. For our prophets have said that he should be born not in Jerusalem, but in Bethlehem of Judah. May the Lord bring thee in safety to that place, because thou hast had pity upon the sick."

It was already long past midnight. Artaban rose in haste, and Vasda, restored by the brief rest, ran eagerly through the silent plain and swam the channels of the river. She put forth the remnant of her strength, and fled over the ground like a gazelle.

But the first beam of the sun sent her shadow before her as she entered upon the final stadium of the journey, and the eyes of Artaban, anxiously scanning the great mound of Nimrod and the Temple of the Seven Spheres, could discern no trace of his friends.

The many-colored terraces of black and orange and red and yellow and green and blue and white, shattered by the convulsions of nature, and crumbling under the repeated blows of human violence, still glittered like a ruined rainbow in the morning light.

Artaban rode swiftly around the hill. He dismounted and climbed to the highest terrace, looking out toward the west.

The huge desolation of the marshes stretched away to the horizon and the border of the desert. Bitterns stood by the stagnant pools and jackals skulked through the low bushes; but there was no sign of the caravan of the Wise Men, far or near.

At the edge of the terrace he saw a little cairn of broken bricks, and under them a piece of parchment. He caught it up and read: "We have waited past the midnight, and can delay no longer. We go to find the King. Follow us across the desert."

Artaban sat down upon the ground and covered his head in despair.

"How can I cross the desert," said he, "with no food and with a spent horse? I must return to Babylon, sell my sapphire, and buy a train of camels, and provision for the journey. I may never over-take my friends. Only God the merciful knows whether I shall not lose the sight of the King because I tarried to show mercy."

For the Sake of a Little Child

There was a silence in the Hall of Dreams, where I was listen-ing to the story of the Other Wise Man. And through this silence I saw, but very dimly, his figure passing over the dreary undulations of the desert, high upon the back of his camel, rocking steadily onward like a ship over the waves.

The land of death spread its cruel net around him. The stony wastes bore no fruit but briers and thorns. The dark ledges of rock thrust themselves above the surface here and there, like the bones of perished monsters. Arid and inhospitable mountain ranges rose before him, furrowed with dry channels of ancient torrents, white and ghastly as scars on the face of Nature. Shifting hills of treach-erous sand were heaped like tombs along the horizon. By day, the fierce heat pressed its intolerable burden on the quivering air; and no living creature moved on the dumb, swooning earth, but tiny jerboas scuttling through the parched bushes, or lizards vanishing in the clefts of the rock. By night the jackals prowled and barked in the distance, and the lion made the black ravines echo with his hollow roaring, while a bitter blighting chill followed the fever of the day. Through heat and cold, the Magian moved steadily onward.

Then I saw the gardens and orchards of Damascus, watered by

the streams of Abana and Pharpar with their sloping swards inlaid with bloom, and their thickets of myrrh and roses. I saw also the long, snowy ridge of Hermon, and the dark groves of cedars, and the valley of the Jordan, and the blue waters of the Lake of Galilee, and the fertile plain of Esdraelon, and the hills of Ephraim, and the highlands of Judah. Through all these I followed the figure of Artaban moving steadily onward, until he arrived at Bethlehem. And it was the third day after the three wise men had come to that place and had found Mary and Joseph, with the young child, Jesus, and had laid their gifts of gold and frankincense and myrrh at his feet.

Then the other wise man drew near, weary, but full of hope, bearing his ruby and his pearl to offer to the King. "For now at last," he said, "I shall surely find him, though it be alone, and later than my brethren. This is the place of which the Hebrew exile told me that the prophets had spoken, and here I shall behold the rising of the great light. But I must inquire about the visit of my brethren, and to what house the star directed them, and to whom they presented their tribute."

The streets of the village seemed to be deserted, and Artaban wondered whether the men had all gone up to the hill-pastures to bring down their sheep. From the open door of a low stone cottage he heard the sound of a woman's voice singing softly. He entered and found a young mother hushing her baby to rest. She told him of the strangers from the far East who had appeared in the village three days ago, and how they said that a star had guided them to the place where Joseph of Nazareth was lodging with his wife and her newborn child, and how they had paid reverence to the child and given him many rich gifts.

"But the travelers disappeared again," she continued, "as suddenly as they had come. We were afraid at the strangeness of their visit. We could not understand it. The man of Nazareth took the babe and his mother and fled away that same night secretly, and it was whispered that they were going far away to Egypt. Ever since, there has been a spell upon the village; something evil hangs over it. They say that the Roman soldiers are coming from Jerusalem to force a new tax from us, and the men have driven the flocks and herds far back among the hills, and hidden themselves to escape it."

Artaban listened to her gentle, timid speech, and the child in her arms looked up in his face and smiled, stretching out its rosy hands to grasp at the winged circle of gold on his breast. His heart warmed to the touch. It seemed like a greeting of love and trust to one who had journeyed long in loneliness and perplexity, fighting with his own doubts and fears, and following a light that was veiled in clouds.

"Might not this child have been the promised Prince?" he asked within himself, as he touched its soft cheek. "Kings have been born ere now in lowlier houses than this, and the favorite of the stars may rise even from a cottage. But it has not seemed good to the God of wisdom to reward my search so soon and so easily. The one whom I seek has gone before me; and now I must follow the King to Egypt."

The young mother laid the babe in its cradle, and rose to minister to the wants of the strange guest that fate had brought into her house. She set food before him, the plain fare of peasants, but willingly offered, and therefore full of refreshment for the soul as well as for the body. Artaban accepted it gratefully; and, as he ate, the child fell into a happy slumber, and murmured sweetly in its dreams, and a great peace filled the quiet room.

But suddenly there came the noise of a wild confusion and uproar in the streets of the village, a shrieking and wailing of women's voices, a clangor of brazen trumpets and a clashing of swords, and a desperate cry: "The soldiers! the soldiers of Herod! They are killing our children."

The young mother's face grew white with terror. She clasped her child to her bosom, and crouched motionless in the darkest corner of the room, covering him with the folds of her robe, lest he should wake and cry.

But Artaban went quickly and stood in the doorway of the house. His broad shoulders filled the portal from side to side, and the peak of his white cap all but touched the lintel.

The soldiers came hurrying down the street with bloody hands and dripping swords. At the sight of the stranger in his imposing dress they hesitated with surprise. The captain of the band approached the threshold to thrust him aside. But Artaban did not stir. His face was as calm as though he were watching the stars, and in his eyes there burned that steady radiance before which even the half-tamed hunting leopard shrinks and the fierce blood-hound pauses in his leap. He held the soldier silently for an instant, and then said in a low voice:

"I am all alone in this place, and I am waiting to give this jewel to the prudent captain who will leave me in peace."

He showed the ruby, glistening in the hollow of his hand like a great drop of blood.

The captain was amazed at the splendor of the gem. The pupils of his eyes expanded with desire, and the hard lines of greed wrinkled around his lips. He stretched out his hand and took the ruby.

"March on!" he cried to his men, "there is no child here. The house is still."

The clamor and the clang of arms passed down the street as the headlong fury of the chase sweeps by the secret covert where the trembling deer is hidden. Artaban re-entered the cottage. He turned his face to the east and prayed:

"God of truth, forgive my sin! I have said the thing that is not, to save the life of a child. And two of my gifts are gone. I have spent for man that which was meant for God. Shall I ever be worthy to see the face of the King?"

But the voice of the woman, weeping for joy in the shadow behind him, said very gently:

"Because thou hast saved the life of my little one, may the Lord bless thee and keep thee; the Lord make His face to shine upon thee and be gracious unto thee; the Lord lift up His countenance upon thee and give thee peace."

In the Hidden Way of Sorrow

Then again there was a silence in the Hall of Dreams, deeper and more mysterious than the first interval, and I understood that the years of Artaban were flowing very swiftly under the stillness of that clinging fog, and I caught only a glimpse, here and there, of the river of his life shining through the shadows that concealed its course.

I saw him moving among the throngs of men in populous Egypt, seeking everywhere for traces of the household that had come down from Bethlehem, and finding them under the spreading sycamore trees of Heliopolis, and beneath the walls of the Roman fortress of New Babylon beside the Nile—traces so faint and dim that they vanished before him continually, as footprints on the hard river-sand glisten for a moment with moisture and then disappear.

I saw him again at the foot of the pyramids, which lifted their sharp points into the intense saffron glow of the sunset sky, changeless monuments of the perishable glory and the imperishable hope of man. He looked up into the vast countenance of the crouching Sphinx, and vainly tried to read the meaning of [the] calm eyes and smiling mouth. Was it, indeed, the mockery of all effort and all aspiration, as Tigranes had said—the cruel jest of a riddle that has no answer, a search that never can succeed? Or was there a touch of pity and encouragement in that inscrutable smile—a promise that even the defeated should attain a victory, and the disappointed should discover a prize, and the ignorant should be made wise, and the blind should see, and the wandering should come into the haven at last?

I saw him again in an obscure house of Alexandria, taking counsel with a Hebrew rabbi. The venerable man, bending over the rolls of parchment on which the prophecies of Israel were written, read aloud the pathetic words which foretold the sufferings of the promised Messiah—the despised and rejected of men, the man of sorrows and the acquaintance of grief.

"And remember, my son," said he, fixing his deep-set eyes upon the face of Artaban, "the King whom you are seeking is not to be found in a palace, nor among the rich and powerful. If the light of the world and the glory of Israel had been appointed to come with the greatness of earthly splendor, it must have appeared long ago. For no son of Abraham will ever again rival the power which Joseph had in the palaces of Egypt, or the magnificence of Solomon throned between the lions in Jerusalem. But the light for which the world is waiting is a new light, the glory that shall rise out of patient and triumphant suffering. And the kingdom which is to be established forever is a new kingdom, the royalty of perfect and unconquerable love.

"I do not know how this shall come to pass, nor how the turbulent kings and peoples of earth shall be brought to acknowledge the Messiah and pay homage to Him. But this I know. Those who seek Him will do well to look among the poor and the lowly, the sorrowful and the oppressed."

So I saw the Other Wise Man again and again, traveling from place to place, and searching among the people of the dispersion, with whom the little family from Bethlehem might, perhaps, have found a refuge. He passed through countries where famine lay heavy upon the land and the poor were crying for bread. He made his dwelling in plague-stricken cities where the sick were languishing in the bitter companionship of helpless misery. He visited the oppressed and the afflicted in the gloom of subterranean prisons, and the crowded wretchedness of slave markets, and the weary toil of galley ships. In all this populous and intricate world of anguish, though he found none to worship, he found many to help. He fed the hungry, and clothed the naked, and healed the sick, and comforted the captive; and his years went by more swiftly than the weaver's shuttle that flashes back and forth through the loom while the web grows and the invisible pattern is completed.

It seemed almost as if he had forgotten his quest. But once I saw him for a moment as he stood alone at sunrise, waiting at the gate of a Roman prison. He had taken from a secret resting-place in his bosom the pearl, the last of his jewels. As he looked at it, a mellower lustre, a soft and iridescent light, full of shifting gleams of azure and rose, trembled upon its surface. It seemed to have absorbed some reflection of the colors of the lost sapphire and ruby. So the profound, secret purpose of a noble life draws into itself the memories of past joy and past sorrow. All that has helped it, all that has hindered it, is transfused by a subtle magic into its very essence. It becomes more luminous and precious the longer it is carried close to the warmth of the beating heart.

Then, at last, while I was thinking of this pearl, and of its meaning, I heard the end of the story of the Other Wise Man.

A Pearl of Great Price

Three-and-thirty years of the life of Artaban had passed away, and he was still a pilgrim, and a seeker after light. His hair, once darker than the cliffs of Zagros, was now white as the wintry snow that covered them. His eyes, that once flashed like flames of fire, were dull as embers smouldering among the ashes.

Worn and weary and ready to die, but still looking for the King, he had come for the last time to Jerusalem. He had often visited the holy city before, and had searched through all its lanes and crowded hovels and black prisons without finding any trace of the family of Nazarenes who had fled from Bethlehem long ago. But now it seemed as if he must make one more effort, and something whispered in his heart that, at last, he might succeed.

It was the season of the Passover. The city was throned with strangers. The children of Israel, scattered in far lands all over the world, had returned to the Temple for the great feast, and there had been a confusion of tongues in the narrow streets for many days.

But on this day there was a singular agitation visible in the multitude. The sky was veiled with a portentous gloom, and currents of excitement seemed to flash through the crowd like the thrill which shakes the forest on the eve of a storm. A secret tide was sweeping them all one way. The clatter of sandals, and the soft, thick sound of thousands of bare feet shuffling over the stones, flowed unceasingly along the street that leads to the Damascus gate.

Artaban joined company with a group of people from his own country, Parthian Jews who had come up to keep the Passover, and inquired of them the cause of the tumult, and where they were going.

"We are going," they answered, "to the place called Golgotha, outside the city walls, where there is to be an execution. Have you not heard what has happened? Two famous robbers are to be crucified, and with them another, called Jesus of Nazareth, a man who has done many wonderful works among the people, so that they love him greatly. But the priests and elders have said that he must die, because he gave himself out to be the Son of God. And Pilate has sent him to the cross because he said that he was the 'King of the Jews.'"

How strangely these familiar words fell upon the tired heart of Artaban! They had led him for a lifetime over land and sea. And now they came to him darkly and mysteriously like a message of despair. The King had arisen, but He had been denied and cast out. He was about to perish. Perhaps He was already dying. Could it be the same who had been born in Bethlehem thirty-three years ago, at whose birth the star had appeared in heaven, and of whose coming the prophets had spoken?

Artaban's heart beat unsteadily with that troubled, doubtful apprehension which is the excitement of old age. But he said within himself: "The ways of God are stranger than the thoughts of men, and it may be that I shall find the King, at last, in the hands of His enemies, and shall come in time to offer my pearl for his ransom before He dies."

So the old man followed the multitude with slow and painful steps toward the Damascus gate of the city. Just beyond the entrance of the guard-house a troop of Macedonian soldiers came down the street, dragging a young girl with torn dress and dishevelled hair. As the Magian paused to look at her with compassion, she broke suddenly from the hands of her tormentors and threw herself at his feet, clasping him around the knees. She had seen his white cap and the winged circle on his breast.

"Have pity on me," she cried, "and save me, for the sake of the God of purity! I also am a daughter of the true religion which is taught by the Magi. My father was a merchant of Parthia, but he is dead, and I am seized for his debts to be sold as a slave. Save me from worse than death."

Artaban trembled.

It was the old conflict in his soul, which had come to him in the palm grove of Babylon and in the cottage at Bethlehem—the conflict between the expectation of faith and the impulse of love. Twice the gift which he had consecrated to the worship of religion had been drawn from his hand to the service of humanity. This was the third trial, the ultimate probation, the final and irrevocable choice.

Was it his great opportunity or his last temptation? He could not tell. One thing only was clear in the darkness of his mind—it was inevitable. And does not the inevitable come from God?

One thing only was sure to his divided heart—to rescue this helpless girl would be a true deed of love. And is not love the light of the soul?

He took the pearl from his bosom. Never had it seemed so luminous, so radiant, so full of tender, living lustre. He laid it in the hand of the slave.

"This is thy ransom, daughter! It is the last of my treasures which I kept for the King."

While he spoke the darkness of the sky thickened, and shuddering tremors ran through the earth, heaving convulsively like the breast of one who struggles with mighty grief.

The walls of the houses rocked to and fro. Stones were loosened and crashed into the street. Dust clouds filled the air. The soldiers fled in terror, reeling like drunken men. But Artaban and the girl whom he had ransomed crouched helpless beneath the wall of the Praetorium.

What had he to fear? What had he to live for? He had given away the last remnant of his tribute for the King. He had parted with the last hope of finding Him. The quest was over, and it had failed. But even in that thought, accepted and embraced, there was peace. It was not resignation. It was not submission. It was something more profound and searching. He knew that all was well, because he had done the best that he could, from day to day. He had been true to the light that had been given to him. He had looked for more. And if he had not found it, if a failure was all that came out of his life, doubtless that was the best that was possible. He had not seen the revelation of "life everlasting, incorruptible and immortal." But he knew that even if he could live his earthly life over again, it could not be otherwise than it had been.

One more lingering pulsation of the earthquake quivered through the ground. A heavy tile, shaken from the roof, fell and struck the old man on the temple. He lay breathless and pale, with his gray head resting on the young girl's shoulder, and the blood trickling from the wound. As she bent over him, fearing that he was dead, there came a voice through the twilight, very small and still, like music sounding from a distance, in which the notes are clear but the words are lost. The girl turned to see if someone had spoken from the window above them, but she saw no one.

Then the old man's lips began to move, as if in answer, and she heard him say in the Parthian tongue:

"Not so, my Lord: For when saw I thee an hungered and fed thee? Or thirsty, and gave thee drink? When saw I thee a stranger, and took thee in? Or naked, and clothed thee? When saw I thee sick or in prison, and came unto thee? Three-and-thirty years have I looked for thee; but I have never seen thy face, nor ministered to thee, my King."

He ceased, and the sweet voice came again. And again the maid heard it, very faintly and far away. But now it seemed as though she understood the words:

"Verily I say unto thee, Inasmuch as thou hast done it unto one of the least of these my brethren, thou hast done it unto me."

A calm radiance of wonder and joy lighted the pale face of Artaban like the first ray of dawn on a snowy mountain-peak. One long, last breath of relief exhaled gently from his lips.

His journey was ended. His treasures were accepted. The Other Wise Man had found the King.

THE GHOST OF CHRISTMAS PRESENT

CHARLES DICKENS *

Scrooge awoke in his bedroom. There was no doubt about that. But it and his own adjoining sitting-room, into which he shuffled in his slippers, attracted by a great light there, had undergone a surprising transformation. The walls and ceiling were so hung with living green, that it looked a perfect grove. The leaves of holly, mistletoe, and ivy reflected back the light, as if many little mirrors had been scattered there; and such a mighty blaze went roaring up the chimney, as that petrifaction of a hearth had never known in Scrooge's time, or Marley's, or for many and many a winter season gone. Heaped upon the floor, to form a kind of throne, were turkeys, geese, game, brawn, great joints of meat, sucking pigs, long wreaths of sausages, mince-pies, plum-puddings, barrels of oysters, red-hot chestnuts, cherry-cheeked apples, juicy oranges, luscious pears, immense twelfth-cakes, and great bowls of punch. In easy state upon this couch there sat a

---

*From *A Christmas Carol*, as condensed by himself, for his *Readings*.

Giant glorious to see; who bore a glowing torch, in shape not unlike Plenty's horn, and who raised it high to shed its light on Scrooge, as he came peeping round the door.

"Come in—come in! and know me better, man! I am the Ghost of Christmas Present. Look upon me! You have never seen the like of me before!"

"Never."

"Have never walked forth with the younger members of my family; meaning (for I am very young) my elder brothers born in these late years?" pursued the Phantom.

"I don't think I have, I am afraid I have not. Have you had many brothers, Spirit?"

"More than eighteen hundred."

"A tremendous family to provide for! Spirit, conduct me where you will. I went forth last night on compulsion, and I learnt a lesson which is working now. Tonight, if you have ought to teach me, let me profit by it."

"Touch my robe!"

Scrooge did as he was told, and held it fast.

The room and its contents all vanished instantly, and they stood in the city streets upon a snowy Christmas morning.

Scrooge and the Ghost passed on, invisible, straight to Scrooge's clerk's; and on the threshold of the door the Spirit smiled, and stopped to bless Bob Cratchit's dwelling with the sprinklings of his torch. Think of that! Bob had but fifteen "Bob" a week himself; he pocketed on Saturdays but fifteen copies of his Christian name; and yet the Ghost of Christmas Present blessed his four-roomed house!

Then up rose Mrs. Cratchit, Cratchit's wife, dressed out but poorly in a twice-turned gown, brave in ribbons, which are cheap and make a goodly show for sixpence; and she laid the cloth, assisted by Belinda Cratchit, second of her daughters, also brave in ribbons; while Master Peter Cratchit plunged a fork into the saucepan of potatoes, and, getting the corners of his monstrous shirt-collar (Bob's private property, conferred upon his son and heir in honor of the day) into his mouth, rejoiced to find himself so gallantly attired, and yearned to show his linen in the fashionable Park. And now two smaller Cratchits, boy and girl came tearing in, screaming that outside the baker's they had smelt the goose, and known it for their own; and, basking in luxurious thoughts of sage and onion, these young Cratchits danced about the table, and exalted Master Peter Cratchit to the skies, while he (not proud, although his collars nearly choked him) blew the fire, until the slow potatoes, bubbling up, knocked loudly at the saucepan-lid to be let out and peeled.

"What has ever got your precious father then?" said Mrs. Cratchit. "And your brother Tiny Tim! And Martha warn't as late last Christmas day by half an hour!"

"Here's Martha, mother!" said a girl, appearing as she spoke.

"Here's Martha, mother!" cried the two young Cratchits. "Hurrah! There's *such* a goose, Martha!"

"Why, bless your heart alive, my dear, how late you are!" said Mrs. Cratchit, kissing her a dozen times, and taking off her shawl and bonnet for her.

"We'd a deal of work to finish up last night," replied the girl, "and had to clear away this morning, mother!"

"Well! Never mind so long as you are come," said Mrs. Cratchit. "Sit ye down before the fire, my dear, and have a warm, Lord bless ye!"

"No, no! There's father coming," cried the two young Cratchits, who were everywhere at once. "Hide, Martha, hide!"

So Martha hid herself, and in came little Bob, the father, with at least three feet of comforter, exclusive of the fringe, hanging down before him; and his threadbare clothes darned up and brushed, to look seasonable; and Tiny Tim upon his shoulder. Alas for Tiny Tim, he bore a little crutch, and had his limbs supported by an iron frame!

"Why, where's our Martha?" cried Bob Cratchit, looking round.

"Not coming," said Mrs. Cratchit.

"Not coming!" said Bob, with a sudden declension in his high spirits; for he had been Tim's blood-horse all the way from church, and had come home rampant—"not coming upon Christmas day!"

Martha didn't like to see him disappointed, if it were only in joke; so she came out prematurely from behind the closet door, and ran into his arms, while the two young Cratchits hustled Tiny Tim, and bore him off to the wash-house that he might hear the pudding singing in the copper.

"And how did little Tim behave?" asked Mrs. Cratchit, when she had rallied Bob on his credulity, and Bob had hugged his daughter to his heart's content.

"As good as gold," said Bob, "and better. Somehow he gets thoughtful, sitting by himself so much, and thinks the strangest things you ever heard. He told me, coming home, that he hoped the people saw him in the church, because he was a cripple, and it might be pleasant to them to remember, upon Christmas day, who made lame beggars walk and blind men see."

Bob's voice was tremulous when he told them this, and trembled more when he said that Tiny Tim was growing strong and hearty.

His active little crutch was heard upon the floor, and back came Tiny Tim before another word was spoken, escorted by his brother and sister to his stool before the fire; and while Bob, turning up his cuffs—as if, poor fellow, they were capable of being made more shabby—compounded some hot mixture in a jug with gin and lemons, and stirred it round and round and put it on the hob to simmer; Master Peter, and the two ubiquitous young Cratchits went to fetch the goose, with which they soon returned in high procession.

Mrs. Cratchit made the gravy (ready beforehand in a little saucepan) hissing hot; Master Peter mashed the potatoes with incredible vigor; Miss Belinda sweetened up the apple-sauce; Martha dusted the hot plates; Bob took Tiny Tim beside him in a tiny corner at the table; the two young Cratchits set chairs for everybody, not forgetting themselves, and mounting guard upon their posts, crammed spoons into their mouths, lest they should shriek for goose before their turn came to be helped. At last the dishes were set on, and grace was said. It was succeeded by a breathless pause, as Mrs. Cratchit, looking slowly all along the carving-knife, prepared to plunge it in the breast; but when she did, and when the long-expected gush of stuffing issued forth, one murmur of delight arose all round the board, and even Tiny Tim, excited by the two young Cratchits, beat on the table with the handle of his knife, and feebly cried, Hurrah!

There never was such a goose. Bob said he didn't believe there ever was such a goose cooked. Its tenderness and flavor, size and cheapness, were the themes of universal admiration. Eked out by apple-sauce and mashed potatoes, it was a sufficient dinner for the whole family; indeed, as Mrs. Cratchit said with great delight (surveying one small atom of a bone upon the dish), they hadn't ate it all at last! Yet everyone had had enough, and the youngest Cratchits in particular, were steeped in sage and onion to the eyebrows! But now, the plates being changed by Miss Belinda, Mrs. Cratchit left the room alone—too nervous to bear witnesses—to take the pudding up and bring it in.

Suppose it should not be done enough! Suppose it should break in turning out! Suppose somebody should have got over the wall of the back-yard, and stolen it, while they were merry with the goose—a supposition at which the two young Cratchits became livid! All sorts of horrors were supposed.

Hallo! A great deal of steam! The pudding was out of the copper. A smell like a washing-day! That was the cloth. A smell like an eating-house and a pastry-cook's next door to each other, with a laundress's next door to that! That was the pudding! In half a minute Mrs. Cratchit entered—flushed but smiling proudly—with the pudding, like a speckled cannon-ball, so hard and firm, blazing in half of half-a-quartern of ignited brandy, and bedight with Christmas holly stuck into the top.

O, a wonderful pudding! Bob Cratchit said, and calmly too, that he regarded it as the greatest success achieved by Mrs. Cratchit since their marriage. Mrs. Cratchit said that now the weight was off her mind, she would confess she had had her doubts about the quantity of flour. Everybody had something to say about it, but nobody thought it was at all a small pudding for a large family. Any Cratchit would have blushed to hint at such a thing.

At last the dinner was all done, the cloth was cleared, the hearth swept, and the fire made up. The compound in the jug being tasted, and considered perfect, apples and oranges were put upon the table, and a shovelful of chestnuts on the fire.

Then all the family drew round the hearth, in what Bob Cratchit called a circle, and at Bob Cratchit's elbow stood the family display of glass, two tumblers, and a custard-cup without a handle.

These held the hot stuff from the jug, however, as well as golden goblets would have done; and Bob served it out with beaming looks, while the chestnuts on the fire sputtered and crackled noisily. Then Bob proposed:—

"A merry Christmas to us all, my dears. God bless us!"

Which all the family re-echoed.

"God bless us every one!" said Tiny Tim, the last of all.

He sat very close to his father's side, upon his little stool. Bob held his withered little hand in his, as if he loved the child, and wished to keep him by his side, and dreaded that he might be taken from him.

Scrooge raised his head speedily, on hearing his own name.

"Mr. Scrooge," said Bob; "I'll give you Mr. Scrooge, the Founder of the Feast!"

"The Founder of the Feast indeed!" cried Mrs. Cratchit, reddening. "I wish I had him here I'd give him a piece of my mind to feast upon and I hope he'd have a good appetite for it."

"My dear," said Bob, "the children! Christmas day."

"It should be Christmas day, I am sure," said she, "on which one drinks the health of such a odious, stingy, hard, unfeeling man as Mr. Scrooge. You know he is, Robert! Nobody knows it better than you do, poor fellow!"

"My dear," was Bob's mild answer, "Christmas day."

"I'll drink his health for your sake and the day's," said Mrs. Cratchit, "not for his. Long life to him! A merry Christmas and a happy New Year! He'll be very merry and very happy, I have no doubt!"

The children drank the toast after her. It was the first of their proceedings which had no heartiness in it. Tiny Tim drank it last of all, but he didn't care twopence for it. Scrooge was the ogre of the family. The mention of his name cast a dark shadow on the party, which was not dispelled for full five minutes.

After it had passed away, they were ten times merrier than before, from the mere relief of Scrooge the Baleful being done with. Bob Cratchit told them how he had a situation in his eye for Master Peter, which would bring in, if obtained, full five and sixpence weekly. The two young Cratchits laughed tremendously at the idea of Peter's being a man of business; and Peter himself looked thoughtfully at the fire from between his collars, as if he were deliberating what particular investments he should favor when he came into the receipt of that bewildering income. Martha, who was a poor apprentice at a milliner's, then told them what kind of work she had to do, and how many hours she worked at a stretch, and how she meant to lie abed to-morrow morning for a good long rest; to-morrow being a holiday she passed at home. Also how she had seen a countess and a lord some days before, and how the lord "was much about as tall as Peter"; at which Peter pulled up his collars so high that you couldn't have seen his head if you had been there. All this time the chestnuts and the jug went round and round; and by and by they had a song, about a lost child travelling in the snow, from Tiny Tim, who had a plaintive little voice, and sang it very well indeed.

There was nothing of high mark in this. They were not a handsome family; they were not well dressed; their shoes were far from being water proof; their clothes were scanty; and Peter might have known, and very likely did, the inside of a pawnbroker's. But they were happy, grateful, pleased with one another, and contented with the time; and when they faded, and looked happier yet in the bright sprinklings of the Spirit's torch at parting, Scrooge had his eye upon them, and especially on Tiny Tim, until the last.

It was a great surprise to Scrooge, as this scene vanished, to hear a hearty laugh. It was a much greater surprise to Scrooge to recognize it as his own nephew's, and to find himself in a bright, dry, gleaming room, with the Spirit standing smiling by his side, and looking at that same nephew.

It is a fair, even-handed, noble adjustment of things, that while there is infection in disease and sorrow, there is nothing in the world so irresistibly contagious as laughter and good-humor. When Scrooge's nephew laughed, Scrooge's niece by marriage laughed as heartily as he. And their assembled friends, being not a bit behindhand, laughed out lustily.

"He said that Christmas was a humbug, as I live!" cried Scrooge's nephew. "He believed it too!"

"More shame for him, Fred!" said Scrooge's niece, indignantly. Bless those women! they never do anything by halves. They are always in earnest.

She was very pretty; exceedingly pretty. With a dimpled, surprised-looking, capital face; a ripe little mouth that seemed made to be kissed—as no doubt it was; all kinds of good little dots about her chin, that melted into one another when she laughed; and the sunniest pair of eyes you ever saw in any little creature's head. Altogether she was what you would have called provoking, but satisfactory, too. O, perfectly satisfactory.

"He's a comical old fellow," said Scrooge's nephew, "that's the truth; and not so pleasant as he might be. However, his offences carry their own punishment, and I have nothing to say against him. Who suffers by his ill whims? Himself, always. Here he takes it into his head to dislike us, and he won't come and dine with us. What's the consequence? He don't lose much of a dinner."

"Indeed, I think he loses a very good dinner," interrupted Scrooge's niece. Everybody else said the same, and they must be allowed to have been competent judges, because they had just had dinner; and, with the dessert upon the table, were clustered round the fire, by lamplight.

"Well, I am very glad to hear it," said Scrooge s nephew, "because I haven't any great faith in these young housekeepers. What do *you* say, Topper?"

Topper clearly had his eye on one of Scrooge's niece's sisters, for he answered that a bachelor was a wretched outcast, who had no right to express an opinion on the subject. Whereat Scrooge's niece's sister—the plump one with the lace tucker; not the one with the roses—blushed.

After tea they had some music. For they were a musical family, and knew what they were about, when they sung a Glee or Catch, I can assure you—especially Topper, who could growl away in the bass like a good one, and never swell the large veins in his forehead, or get red in the face over it.

But they didn't devote the whole evening to music. After a while they played at forfeits; for it is good to be children sometimes, and never better than at Christmas, when its mighty Founder was a child himself: There was first a game at blindman's-buff though. And I no more believe Topper was really blinded than I believe he had eyes in his boots. Because the way in which he went after that plump sister in the lace tucker was an outrage on the credulity of human nature. Knocking down the fire-irons, tumbling over the, chairs, bumping up against the piano, smothering himself among the curtains, wherever she went there went he! He always knew where the plump sister was. He wouldn't catch anybody else. If you had fallen up against him, as some of them did, and stood there, he would have made a feint of endeavoring to seize you, which would have been an reply to affront to your understanding, and would instantly have sidled off in the direction of the plump sister.

"Here is a new game," said Scrooge. "One half-hour, Spirit, only one!"

It was a Game called Yes and No, where Scrooge's nephew had to think of something, and the rest must find out what; he only answering to their questions yes or no, as the case was. The fire of questioning to which he was exposed elicited from him that he was thinking of an animal, a live animal, rather a disagreeable animal, a savage animal, an animal that growled and grunted sometimes, and talked sometimes, and lived in London, and walked about the streets, and wasn't made a show of, and wasn't led by anybody, and didn't live in a menagerie, and was never killed in a market, and was not a horse, or an ass, or a cow, or a bull, or a tiger, or a dog, or a pig, or a cat, or a bear. At every new question put to him, this nephew burst into a fresh roar of laughter; and was so inexpressibly tickled, that he was obliged to get up off the sofa and stamp. At last the plump sister cried out:—

"I have found it out! I know what it is, Fred! I know what it is!"

"What is it?" cried Fred.

"It's your uncle Scro-o-o-o-oge!"

Which it certainly was. Admiration was the sentiment, though some objected that the reply to "Is it a bear?" ought to have been "Yes."

Uncle Scrooge had imperceptibly become so gay and light of heart, that he would have drank to the unconscious company in an inaudible speech. But the whole scene passed off in the breath of the last word spoken by his nephew; and he and the Spirit were again upon their travels.

Much they saw, and far they went, and many homes they visited, but always with a happy end. The Spirit stood beside sick-beds, and they were cheerful; on foreign lands, and they were close at home; by struggling men, and they were patient in their greater hope; by poverty, and it was rich. In almshouse, hospital, and jail, in misery's every refuge, where vain man in his little brief authority had not made fast the door, and barred the Spirit out, he left his blessing, and taught Scrooge his precepts.

A FATHER FOR CHRISTMAS

A U T H O R   U N K N O W N

Sheriff John Charles Olsen let out a sigh so hefty it blew an apple core clear off his desk. There'd been times in his life when he'd felt worse. The night he'd spent in the swamp behind the Sundquist place with a broken leg and about a million mosquitoes for company was one such time. But there'd never been a time when he'd wanted less to be a sheriff.

"Are you deaf?" Mart Dahlberg demanded.

Sheriff Olsen looked across at where his deputy was typing out letters in his usual neat and fast way. "Did you say something?"

"Only three times. Didn't you promise the fellow you'd be out there by noon?"

"It ain't noon yet."

"It will be by the time you get there."

Sheriff Olsen hauled himself, slow and heavy, to his feet.

"Sure you don't want me to go along?" Mart asked, and his voice was gentler sounding.

The sheriff shook his head. "No, not much stuff out there. Just four chairs and a table and the kids' clothes and some bedding."

"Well, I wish you'd get started," Mart said. "You got to be back here and into your Santa Claus outfit by three, remember."

"I haven't forgotten," the sheriff answered. He sounded snappish, but he couldn't help it.

Mart got up from his desk. "Look, John," he said, "take it easy. Folks get evicted from their homes all the time."

"Not a week before Christmas, they don't," the sheriff growled.

201

He slammed shut the office door and went out of the court-house to where his car was parked. He gave a quick look at how the trailer was fastened, then he got into the car and slammed that door shut, too.

Maybe it wasn't anybody's fault what had happened. But it made the sheriff feel awfully queer in his stomach to have to move three little kids out of their home just before he was going to dress up in a Santa Claus outfit and hand out gifts to other kids at the annual Christmas celebration!

Sheriff Olsen started up the engine and turned on the heater. Then he turned it off and wiped the sweat off his forehead with his mitten. Likely a man with more brains than the sheriff had could have fixed things right for Stephen Reade.

Sam Merske called Stephen Reade a deadbeat and a phony, but that was because Reade hadn't made a good tenant farmer. Two years ago, when Reade had rented the farm from Merske, Merske had called Reade a fine, upstanding personality.

Sheriff Olsen had argued for months with Merske about Reade and the kids, figuring that all Reade needed was another summer to get things going right. But Sam Merske was a business-man and he expected his farm to produce and make money for him. Finally he'd taken Reade to court.

After that, the sheriff had done his arguing with Judge Martinson, but the judge said that Sam Merske had been very gen-erous and patient with Reade, and that it was understandable Sam's wanting to get a competent man settled on his farm before spring came.

"This man, Reade," the judge had said, "is obviously not fitted to farm. That has been proven to my satisfaction, not only by his inability to make his rent payments but also by the condition the county agent tells me the farm is in. Let us not fog our judgment,

John, with undue sentimentality. It will be far better for both Reade and his children if we face the issue squarely."

It wasn't Stephen Reade's fault what had happened. You have to be kind of raised to it to know what to do when your cow takes sick or the weather mildews your raspberries. All his life since he was a kid, Reade had been in the selling business in New York City, going from door to door, first with magazine subscriptions, and then with stockings, and finally with vacuum cleaners. It took hard work and brains and a lot more courage than the sheriff himself had to go around ringing doorbells and asking strange women to buy things from you. But Stephen Reade had sold enough to support a wife and three children.

After the third child was born, Mrs. Reade had been sick all the time. She'd been raised on a farm in Oregon, and she figured living in a big city was what made her sick. So when she knew she wasn't going to live, she'd made her husband promise he'd take the kids to the country.

Reade had promised faithfully, and after his wife was gone he'd taken what was left of their savings and headed for Oregon. He'd gone as far as the bus depot in St. Paul when he'd read an ad. The ad had said that anyone with initiative and enterprise wanting to rent an A-one farm should apply to Sam Merske, proprietor of the Merske Dry Goods Store in Minnewashta County.

Sam had demanded three months' rent in advance, and that was all he'd ever gotten out of Reade. The cow and the chickens had taken all the leftover cash that Reade had, and the cow hadn't lived very long.

Johanna Olsen, the sheriff's wife, had bought all her eggs off of Reade for two months. After that, for another two months she'd bought as many as Reade had to sell. And, after that, there weren't enough hens left to give the Reade youngsters an egg each for their breakfasts.

The plan was to move the Reade family into the two empty rooms above the Hovander Grain and Feed Store. It wasn't a permanent arrangement, because Hovander didn't like the idea. "Eight days is all they can stay. I ain't no charitable institution, and I wouldn't do the favor for nobody but you, John."

But the eight days would get the Reade kids through Christmas.

Sheriff Olsen brought the car and the trailer up alongside the farmhouse. There was a big railed-in porch running around three sides of the house and you could see how a widower with three children would have liked the looks of the porch the minute he saw it—forgetting how hard a big old house was to heat.

The sheriff knocked at the door. After a minute he heard someone running and then Ellen's voice said, "Robbie, don't go near that door; I'm supposed to answer." In another minute, the door opened a crack.

Sheriff Olsen said, "'Lo, Ellen."

Ellen said, "Hello, Mr. Olsen," but she didn't smile back. "My father's out for the present, but you're welcome to wait in the kitchen. It's warmest there."

Sheriff Olsen sat down on one of the four chairs pulled up to a card table. On the table was a bundle tied up in a blanket; near the back door was a barrel covered with newspapers, and three suitcases fastened with ropes.

The sheriff said, "You sure been busy."

"I helped with everything," Robbie said.

Ellen said, "The stove belongs to Mr. Merske, and so do the beds and the clock. But the chairs and the table are all paid for and so they belong to us."

Sheriff Olsen looked at the clock. "Did your pa say when he'd be back?"

"He's gone for something," Ellen said.

Robbie said, "Dad's gone to get us a surprise. Letty thinks he's buying her a doll, but Dad said what he's getting for us is heaps more important than anything you can buy in a store."

Sheriff Olsen smiled at Letty and she came over and put her head down on his knee. She was about 4 and she wasn't worried yet about how things were in the world.

When it got to be about half past 12, the sheriff said, "Maybe we should all drive down the road a ways and give a lift to your pa!"

Ellen slid down from the window sill. "Are you getting restless, Mr. Olsen?" she asked.

"Kinda."

"Well, when you get awful restless, I'm supposed to give you a letter." She started toward the parlor door. Then she turned. "But first, you have to be awful restless."

"I am awful restless," he answered with a worried look on his kind face.

In half a minute, she was back with an envelope. Inside was a sheet of paper that had been written on with pencil:

"To the Sheriff of Minnewashta County:

I, Stephen Reade, being of sound mind and body, do herewith declare that I relinquish all legal claim to my three children, Ellen, Robert, and Letitia Reade. I do this as my Christmas gift to them, so that they may be legally adopted by some family that will take care of them. I herewith swear never to make myself known to their new parents. They are good children and will make their new parents happy.

Yours very truly,

Your grateful friend, Stephen Reade."

"Does it tell about my doll?" Letty asked, jumping up and down.

"Does my father say when he'll be back, Mr. Olsen?" Ellen asked. She was standing very straight at the sink, making little pleats in her dress. "Does he?"

Sheriff Olsen looked at the clock, and then at his watch. There'd be a freight train pulling out of the station in 38 minutes, and if Reade hadn't hitched a ride on a truck, he'd be waiting to bum one on the freight. But you couldn't chase after a deserting father with the fellow's kids in the back of your car.

"Does he?" Ellen asked again.

Sheriff Olsen gave a big hearty smile. "Well, what do you know about that? Your dad's changed his plans. He wants you should stay the afternoon with my wife. So, quick now, put on your coats and caps and boots while I unhitch the trailer."

"But aren't we taking our chairs and things, Mr. Olsen?" Ellen asked.

"I'll come back for 'em later. Where's your boots, Letty?"

"Mr. Olsen, I don't think my father would want us to leave without taking our furniture with us."

"Look, my wife's going to take you to the Christmas celebration and you'll get presents from Santa Claus and everything. Only we gotta hurry, see?"

"Daddy's getting me a present," Letty said.

Robbie shouted, "I think we'd better wait here for Daddy."

"There'll be a Christmas tree," the sheriff said, "and hot cocoa to drink and peanut butter sandwiches. Robbie, you got brains, see if you can find Letty's mittens. I got her boots here."

Next Ellen spoke up: "We aren't supposed to go to the Christmas celebration, Mr. Olsen. My father told us it's just for the children who live in town."

"Well, that's the big surprise your pa's got for you. Santa Claus wants the three Reade kids to be special guests. Letty, stick your thumb in the hole that was meant for your thumb in this mitten."

"I want my daddy," Letty squealed. "I want my daddy to take me to see Santa Claus."

"She's scared because Daddy isn't here," Robbie said. "Aren't you scared 'cause Daddy isn't here, Letty?"

Sheriff Olsen grabbed hold of Letty. "How good can you ride piggyback?" With that, he rushed her off to the car.

Going over the slippery road with the three children, the sheriff had to drive slowly and carefully back into town. Right away, when the sheriff honked, Johanna came running out of the house.

"Johanna, they haven't eaten yet. And could you please phone down to the Christmas committee and tell them that you're bringing three extra children so they will have time to get their gifts wrapped right."

Johanna opened the back door to the car, and the three Reade youngsters moved out toward the smile she gave them like they were three new-hatched chicks heading for the feel of something warm.

"Wow!" said Johanna. "Am I ever lucky! There's a whole big chocolate cake in the kitchen, and me worrying who was going to help to frost and eat it."

With the kids out of the car, the sheriff drove kind of crazy. Once he was past the courthouse and heading for the station, the traffic thinned out and there wasn't anybody's neck to worry about except his own.

The freight was in, and the sheriff drove straight up onto the platform. Lindahl, who was stationmaster, gave a yelp, but when he saw it was the sheriff, he yelled, "What's he look like?" and started running down the length of the train.

Sheriff Olsen headed east toward the engine, and found where somebody had once been crouching down in the snow on the embankment.

It was an open boxcar, and likely Reade had seen the sheriff already, but the sheriff called out Reade's name anyhow. Then he pulled himself up into the car.

It took half a minute for the sheriff to get used to the half light, but all that time Stephen Reade didn't move or try to get past him through the door. He just sat huddled up in his corner, pretending like he wasn't there.

Sheriff Olsen went over to him and put his hands under Reade's elbows and pulled him to his feet. Reade didn't say anything when the sheriff shoved him down off the boxcar into the snow. But when they were in the sheriff's car, the train gave a whistle and Reade said, in a whisper, "I was close to making it."

The sheriff drove around behind where the Ladies' Shakespeare Study Society had put a row of evergreens. He kept the heater going, and after a couple of minutes Stephen Reade stopped shaking some. . . .

All of a sudden Reade gave a groan. "Let me out of here! For their sake, you've got to let me get away!" He started to rock back and forth, with his hands holding tight to his knees. "You've got to believe me! I'm no good for those kids! I've lost my nerve. I'm frightened. I'm frightened sick!"

For a long time the sheriff just sat next to Stephen Reade, wanting one minute to break the guy's neck for him, and the next minute to put his arm around him, and not knowing any of the time what was right to do.

After a couple of minutes he said, "A while back, you claimed I didn't know what it was like to be scared. Well, sometimes I get scared, too. Take like this afternoon. This afternoon I got to dress up crazy and hand out presents to a whole roomful of kids. Last night I didn't sleep so good either, worrying about it."

Stephen Reade snorted.

"Well, it ain't easy like maybe you think," Sheriff John went on.

"I have to get up on a platform, and all the kids'll be staring at me, and sometimes their folks come too."

"You certainly make it sound tragic."

"OK, if you don't figure it's so hard, you do it. I'll make a bargain with you. You be Santa Claus for me, and I'll find you a job. And while you're doing a good turn for both me and yourself, Ellen and Robbie and Letty will sure get a kick out of seeing their pa acting Santa Claus to all the kids in town."

For a long time Reade just sat staring through the windshield. Then he said, with his voice low and sober, "You couldn't find me a job. There isn't a man in the whole county who'd be half-wit enough to hire the loony that made hash out of Merske's farm. And you know it." Then he faced around to the sheriff. "But I'll play at being Santa Claus if you want me to. I've been owing you some sort of thanks for a couple of years."

Ten minutes later, the sheriff had Stephen Reade holed up in the washroom opposite his office. He pointed out where the outfit was hanging in the corner. "You better put the whiskers and cap on, too, while you got a mirror," he said. "I'll keep watch outside."

Sheriff Olsen closed the washroom door and stepped back almost into his deputy's arms.

"What you got in there?" Mart Dahlberg said.

"Stephen Reade. He's going to be Santa Claus."

"You crazy or something?" Mart asked. "You've been Santa Claus for five years. What you want to go and give your part to that dope for?"

"Look, Mart, don't yell. Reade's feeling awful low, see? Getting evicted and not having a job or nothing. And I kinda figured handing out the presents to all the kids would maybe pep him up some."

"The committee won't let him."

"The committee won't know until it's too late," the sheriff

explained. "Maybe I figured crazy, but I had to figure something. And, anyhow, he promised his kids a good surprise."

Mart gave a gentle pat on the sheriff's back. "Well," he said, "I can pray for you, but I don't figure it will help much."

Twenty minutes later, Sheriff Olsen poked his head into the kitchen behind the church's big recreation room.

Mrs. Bengtson looked around from washing cocoa cups. "The eating's done with, John," she said. "And they're singing carols while they wait for you."

Sheriff Olsen said, "Thanks." He motioned Stephen Reade to slip past through the kitchen to the door that opened out on the little stage. Then he moved himself, quiet and unnoticed, around to the back of the recreation room.

The piano was playing "Silent Night" and the place was jam-packed. The sheriff took off his hat and wiped his face. Then he sat down at the end of the bench that held Johanna and the three Reade kids. He smiled across the heads of the three kids at Johanna, and then he closed his hand over the hot paw that little Ellen had wriggled onto his knee.

Up on the stage the tree was a beautiful sight. It was nine feet tall, and the committee had decorated it with pretty balls, lights, and popcorn chains. Under the tree were the presents. The wrapping paper had all come from Merske's Dry Goods Store because this year Sam Merske was chairman of the committee and most of the presents had been bought at his store. Some of the paper was white and had green bells on it and some was red with white bells, and each bell had printed on it one of the letters of M E R S K E. And they were a beautiful sight, too. But sitting next to the presents, low under the tree, hunched up like a discouraged rabbit, was Santa Claus.

Sheriff Olsen flattened his hat out on his knee. Mart had been right. Wearing a beard on his chin and putting stuffing over his stomach weren't going to put pep into Stephen Reade. All they were going to do was spoil the show for the children and make Reade feel more miserable even than before! Then the music stopped and the sheriff folded his hat in two. Mart had said he would pray and maybe he wasn't forgetting to.

All of a sudden a little kid down front squealed, "Merry Christmas, Santa Claus!" And after that, the whole room was full of loving squeals and chirpings and calls of "Hi, Santa!"

Stephen Reade straightened up his shoulders a bit and then he reached out a hand for one of the packages. Sheriff Olsen began to feel some better. At least, Reade was remembering what he was up on the stage for, and maybe the kids wouldn't notice that Santa Claus didn't have his whole heart in the business.

Then a voice said, hoarse and angry, "Move over," and Sam Merske plunked himself down at the end of the bench.

Sheriff Olsen gave a low groan, and Merske said, "Surprised to see me, huh?"

"Kinda," the sheriff muttered.

"You got the nerve to be sitting here," Merske said. "Who you got up there behind those whiskers?"

Sheriff Olsen wet his lips and then he opened his mouth, figuring to say it was a friend. But Ellen Reade was quicker at opening hers. Ellen leaned over the sheriff's knees and lifted her face up, eager and excited.

"It's my father, Mr. Merske," she whispered. "Isn't he *wonderful?*" Then she gave a sigh like she was stuffed full of a good dinner, and turned back to stare at the stage again.

Sheriff Olsen stared at the stage too, but the tree and Santa Claus and the little boy who was getting his present were all blurred together because of the awful way the sheriff was feeling.

Sam Merske said, "So you put Stephen Reade up there in the

whiskers and clothes and things that I supplied. Ain't that just beautiful?"

On the stage, a little girl was getting her package, and being a little girl, was remembering to say "Thank you.

Sam Merske said, "I'll get you for this. Putting a dead beat up there to hand out stuff that's wrapped with my paper and tied with my string! A no-good loafer that'll ruin the whole show! A no-good—"

His voice was getting louder, and the sheriff stuck his elbow hard into Sam Merske's ribs to make him shut up before the Reade kids could hear what he was saying.

But just shutting him up for now wasn't going to help. There were an awful lot of ways Merske could shame Stephen Reade in front of his children—like taking away the table and chairs that Ellen had counted on belonging to her family.

Sheriff Olsen tried to swallow, but his mouth was too dry. His throat was dry the same as his mouth. But his face and neck were so wet it would have taken a couple of bath towels to mop them.

It wasn't just a dumb thing the sheriff had gone and done; it was a plain crazy thing.

"Look, Sam," the sheriff whispered, "I gotta talk with you outside."

"Not with me," Merske said. "I'm sitting right here until I can lay my hands personal on that bum."

"Crazy" was what his deputy had called the sheriff's scheme. But Mart Dahlberg had been kind and generous. "Wicked" was the word he ought to have used.

And then all of a sudden a little boy began to yowl.

"It's Johnny Pilshek," Ellen said. "He's mad 'cause Louie Horbetz got a cowboy hat and all he got was mittens."

Every year it happened like that. Two or maybe three or four kids would complain about their presents, and that was why the committee always hid half a dozen boxes of something such as crayons under the sheet to give them. But Stephen Reade didn't know about the extras, because the sheriff had forgotten to tell him.

Johnny Pilshek marched back up on the stage. He stuck out his lower lip and shoved the mittens at Santa Claus. "I don't want mittens," Johnny howled. "Mittens aren't a real present."

Santa Claus took the mittens and inspected them. "Most mittens aren't a real present," he said, "but these mittens are something special. They're made of interwoven, reprocessed wool, Johnny. That's what the label says. And we had to order them especially for you at the North Pole, Johnny! Everywhere, boys have been asking me to bring them this special kind of mitten, but we haven't been able to supply the demand."

"I've got mittens already," Johnny muttered. "I don't want no more."

Santa reached out and took one of Johnny's hands and inspected it careful as he had the mittens.

"Certainly you've got mittens already, Johnny. But they aren't like these. Do you know why we had these made for you, Johnny? We had these made for you because your hands are rather special. You've got to keep those fingers of yours supple, Johnny. A baseball player, when he's your age, gets his fingers stiff from the cold, and what happens? He winds up in the minor leagues, that's what happens."

He put the mittens back into Johnny's hand. "And we don't want you in anything except the major teams, Johnny."

"Gee," said Johnny. Then he turned around and walked down off the platform, flexing the fingers of his right hand, slow and thoughtful all the way.

Sheriff Olsen let out the breath he'd been holding; he could see now how Stephen Reade had made a living for his wife and kids out of going from door to door with magazines and hosiery and vacuum cleaners. The sheriff looked down at Ellen, and Ellen looked up at the sheriff and gave a big smile.

"He sure *is* wonderful!" the sheriff whispered to her.

And then a little girl sitting next to Johnny Pilshek stood up and asked, solemn and polite, if she could bring her present back too. She'd wrapped it up in the paper again, and she kept it hidden behind her until she was up on the stage.

"I think it's a mistake," she said in an unhappy kind of a whisper. "What I got wasn't meant for a girl."

Santa took the package. "We don't often make a mistake, April," he told her, "but let's see." He opened the package up on his knees.

"I don't mind it's being a muffler," April said, "but that one's meant for a boy. I know, because it's just like one they've got in Mr. Merske's store in the boy's section for 69 cents. And it's not one bit pretty, either."

Stephen Reade held up the heavy gray scarf. "You're right, April," he said. "This was made for a boy and it's not one bit pretty. All the same, we chose it for you. And here's the reason why. It was chosen especially to protect your voice."

"I don't care. I don't want to wear it."

"You're pretty, April, and someday you'll be even prettier. But this is a fact. To get into the movies or on TV you've got to have a pretty face, but you've got to have something else too. You've got to have a pretty voice, one that's been properly protected by"—he turned over one corner of the scarf—"by 40 percent wool, 60 percent cotton, var-dyed."

He draped the thing over April's arm, and after a little bit, April began to stroke it.

"Should I wear it all the time, Santa?"

"No. Just when the temperature's below freezing, April. Have your mother check the thermometer every time you go out, and when it's below 32, then you wear it."

"Yes, sir—I mean, yes, thank you, Santa Claus."

Five minutes later, the lady who played the piano sat down again and started in on "Hark the Herald Angels Sing." On the stage Stephen Reade was standing up, singing, and motioning with his arms for everybody to join in. But the sheriff couldn't join in. He couldn't even open his mouth, let alone get any singing out.

Stephen Reade had done what the sheriff had asked him to, and he'd made a good job of it. And in return the sheriff had got Reade and his kids in a worse fix than ever.

The sheriff turned and looked at Sam Merske. He wasn't singing either—just scowling and muttering to himself.

The sheriff wet his lips. "Sam," he said.

Merske turned and glared. "So that was the gag," he said. "Pretty slick, pretty slick, arranging for him to give me a personal demonstration of his selling ability. Pretty slick."

"Huh?" said the sheriff, and when the song ended and the next one hadn't yet begun, he said, "Huh?" again.

"OK," said Merske, "you win this time. He gets the job."

"What do you mean?" the sheriff asked slow and careful. "You mean you're fixing to give Stephen Reade a job in your store?"

"With the competition I've got from the mail orders, I'd give a shoplifter a job if he could sell like that guy can. He may not be a farmer, but he's a real salesman." Then he scratched at the top of his head and glared some more at the sheriff. "What gets me is that I never put you down for having either the brains or the brass to swing a deal like that. How'd you hit on it?"

Sheriff Olsen didn't answer. It would take an awful lot of talking to explain to Merske how sometimes things worked out fine even without any brains to help you. And, besides, the piano was getting started on "Jingle Bells," which was a tune the sheriff knew extra well.

Sheriff Olsen opened his mouth wide. He could tell from the way the folks in front turned around to frown at him that he was drowning them out. But he didn't care. There wasn't any better time than a week before Christmas, he figured, for bursting out loud and merry . . .

A LITTLE WOMEN CHRISTMAS*

LOUISA MAY ALCOTT

Christmas won't be Christmas without any presents," grumbled Jo, lying on the rug.

"It's so dreadful to be poor!" sighed Meg, looking down at her old dress.

"I don't think it's fair for some girls to have plenty of pretty things, and other girls nothing at all," added little Amy, with an injured sniff.

"We've got Father and Mother, and each other," said Beth contentedly from her corner.

The four young faces on which the firelight shone brightened at the cheerful words, but darkened again as Jo said sadly, "We haven't got Father, and shall not have him for a long time." She

---

* Adapted from *Little Women*, chapters 1 and 2.

didn't say "perhaps never," but each silently added it, thinking of Father far away, where the fighting was.

Nobody spoke for a minute; then Meg said in an altered tone, "You know the reason Mother proposed not having any presents this Christmas was because it is going to be a hard winter for everyone; and she thinks we ought not to spend money for pleasure, when our men are suffering so in the army. We can't do much, but we can make our little sacrifices, and ought to do it gladly. But I am afraid I don't." And Meg shook her head, as she thought regretfully of all the pretty things she wanted.

"But I don't think the little we should spend would do any good. We've each got a dollar, and the army wouldn't be much helped by our giving that. I agree not to expect anything from Mother or you, but I do want to buy *Undine and Sintram* for myself. I've wanted it so long," said Jo, who was a bookworm.

"I planned to spend mine in new music," said Beth, with a little sigh, which no one heard but the hearth brush and kettle holder.

"I shall get a nice box of Faber's drawing pencils. I really need them," said Amy decidedly.

"Mother didn't say anything about our money, and she won't wish us to give up everything. Let's each buy what we want, and have a little fun. I'm sure we work hard enough to earn it," cried Jo, examining the heels of her shoes in a gentlemanly manner.

"I know *I* do—teaching those tiresome children nearly all day, when I'm longing to enjoy myself at home," began Meg, in the complaining tone again.

"You don't have half such a hard time as I do," said Jo. "How would you like to be shut up for hours with a nervous, fussy old lady, who keeps you trotting, is never satisfied, and worries you till you're ready to fly out the window or cry?"

"It's naughty to fret, but I do think washing dishes and keeping things tidy is the worst work in the world. It makes me cross, and my hands get so stiff, I can't practice well at all." And Beth looked at her rough hands with a sigh that anyone could hear that time.

"I don't believe any of you suffer as I do," cried Amy, "for you don't have to go to school with impertinent girls, who plague you if you don't know your lessons, and laugh at your dresses, and label your father if he isn't rich, and insult you when your nose isn't nice."

"If you mean *libel,* I'd say so, and not talk about *labels,* as if Papa was a pickle bottle," advised Jo, laughing.

"I know what I mean, and you needn't be statirical about it. It's proper to use good words, and improve your *vocabilary,*" returned Amy, with dignity.

"Don't peck at one another, children. . . ." said Meg. . . .

The clock struck six and, having swept up the hearth, Beth put a pair of slippers down to warm. Somehow the sight of the old shoes had a good effect upon the girls, for Mother was coming, and everyone brightened to welcome her. Meg stopped lecturing, and lighted the lamp, Amy got out of the easy chair without being asked, and Jo forgot how tired she was as she sat up to hold the slippers nearer to the blaze.

"They are quite worn out. Marmee must have a new pair."

"I thought I'd get her some with my dollar," said Beth.

"No, I shall!" cried Amy.

"I'm the oldest," began Meg, but Jo cut in with a decided, "I'm the man of the family now Papa is away, and I shall provide the slippers, for he told me to take special care of Mother while he was gone."

"I'll tell you what we'll do," said Beth, "let's each get her something for Christmas, and not get anything for ourselves."

"That's like you, dear! What will we get?" exclaimed Jo.

Everyone thought soberly for a minute, then Meg announced,

as if the idea was suggested by the sight of her own pretty hands, "I shall give her a nice pair of gloves."

"Army shoes, best to be had," cried Jo.

"Some handkerchiefs, all hemmed," said Beth.

"I'll get a little bottle of cologne. She likes it, and it won't cost much, so I'll have some left to buy my pencils," added Amy.

"How will we give the things?" asked Meg.

"Put them on the table, and bring her in and see her open the bundles. Don't you remember how we used to do on our birthdays?" answered Jo. . . .

"Glad to find you so merry, my girls," said a cheery voice at the door, and [the girls] turned to welcome a tall, motherly lady with a "can I help you" look about her which was truly delightful. She was not elegantly dressed, but a noble-looking woman, and the girls thought the gray cloak and unfashionable bonnet covered the most splendid mother in the world.

"Well, dearies, how have you got on today? There was so much to do, getting the boxes ready to go tomorrow, that I didn't come home to dinner. Has anyone called, Beth? How is your cold, Meg? Jo, you look tired to death. Come and kiss me, baby."

While making these maternal inquiries Mrs. March got her wet things off, her warm slippers on, and sitting down in the easy chair, drew Amy to her lap, preparing to enjoy the happiest hour of her busy day. The girls flew about, trying to make things comfortable, each in her own way. Meg arranged the tea table, Jo brought wood and set chairs, dropping, over-turning, and clattering everything she touched. Beth trotted to and fro between parlor kitchen, quiet and busy, while Amy gave directions to everyone, as she sat with her hands folded.

As they gathered about the table, Mrs. March said, with a particularly happy face, "I've got a treat for you after supper."

A quick, bright smile went round like a streak of sunshine.

Beth clapped her hands, regardless of the biscuit she held, and Jo tossed up her napkin, crying, "A letter! A letter! Three cheers for Father!"

"Yes, a nice long letter. He is well, and thinks he shall get through the cold season better than we feared. He sends all sorts of loving wishes for Christmas, and an especial message to you girls," said Mrs. March, patting her pocket as if she had got a treasure there.

"Hurry and get done! Don't stop to quirk your little finger and simper over your plate, Amy," cried Jo, choking on her drink and dropping her bread, butter side down, on the carpet in her haste to get at the treat.

Beth ate no more, but crept away to sit in her shadowy corner and brood over the delight to come, till the others were ready.

"I think it was so splendid in Father to go as chaplain when he was too old to be drafted, and not strong enough for a soldier," said Meg warmly. . . .

"When will he come home, Marmee? asked Beth, with a little quiver in her voice.

"Not for many months, dear, unless he is sick. He will stay and do his work faithfully as long as he can, and we won't ask for him back a minute sooner than he can be spared. Now come and hear the letter."

They all drew to the fire, Mother in the big chair with Beth at her feet, Meg and Amy perched on either arm of the chair, and Jo leaning on the back, where no one would see any sign of emotion if the letter should happen to be touching. Very few letters were written in those hard times that were not touching, especially those which fathers sent home. In this one little was said of the hardships endured, the dangers faced, or the homesickness conquered. It was a cheerful, hopeful letter, full of lively descriptions of camp life, marches, and military news, and only at the end did the writer's heart overflow with fatherly love and longing for the little girls at home.

"Give them all of my dear love and a kiss. Tell them I think of them by day, pray for them by night, and find my best comfort in their affection at all times. A year seems very long to wait before I see them, but remind them that while we wait we may all work, so that these hard days need not be wasted. I know they will remember all I said to them, that they will be loving children to you, will do their duty faithfully, fight their bosom enemies bravely, and conquer themselves so beautifully that when I come back to them I may be fonder and prouder than ever of my little women."

Everybody sniffed when they came to that part. Jo wasn't ashamed of the great tear that dropped off the end of her nose, and Amy never minded the rumpling of her curls as she hid her face on her mother's shoulder and sobbed out, "I am a selfish girl! But I'll truly try to be better, so he mayn't be disappointed in me by-and-by."

"We all will," cried Meg. "I think too much of my looks and hate to work, but won't any more, if I can help it."

"I'll try and be what he loves to call me, 'a little woman' and not be rough and wild, but do my duty here instead of wanting to be somewhere else," said Jo, thinking that keeping her temper at home was a much harder task than facing a rebel or two down South.

Beth said nothing, but wiped away her tears with the blue army sock and began to knit with all her might, losing no time in doing the duty that lay nearest her, while she resolved in her quiet little soul to be all that Father hoped to find her when the year brought round the happy coming home. . . .

Jo was the first to wake in the gray dawn of Christmas morning. No stockings hung at the fireplace, and for a moment she felt as much disappointed as she did long ago, when her little sock fell down because it was crammed so full of goodies. Then she remembered her mother's promise and, slipping her hand under her pillow, drew out a little crimson-covered book. She knew it very well, for it was that beautiful old story of the best life ever lived, and Jo felt that it was a true guidebook for any pilgrim going on a long journey. She woke Meg with a "Merry Christmas," and bade her see what was under her pillow. A green-covered book appeared, with the same picture inside, and a few words written by their mother, which made their one present very precious in their eyes. Presently Beth and Amy woke to rummage and find their little books also, one dove-colored, the other blue, and all sat looking at and talking about them, while the east grew rosy with the coming day.

In spite of her small vanities, Margaret had a sweet and pious nature, which unconsciously influenced her sisters, especially Jo, who loved her very tenderly, and obeyed her because her advice was so gently given.

"Girls," said Meg seriously, looking from the tumbled head beside her to the two little night-capped ones in the room beyond, "Mother wants us to read and love and mind these books, and we must begin at once. We used to be faithful about it, but since Father went away and all this war trouble unsettled us, we have neglected many things. You can do as you please, but I shall keep my book on the table here and read a little every morning as soon as I wake, for I know it will do me good and help me through the day."

Then she opened her new book and began to read. Jo put her arm round her and, leaning cheek to cheek, read also, with the quiet expression so seldom seen on her restless face.

"How good Meg is! Come, Amy, let's do as they do. I'll help you with the hard words, and they'll explain things if we don't understand," whispered Beth, very much impressed by the pretty books and her sisters' example.

"I'm glad mine is blue," said Amy and then the rooms were very still while the pages were softly turned, and the winter sunshine crept in to touch the bright heads and serious faces with a Christmas greeting.

"Where is Mother?" asked Meg, as she and Jo ran down to thank her for their gifts, half an hour later.

"Goodness only knows some poor creeter came a-beggin', and your ma went straight off to see what was needed. There never was such a woman for givin' away vittles and drink, clothes and firin'," replied Hannah, who had lived with the family since Meg was born, and was considered by them all more as a friend than a servant.

"She will be back soon, I think, so fry your cakes, and have everything ready," said Meg, looking over the presents which were collected in a basket and kept under the sofa, ready to be produced at the proper time. "Why, where is Amy's bottle of cologne?" she added, as the little flask did not appear.

"She took it out a minute ago, and went off with it to put a ribbon on it, or some such notion," replied Jo, dancing about the room to take the first stiffness off the new army slippers.

"How nice my handkerchiefs look, don't they? Hannah washed and ironed them for me, and I marked them all myself," said Beth, looking proudly at the somewhat uneven letters which had cost her such labor.

"Bless the child! She's gone and put 'Mother' on them instead of 'M. March.' How funny!" cried Jo, taking one up.

"Isn't that right? I thought it was better to do it so, because Meg's initials are M.M., and I don't want anyone to use these but Marmee," said Beth, looking troubled.

"It's all right, dear, and a very pretty idea, quite sensible too, for no one can ever mistake now. It will please her very much, I know," said Meg, with a frown for Jo and a smile for Beth.

"There's Mother. Hide the basket, quick!" cried Jo, as a door slammed and steps sounded in the hall.

Amy came in hastily, and looked rather abashed when she saw her sisters all waiting for her.

"Where have you been, and what are you hiding behind you?" asked Meg, surprised to see, by her hood and cloak, that lazy Amy had been out so early.

"Don't laugh at me, Jo! I didn't mean anyone should know till the time came. I only meant to change the little bottle for a big one, and I gave all my money to get it, and I'm truly trying not to be selfish any more."

As she spoke, Amy showed the handsome flask which replaced the cheap one, and looked so earnest and humble in her little effort to forget herself that Meg hugged her on the spot, and Jo pronounced her 'a trump,' while Beth ran to the window, and picked her finest rose to ornament the stately bottle.

"You see, I felt ashamed of my present, after reading and talking about being good this morning, so I ran round the corner and changed it the minute I was up, and I'm so glad, for mine is the handsomest now."

Another bang of the street door sent the basket under the sofa, and the girls to the table, eager for breakfast.

"Merry Christmas, Marmee! Many of them! Thank you for our books. We read some, and mean to every day," they all cried in chorus.

"Merry Christmas, little daughters! I'm glad you began at once, and hope you will keep on. But I want to say one word before we sit down. Not far away from here lies a poor woman with a little newborn baby. Six children are huddled into one bed to keep from freezing, for they have no fire. There is nothing to eat over there, and the oldest boy came to tell me they were suffering hunger and cold. My girls, will you give them your breakfast as a Christmas present?"

They were all unusually hungry, having waited nearly an hour, and for a minute no one spoke, only a minute, for Jo exclaimed impetuously, "I'm so glad you came before we began!"

"May I go and help carry the things to the poor little children?" asked Beth eagerly.

"*I* shall take the cream and the muffins," added Amy, heroically giving up the articles she most liked.

Meg was already covering the buckwheats, and piling the bread into one big plate.

"I thought you'd do it," said Mrs. March, smiling as if satisfied. "You shall all go and help me, and when we come back we will have bread and milk for breakfast, and make it up at dinnertime."

They were soon ready, and the procession set out. Fortunately it was early, and they went through back streets, so few people saw them, and no one laughed at the queer party.

A poor, bare, miserable room it was, with broken windows, no fire, ragged bedclothes, a sick mother, wailing baby, and a group of pale, hungry children cuddled under one old quilt, trying to keep warm.

How the big eyes stared and the blue lips smiled as the girls went in.

"Ach! It is good angels come to us!" said the poor woman, crying for joy.

"Funny angels in hoods and mittens," said Jo, and set them to laughing.

In a few minutes it really did seem as if kind spirits had been at work there. Hannah, who had carried wood, made a fire, and stopped up the broken panes with old hats and her own cloak. Mrs. March gave the mother hot drink and gruel, and comforted her with promises of help, while she dressed the little baby as tenderly as if it had been her own. The girls meantime spread the table, set the children round the fire, and fed them like so many hungry birds, laughing, talking, and trying to understand the funny broken English.

"Das ist gut!" "Die angel-kinder!" cried the poor things as they ate and warmed their purple hands at the comfortable blaze. The girls had never been called angel children before, and thought it very agreeable, especially Jo, who had been considered a 'Sancho' ever since she was born. That was a very happy breakfast, though they didn't get any of it. And when they went away, leaving comfort behind, I think there were not in all the city four merrier people than the hungry little girls who gave away their breakfasts and contented themselves with bread and milk on Christmas morning.

"That's loving our neighbor better than ourselves, and I like it," said Meg, as they set out their presents while their mother was upstairs collecting clothes for the poor Hummels.

Not a very splendid show, but there was a great deal of love done up in the few little bundles, and the tall vase of red roses, white chrysanthemums, and trailing vines, which stood in the middle, gave quite an elegant air to the table.

"She's coming! Strike up, Beth! Open the door, Amy! Three cheers for Marmee!" cried Jo, prancing about while Meg went to conduct Mother to the seat of honor.

Beth played her gayest march, Amy threw open the door, and Meg enacted escort with great dignity. Mrs. March was both surprised and touched, and smiled with her eyes full as she examined her presents and read the little notes which accompanied them. The slippers went on at once, a new handkerchief was slipped into her pocket, well scented with Amy's cologne, the rose was fastened in her bosom, and the nice gloves were pronounced "a perfect fit."

There was a good deal of laughing and kissing and explaining, in the simple, loving fashion which makes these home festivals so pleasant at the time, so sweet to remember long afterward. . . .

Beth nestled up to her, and whispered softly, "I'm afraid Father isn't having such a merry Christmas as we are."

WHERE LOVE IS GOD IS[*]

LEO TOLSTOY

In a certain town there lived a cobbler, Martin Avdéiteh by name. He had a tiny room in a basement, the one window of which looked out on to the street. Through it one could only see the feet of those who passed by, but Martin recognized the people by their boots. He had lived long in the place and had many acquaintances. There was hardly a pair of boots in the neighbourhood that had not been once or twice through his hands, so he often saw his own handiwork through the window. Some he had re-soled, some patched, some stitched up, and to some he had even put fresh uppers. He had plenty to do, for he worked well, used good material, did not charge too much, and could be relied on. If he could do a job by the day required, he

*Adapted from *Twenty-Three Tales.*

undertook it; if not, he told the truth and gave no false promises; so he was well known and never short of work.

Martin had always been a good man; but in his old age he began to think more about his soul and to draw nearer to God. While he still worked for a master, before he set up on his own account, his wife had died, leaving him with a three-year-old son. None of his elder children had lived, they had all died in infancy. At first Martin thought of sending his little son to his sister's in the country, but then he felt sorry to part with the boy, thinking: "It would be hard for my little Kapitón to have to grow up in a strange family; I will keep him with me."

Martin left his master and went into lodgings with his little son. But he had no luck with his children. No sooner had the boy reached an age when he could help his father and be a support as well as a joy to him, than he fell ill and, after being laid up for a week with a burning fever, died. Martin buried his son, and gave way to despair so great and overwhelming that he murmured against God. In his sorrow he prayed again and again that he too might die, reproaching God for having taken the son he loved, his only son while he, old as he was, remained alive. After that Martin left off going to church.

One day an old man from Martin's native village who had been a pilgrim for the last eight years, called in on his way from Tróitsa Monastery. Martin opened his heart to him, and told him of his sorrow.

"I no longer even wish to live, holy man," he said. "All I ask of God is that I soon may die. I am now quite without hope in the world."

The old man replied: "You have no right to say such things, Martin. We cannot judge God's ways. Not our reasoning, but God's will, decides. If God willed that your son should die and you should live, it must be best so. As to your despair—that comes because you wish to live for your own happiness."

"What else should one live for?" asked Martin.

"For God, Martin," said the old man. "He gives you life, and you must live for Him. When you have learnt to live for Him, you will grieve no more, and all will seem easy to you."

Martin was silent awhile, and then asked: "But how is one to live for God?"

The old man answered. "How one may live for God has been shown us by Christ. Can you read? Then buy the Gospels, and read them: there you will see how God would have you live. You have it all there."

These words sank deep into Martin's heart, and that same day he went and bought himself a Testament in large print, and began to read.

At first he meant only to read on holidays, but having once begun he found it made his heart so light that he read every day. Sometimes he was so absorbed in his reading that the oil in his lamp burnt out before he could tear himself away from the book. He continued to read every night, and the more he read the more clearly he understood what God required of him, and how he might live for God. And his heart grew lighter and lighter. Before, when he went to bed he used to lie with a heavy heart, moaning as he thought of his little Kapitón; but now he only repeated again and again: "Glory to Thee, glory to Thee, O Lord! Thy will be done!"

From that time Martin's whole life changed. Formerly, on holidays he used to go and have tea at the public house, and did not even refuse a glass or two of vodka. Sometimes, after having had a drop with a friend, he left the public house not drunk, but rather merry, and would say foolish things: shout at a man, or abuse him. Now, all that sort of thing passed away from him. His life became peaceful and joyful. He sat down to his work in the morning, and when he had finished his day's work he took the lamp down from the wall, stood it on the table, fetched his book from the shelf, opened it, and sat down to read. The more he read the better he understood, and the clearer and happier he felt in his mind.

It happened one Christmas season that Martin sat up late, absorbed in his book. He was reading Luke's Gospel; and in the sixth chapter he came upon the verses:

"To him that smiteth thee on the one cheek offer also the other; and from him that taketh away thy cloke withhold not thy coat also. Give to every man that asketh thee; and of him that taketh away thy goods ask them not again. And as ye would that men should do to you, do ye also to them likewise."

He also read the verses where our Lord says:

"And why call ye me, Lord, Lord, and do not the things which I say? Whosoever cometh to me, and heareth my sayings, and doeth them, I will shew you to whom he is like: He is like a man which built an house, and digged deep, and laid the foundation on a rock: and when the flood arose, the stream beat vehemently upon that house, and could not shake it: for it was founded upon a rock. But he that heareth and doeth not, is like a man that without a foundation built an house upon the earth, against which the stream did beat vehemently, and immediately it fell; and the ruin of that house was great."

When Martin read these words his soul was glad within him. He took off his spectacles and laid them on the book, and leaning his elbows on the table pondered over what he had read. He tried his own life by the standard of those words, asking himself:

"Is my house built on the rock, or on sand? If it stands on the rock, it is well. It seems easy enough while one sits here alone, and one thinks one has done all that God commands; but as soon as I cease to be on my guard, I sin again. Still I will persevere. It brings such joy. Help me, O Lord!"

He thought all this, and was about to go to bed, but was loth to leave his book. So he went on reading the seventh chapter—about the centurion, the widow's son, and the answer to John's disciples—and he came to the part where a rich Pharisee invited the Lord to his house; and he read how the woman who was a sinner, anointed his feet and washed them with her tears, and how he justified her. Coming to the forty-fourth verse, he read:

"And turning to the woman, he said unto Simon, Seest thou this woman? I entered into thine house thou gavest me no water for my feet: but she hath wetted my feet with her tears, and wiped them with her hair. Thou gavest me no kiss; but she, since the time I came in, hath not ceased to kiss my feet. My head with oil thou didst not anoint: but she hath anointed my feet with ointment."

He read these verses and thought: "He gave no water for his feet, gave no kiss, his head with oil he did not anoint. . . ." And Martin took off his spectacles once more, laid them on his book, and pondered.

"He must have been like me, that Pharisee. He too thought only of himself—how to get a cup of tea, how to keep warm and comfortable; never a thought of his guest. He took care of himself, but for his guest he cared nothing at all. Yet who was the guest? The Lord himself! If he came to me, should I behave like that?"

Then Martin laid his head upon both his arms and, before he was aware of it, he fell asleep.

"Martin!" he suddenly heard a voice, as if someone had breathed the word above his ear.

He started from his sleep. "Who's there?" he asked.

He turned round and looked at the door; no one was there.

He called again. Then he heard quite distinctly: "Martin, Martin! Look out into the street tomorrow, for I shall come."

Martin roused himself, rose from his chair and rubbed his eyes, but did not know whether he had heard these words in a dream or awake. He put out the lamp and lay down to sleep.

Next morning he rose before daylight, and after saying his prayers he lit the fire and prepared his cabbage soup and buck-wheat porridge. Then he lit the samovár, put on his apron, and sat down by the window to his work. As he sat working Martin thought over what had happened the night before. At times it seemed to him like a dream, and at times he thought that he had really heard the voice. "Such things have happened before now," thought he.

So he sat by the window, looking out into the street more than he worked, and whenever anyone passed in unfamiliar boots he would stoop and look up, so as to see not the feet only but the face of the passerby as well. A house porter passed in new felt boots; then a water-carrier. Presently an old soldier of Nicholas's reign came near the window, spade in hand. Martin knew him by his boots, which were shabby old felt ones, goloshed with leather. The old man was called Stepánitch: a neighbouring tradesman kept him in his house for charity, and his duty was to help the house-porter. He began to clear away the snow before Martin's window. Martin glanced at him and then went on with his work.

"I must be growing crazy with age," said Martin, laughing at his fancy. "Stepánitch comes to clear away the snow, and I must needs imagine it's Christ coming to visit me. Old dotard that I am!"

Yet after he had made a dozen stitches he felt drawn to look out of the window again. He saw that Stepánitch had leaned his spade against the wall, and was either resting himself or trying to get warm. The man was old and broken down, and had evidently not enough strength even to clear away the snow.

"What if I called him in and gave him something warm to drink?" thought Martin. "The samovár is just on the boil."

He stuck his awl in its place, rose, and put the samovár on the table. Then he tapped the window with his fingers. Stepánitch turned and came to the window. Martin beckoned to him to come in, and went himself to open the door.

"Come in," he said, "and warm yourself a bit. I'm sure you must be cold."

"May God bless you!" Stepánitch answered. "My bones do ache to be sure." He came in, first shaking off the snow, and lest he should leave marks on the floor he began wiping his feet; but as he did so he tottered and nearly fell.

"Don't trouble to wipe your feet," said Martin "I'll wipe up the floor—it's all in the day's work. Come, friend, sit down and have something to drink."

Filling two tumblers, he passed one to his visitor, and pouring his own out into the saucer, began to blow on it.

Stepánitch emptied his glass, and, turning it upside down, put the remains of his piece of sugar on the top. He began to express his thanks, but it was plain that he would be glad of some more.

"Have another glass," said Martin, refilling the visitor's tumbler and his own. But while he drank, Martin kept looking out into the street.

"Are you expecting anyone?" asked the visitor.

"Am I expecting anyone? Well, now, I'm ashamed to tell you. It isn't that I really expect anyone; but I heard something last night which I can't get out of my mind. Whether it was a vision, or only a fancy, I can't tell. You see, friend, last night I was reading the Gospel, about Christ the Lord, how he suffered, and how he walked on earth. You have heard tell of it, I dare say."

"I have heard tell of it," answered Stepánitch; "but I'm an ignorant man and not able to read."

"Well, you see, I was reading of how he walked on earth. I came to that part, you know, where he went to a Pharisee who did not receive him well. Well, friend, as I read about it, I thought how that man did not receive Christ the Lord with proper honour. Suppose such a thing could happen to such a man as myself, I thought, what would I not do to receive him! But that man gave him no reception at all. Well, friend, as I was thinking of this, I began to doze, and as I dozed I heard someone call me by name. I got up, and thought I heard someone whispering, "Expect me; I will come tomorrow." This happened twice over. And to tell you the truth, it sank so into my mind that, though I am ashamed of it myself, I keep on expecting him, the dear Lord!"

Stepánitch shook his head in silence, finished his tumbler and laid it on its side; but Martin stood it up again and refilled it for him.

"Here, drink another glass, bless you! And I was thinking, too, how he walked on earth and despised no one, but went mostly among common folk. He went with plain people, and chose his disciples from among the likes of us, from workmen like us, sinners that we are. 'He who raises himself,' he said, 'shall be humbled and he who humbles himself shall be raised.' 'You call me Lord,' he said, 'and I will wash your feet.' 'He who would be first,' he said, 'let him be the servant of all; because,' he said, 'blessed are the poor, the humble, the meek, and the merciful.'"

Stepánitch forgot his drink. He was an old man easily moved to tears, and as he sat and listened the tears ran down his cheeks.

"Come, drink some more," said Martin. But Stepánitch crossed himself, thanked him, moved away his tumbler, and rose.

"Thank you, Martin Avdéitch," he said, "you have given me food and comfort both for soul and body."

"You're very welcome. Come again another time. I am glad to have a guest," said Martin.

Stepánitch went away; and Martin poured out the last of the warm drink and drank it up. Then he put away the serving things and sat down to his work, stitching the back seam of a boot. And as he stitched he kept looking out of the window, waiting for Christ, and thinking about him and his doings. And his head was full of Christ's sayings.

Two soldiers went by: one in government boots, the other in boots of his own; then the master of a neighbouring house, in shining goloshes; then a baker carrying a basket. All these passed on. Then a woman came up in worsted stockings and peasant-made shoes. She passed the window, but stopped by the wall. Martin glanced up at her through the window, and saw that she was a stranger, poorly dressed, and with a baby in her arms. She stopped by the wall with her back to the wind, trying to wrap the baby up though she had hardly anything to wrap it in. The woman had only summer clothes on, and even they were shabby and worn. Through the window Martin heard the baby crying, and the woman trying to soothe it, but unable to do so. Martin rose and going out of the door and up the steps he called to her.

"My dear, I say, my dear!"

The woman heard, and turned round.

"Why do you stand out there with the baby in the cold? Come inside. You can wrap him up better in a warm place. Come this way!"

The woman was surprised to see an old man in an apron, with spectacles on his nose, calling to her, but she followed him in.

They went down the steps, entered the little room, and the old man led her to the bed.

"There, sit down, my dear, near the stove. Warm yourself, and feed the baby."

"Haven't any milk. I have eaten nothing myself since early morning," said the woman, but still she took the baby to her breast.

Martin shook his head. He brought out a basin and some bread. Then he opened the oven door and poured some cabbage soup into the basin. He took out the porridge pot also but the porridge was not yet ready, so he spread a cloth on the table and served only the soup and bread.

"Sit down and eat, my dear, and I'll mind the baby. Why, bless me, I've had children of my own; I know how to manage them."

The woman crossed herself, and sitting down at the table began to eat, while Martin put the baby on the bed and sat down by it. He chucked and chucked, but having no teeth he could not do it well and the baby continued to cry. Then Martin tried poking at him with his finger; he drove his finger straight at the baby's mouth and then quickly drew it back, and did this again and again. He did not let the baby take his finger in its mouth, because it was all black with cobbler's wax. But the baby first grew quiet watching the finger, and then began to laugh. And Martin felt quite pleased.

The woman sat eating and talking, and told him who she was, and where she had been.

"I'm a soldier's wife," said she. "They sent my husband somewhere, far away, eight months ago, and I have heard nothing of him since. I had a place as cook till my baby was born, but then they would not keep me with a child. For three months now I have been struggling, unable to find a place, and I've had to sell all I had for food. I tried to go as a wet-nurse, but no one would have me; they said I was too starved-looking and thin. Now I have just been to see a tradesman's wife (a woman from our village is in service with her) and she has promised to take me. I thought it was all settled at last, but she tells me not to come till next week. It is far to her place, and I am fagged out, and baby is quite starved, poor mite. Fortunately our landlady has pity on us, and lets us lodge free, else I don't know what we should do."

Martin sighed. "Haven't you any warmer clothing?" he asked.

"How could I get warm clothing?" said she. "Why I pawned my last shawl for sixpence yesterday."

Then the woman came and took the child, and Martin got up. He went and looked among some things that were hanging on the wall, and brought back an old cloak

"Here," he said, "though it's a worn-out old thing, it will do to wrap him up in."

The woman looked at the cloak, then at the old man, and taking it, burst into tears. Martin turned away, and groping under the bed brought out a small trunk. He fumbled about in it, and again sat down opposite the woman. And the woman said:

"The Lord bless you, friend. Surely Christ must have sent me to your window, else the child would have frozen. It was mild when I started, but now see how cold it has turned. Surely it must have been Christ who made you look out of your window and take pity on me, poor wretch!"

Martin smiled and said; "It is quite true; it was he made me do it. It was no mere chance made me look out."

And he told the woman his dream, and how he had heard the Lord's voice promising to visit him that day.

"Who knows? All things are possible," said the woman. And she got up and threw the cloak over her shoulders, wrapping it round herself and round the baby. Then she bowed, and thanked Martin once more.

"Take this for Christ's sake," said Martin, and gave her sixpence to get her shawl out of pawn. The woman crossed herself, and Martin did the same, and then he saw her out.

After the woman had gone, Martin ate some cabbage soup,

cleared the things away, and sat down to work again. He sat and worked, but did not forget the window, and every time a shadow fell on it he looked up at once to see who was passing. People he knew and strangers passed by, but no one remarkable.

After a while Martin saw an apple-woman stop just in front of his window. She had a large basket, but there did not seem to be many apples left in it; she had evidently sold most of her stock. On her back she had a sack full of chips, which she was taking home. No doubt she had gathered them at some place where building was going on. The sack evidently hurt her, and she wanted to shift it from one shoulder to the other, so she put it down on the foot-path and, placing her basket on a post, began to shake down the chips in the sack. While she was doing this a boy in a tattered cap ran up, snatched an apple out of the basket, and tried to slip away; but the old woman noticed it, and turning, caught the boy by his sleeve. He began to struggle, trying to free himself, but the old woman held on with both hands, knocked his cap off his head, and seized hold of his hair. The boy screamed and the old woman scolded. Martin dropped his awl, not waiting to stick it in its place, and rushed out of the door. Stumbling up the steps, and dropping his spectacles in his hurry, he ran out into the street. The old woman was pulling the boy's hair and scolding him, and threatening to take him to the police. The lad was struggling and protesting, saying, "I did not take it. What are you beating me for? Let me go!"

Martin separated them. He took the boy by the hand and said, "Let him go, Granny. Forgive him for Christ's sake."

"I'll pay him out, so that he won't forget it for a year! I'll take the rascal to the police!"

Martin began entreating the old woman.

"Let him go, Granny. He won't do it again. Let him go for Christ's sake!"

The old woman let go, and the boy wished to run away, but Martin stopped him.

"Ask the Granny's forgiveness!" said he. "And don't do it another time. I saw you take the apple."

The boy began to cry and to beg pardon.

"That's right. And now here's an apple for you," and Martin took an apple from the basket and gave it to the boy, saying, "I will pay you, Granny."

"You will spoil them that way, the young rascals," said the old woman. "He ought to be whipped so that he should remember it for a week."

"Oh, Granny, Granny," said Martin, "that's our way—but it's not God's way. If he should be whipped for stealing an apple, what should be done to us for our sins?"

The old woman was silent.

And Martin told her the parable of the lord who forgave his servant a large debt, and how the servant went out and seized his debtor by the throat. The old woman listened to it all, and the boy, too, stood by and listened.

"God bids us forgive," said Martin, "or else we shall not be forgiven. Forgive everyone; and a thoughtless youngster most of all."

The old woman wagged her head and sighed.

"It's true enough," said she, "but they are getting terribly spoilt."

"Then we old ones must show them better ways," Martin replied.

"That's just what I say," said the old woman. "I have had seven of them myself, and only one daughter is left." And the old woman began to tell how and where she was living with her daughter, and how many grandchildren she had. "There now," she said, "I have but little strength left, yet I work hard for the sake of my grandchildren; and nice children they are, too. No one comes out to meet me but the children. Little Annie, now, won't leave me for anyone. 'It's grandmother, dear grandmother, darling grandmother.'" And the old woman completely softened at the thought.

"Of course, it was only his childishness, God help him," said she, referring to the boy.

As the old woman was about to hoist her sack on her back, the lad sprang forward to her, saying, "Let me carry it for you, Granny. I'm going that way."

The old woman nodded her head, and put the sack on the boy's back, and they went down the street together, the old woman quite forgetting to ask Martin to pay for the apple. Martin stood and watched them as they went along talking to each other.

When they were out of sight Martin went back to the house. Having found his spectacles unbroken on the steps, he picked up his awl and sat down again to work. He worked a little, but could soon not see to pass the bristle through the holes in the leather; and presently he noticed the lamplighter passing on his way to light the street lamps.

"Seems it's time to light up," thought he. So he trimmed his lamp, hung it up, and sat down again to work. He finished off one boot and, turning it about, examined it. It was all right. Then he gathered his tools together, swept up the cuttings, put away the bristles and the thread and the awls, and, taking down the lamp, placed it on the table. Then he took the Gospels from the shelf. He meant to open them at the place he had marked the day before with a bit of morocco, but the book opened at another place. As Martin opened it, his yesterday's dream came back to his mind, and no sooner had he thought of it than he seemed to hear footsteps, as though someone were moving behind him. Martin turned round, and it seemed to him as if people were standing in the dark corner, but he could not make out who they were. And a voice whispered in his ear: "Martin, Martin, don't you know me?"

"Who is it?" muttered Martin.

"It is I," said the voice. And out of the dark corner stepped Stepánitch, who smiled and vanishing like a cloud was seen no more.

"It is I," said the voice again. And out of the darkness stepped the woman with the baby in her arms and the woman smiled and the baby laughed, and they too vanished.

"It is I," said the voice once more. And the old woman and the boy with the apple stepped out and both smiled, and then they too vanished.

And Martin's soul grew glad. He crossed himself, put on his spectacles, and began reading the Gospel just where it had opened; and at the top of the page he read:

"I was an hungered, and ye gave me meat: I was thirsty, and ye gave me drink: I was a stranger, and ye took me in."

And at the bottom of the page he read:

"Inasmuch as ye did it unto one of these my brethren even these least, ye did it unto me" (*Matt.* xxv).

And Martin understood that his dream had come true; and that the Saviour had really come to him that day, and he had welcomed him.

CHRISTMAS EVERY DAY

WILLIAM DEAN HOWELLS

The little girl came into her papa's study, as she always did Saturday morning before breakfast, and asked for a story. He tried to beg off that morning, for he was very busy, but she would not let him. So he began:

"Well, once there was a little pig—"

She put her hand over his mouth and stopped him at the word. She said she had heard little pig stories till she was perfectly sick of them.

"Well, what kind of story *shall* I tell, then?"

"About Christmas. It's getting to be the season. It's past Thanksgiving already."

"It seems to me," argued her papa, "that I've told as often about Christmas as I have about little pigs."

"No difference! Christmas is more interesting."

"Well!" Her papa roused himself from his writing by a great effort. "Well, then, I'll tell you about the little girl that wanted it Christmas every day in the year. How would you like that?"

"First-rate!" said the little girl; and she nestled into comfortable shape in his lap, ready for listening.

"Very well, then, this little pig—Oh, what are you pounding me for?"

"Because you said little pig instead of little girl."

"I should like to know what's the difference between a little pig and a little girl that wanted it Christmas every day!"

"Papa," said the little girl, warningly, "if you don't go on, I'll

242

give it to you!" And at this her papa darted off like lightning, and began to tell the story as fast as he could.

***

Well, once there was a little girl who liked Christmas so much that she wanted it to be Christmas every day in the year; and as soon as Thanksgiving was over she began to send postal cards to the old Christmas Fairy to ask if she mightn't have it. But the old Fairy never answered any of the postals; and after a while, the little girl found out that the Fairy was pretty particular, and wouldn't even notice anything but letters—not even correspondence cards in envelopes; but real letters on sheets of paper, and sealed outside with a monogram—or your initial, anyway. So, then, she began to send her letters; and in about three weeks—or just the day before Christmas, it was—she got a letter from the Fairy, saying she might have it Christmas every day for a year, and then they would see about having it longer.

The little girl was a good deal excited already, preparing for the old-fashioned, once-a-year Christmas that was coming the next day, and perhaps the Fairy's promise didn't make such an impression on her as it would have made at some other time. She just resolved to keep it to herself, and surprise everybody with it as it kept coming true; and then it slipped out of her mind altogether.

She had a splendid Christmas. She went to bed early, so as to let Santa Claus have a chance at the stockings, and in the morning she was up the first of anybody and went and felt them, and found hers all lumpy with packages of candy, and oranges and grapes, and pocket-books and rubber balls, and all kinds of small presents, and her big brother's with nothing but the tongs in them, and her young lady sister's with a new silk umbrella, and her papa's and mamma's with potatoes and pieces of coal wrapped up in tissue paper, just as they always had every Christmas. Then she waited around till the rest of the family were up, and she was the first to burst into the library, when the doors were opened, and look at the large presents laid out on the library-table—books, and portfolios, and boxes of stationery, and breastpins, and dolls, and little stoves, and dozens of handkerchiefs, and ink-stands, and skates, and snow-shovels, and photograph-frames, and little easels, and boxes of watercolors, and Turkish paste, and nougat, and candied cherries, and dolls' houses, and waterproofs—and the big Christmas-tree, lighted and standing in a waste-basket in the middle.

She had a splendid Christmas all day. She ate so much candy that she did not want any breakfast; and the whole forenoon the presents kept pouring in that the expressman had not had time to deliver the night before; and she went 'round giving the presents she had got for other people, and came home and ate turkey and cranberry for dinner, and plum-pudding and nuts and raisins and oranges and more candy, and then went out and coasted and came in with a stomach-ache, crying; and her papa said he would see if his house was turned into that sort of fool's paradise another year; and they had a light supper, and pretty early everybody went to bed cross.

***

Here the little girl pounded her papa in the back, again.

"Well, what now? Did I say pigs?"

"You made them *act* like pigs."

"Well, didn't they?"

"No matter; you oughtn't to put it into a story."

"Very well, then, I'll take it all out."

Her father went on:

***

The little girl slept very heavily, and she slept very late, but she was wakened at last by the other children dancing 'round the bed with their stockings full of presents in their hands.

"What is it?" said the little girl, and she rubbed her eyes and tried to rise up in bed. "Christmas! Christmas! Christmas!" they all shouted, and waved their stockings.

"Nonsense! It was Christmas yesterday."

Her brothers and sisters just laughed. "We don't know about that. It's Christmas today, any way. You come into the library and see."

Then all at once it flashed on the little girl that the Fairy was keeping her promise, and her year of Christmases was beginning. She was dreadfully sleepy, but she sprang up like a lark—a lark that had overeaten itself and gone to bed cross—and darted into the library. There it was again! Books, and portfolios, and boxes of stationery, and breastpins—

***

"You needn't go over it all, Papa; I guess I can remember just what was there," said the little girl.

***

Well, and there was the Christmas-tree blazing away, and the family picking out their presents, but looking pretty sleepy, and her father perfectly puzzled, and her mother ready to cry. "I'm sure I don't see how I'm to dispose of all these things," said her mother, and her father said it seemed to him they had had something just like it the day before, but he supposed he must have dreamed it. This struck the little girl as the best kind of a joke; and so she ate so much candy she didn't want any breakfast, and went 'round carrying presents, and had turkey and cranberry for dinner, and then went out and coasted, and came in with a—

***

"Papa!"

"Well, what now?"

"What did you promise, you forgetful thing?"

"Oh! oh, yes!"

***

Well, the next day, it was just the same thing over again, but everybody getting crosser; and at the end of a week's time so many people had lost their tempers that you could pick up lost tempers anywhere; they perfectly strewed the ground. Even when people tried to recover their tempers they usually got somebody else's, and it made the most dreadful mix.

The little girl began to get frightened, keeping the secret all to herself; she wanted to tell her mother, but she didn't dare to; and she was ashamed to ask the Fairy to take back her gift, it seemed ungrateful and ill-bred, and she thought she would try to stand it, but she hardly knew how she could, for a whole year. So it went on and on, and it was Christmas on St. Valentine's Day and Washington's Birthday, just the same as any day, and it didn't skip even the First of April, though everything was counterfeit that day, and that was some *little* relief.

After a while coal and potatoes began to be awfully scarce, so many had been wrapped up in tissue paper to fool papas and mammas with. Turkeys got to be about a thousand dollars apiece—

***

"Papa!"

"Well, what?"

"You're beginning to fib."

"Well, *two* thousand, then."

***

And they got to passing off almost anything for turkeys—half-grown humming-birds, and even rocs out of the "Arabian Nights"—the real turkeys were so scarce. And cranberries—well, they asked a diamond apiece for cranberries. All the woods and orchards were cut down for Christmas-trees, and where the woods and orchards used to be it looked just like a stubble-field, with the stumps. After a while they had to make Christmas-trees out of rags, and stuff them with bran, like old-fashioned dolls; but there were plenty of rags, because people got so poor, buying presents for one another, that they couldn't get any new clothes, and they just wore their old ones to tatters. They got so poor that everybody had to go to the poor-house, except the confectioners, and the fancy-store keepers, and the picture-book sellers, and the expressmen; and *they* all got so rich and proud that they would hardly wait upon a person when he came to buy. It was perfectly shameful!

Well, after it had gone on about three or four months, the little girl, whenever she came into the room in the morning and saw those great ugly, lumpy stockings dangling at the fireplace, and the disgusting presents around everywhere, used to just sit down and burst out crying. In six months she was perfectly exhausted; she couldn't even cry any more; she just lay on the lounge and rolled her eyes and panted. About the beginning of October she took to sitting down on dolls wherever she found them—French dolls, or any kind—she hated the sight of them so; and by Thanksgiving she was crazy, and just slammed her presents across the room.

By that time people didn't carry presents around nicely any more. They flung them over the fence, or through the window, or anything; and, instead of running their tongues out and taking great pains to write "For dear Papa," or "Mamma," or "Brother," or "Sister," or "Susie," or "Sammie," or "Billie," or "Bobbie," or "Jimmie," or "Jennie," or whoever it was, and troubling to get the spelling right, and then signing their names, and "Xmas, 188—," they used to write in the gift-books, "Take it, you horrid old thing!" and then go and bang it against the front door. Nearly everybody had built barns to hold their presents, but pretty soon the barns overflowed, and then they used to let them lie out in the rain, or anywhere. Sometimes the police used to come and tell them to shovel their presents off the sidewalk, or they would arrest them.

***

"I thought you said everybody had gone to the poor-house," interrupted the little girl.

"They did go, at first," said her papa; "but after a while the poor-houses got so full that they had to send the people back to their own houses. They tried to cry, when they got back, but they couldn't make the least sound."

"Why couldn't they?"

"Because they had lost their voices, saying 'Merry Christmas' so much. Did I tell you how it was on the Fourth of July?"

"No; how was it?" And the little girl nestled closer, in expectation of something uncommon.

***

Well, the night before, the boys stayed up to celebrate, as they always do, and fell asleep before twelve o'clock, as usual, expecting to be wakened by the bells and cannon. But it was nearly eight o'clock before the first boy in the United States woke up, and then he found out what the trouble was. As soon as he could get his clothes on he ran out of the house and smashed a big cannon-torpedo down on the pavement; but it didn't make any more noise than a damp wad of paper; and after he tried about twenty or thirty more, he began to pick them up and look at them.

Every single torpedo was a big raisin! Then he just streaked it upstairs, and examined his firecrackers and toy pistol and two-dollar collection of fireworks, and found that they were nothing but sugar and candy painted up to look like fireworks! Before ten o'clock every boy in the United States found out that his Fourth of July things had turned into Christmas things; and then they just sat down and cried—they were so mad. There are about twenty million boys in the United States, and so you can imagine what a noise they made. Some men got together before night, with a little powder that hadn't turned into purple sugar yet, and they said they would fire off one cannon, anyway. But the cannon burst into a thousand pieces, for it was nothing but rock-candy, and some of the men nearly got killed. The Fourth of July orations all turned into Christmas carols, and when anybody tried to read the Declaration, instead of saying, "When in the course of human events it becomes necessary," he was sure to sing, "God rest you, merry gentlemen." It was perfectly awful.

***

The little girl drew a deep sigh of satisfaction.

"And how was it at Thanksgiving?"

Her papa hesitated. "Well, I'm almost afraid to tell you. I'm afraid you'll think it's wicked."

"Well, tell, anyway," said the little girl.

***

Well, before it came Thanksgiving it had leaked out who had caused all these Christmases. The little girl had suffered so much that she had talked about it in her sleep; and after that hardly anybody would play with her. People just perfectly despised her, because if it had not been for her greediness it wouldn't have happened; and now, when it came Thanksgiving, and she wanted them to go to church, and have squash-pie and turkey, and show their gratitude, they said that all the turkeys had been eaten up for her old Christmas dinners, and if she would stop the Christmases, they would see about the gratitude. Wasn't it dreadful? And the very next day the little girl began to send letters to the Christmas Fairy, and then telegrams, to stop it. But it didn't do any good; and then she got to calling at the Fairy's house, but the girl that came to the door always said, "Not at home," or "Engaged," or "At dinner," or something like that; and so it went

on till it came to the old once-a-year Christmas Eve. The little girl
fell asleep, and when she woke up in the morning—

***

"She found it was all nothing but a dream," suggested the little
girl.

"No, indeed!" said her papa. "It was all every bit true!"

"Well, what *did* she find out, then?"

"Why, that it wasn't Christmas at last, and wasn't ever going to
be, any more. Now it's time for breakfast."

The little girl held her papa fast around the neck.

"You shan't go if you're going to leave it so!"

"How do you want it left?"

"Christmas once a year."

"All right," said her papa; and he went on again.

***

Well, there was the greatest rejoicing all over the country, and
it extended clear up into Canada. The people met together everywhere, and kissed and cried for joy. The city carts went around
and gathered up all the candy and raisins and nuts, and dumped
them into the river; and it made the fish perfectly sick; and the
whole United States, as far out as Alaska, was one blaze of bonfires,
where the children were burning up their gift-books and presents
of all kinds. They had the greatest time!

The little girl went to thank the old Fairy because she had
stopped its being Christmas, and she said she hoped she would
keep her promise and see that Christmas never, never came again.
Then the Fairy frowned, and asked her if she was sure she knew
what she meant; and the little girl asked her, Why not? and the old
Fairy said that now she was behaving just as greedily as ever, and
she'd better look out. This made the little girl think it all over carefully again, and she said she would be willing to have it Christmas
about once in a thousand years; and then she said a hundred, and

then she said ten, and at last she got down to one. Then the Fairy said that was the good old way that had pleased people ever since Christmas began, and she was agreed. Then the little girl said, "What're your shoes made of?" And the Fairy said, "Leather." And the little girl said, "Bargain's done forever," and skipped off, and hippity-hopped the whole way home, she was so glad.

***

"How will that do?" asked the papa.

"First-rate!" said the little girl; but she hated to have the story stop, and was rather sober. However, her mamma put her head in at the door, and asked her papa:

"Are you never coming to breakfast? What have you been telling that child?"

"Oh, just a moral tale."

The little girl caught him around the neck again.

"We know! Don't you tell *what*, Papa! Don't you tell *what!*"

DULCE DOMUM*

KENNETH GRAHAME

The sheep ran huddling together against the hurdles, blowing out thin nostrils and stamping with delicate fore-feet, their heads thrown back and a light steam rising from the

---

*Slightly adapted from *The Wind in the Willows*.

crowded sheep-pen into the frosty air, as the two animals hastened by in high spirits, with much chatter and laughter. They were returning across country after a long day's outing with Otter, hunting and exploring on the wide uplands where certain streams tributary to their own river had their first small beginnings; and the shades of the short winter day were closing in on them, and they had still some distance to go. . . .

"It looks as if we were coming to a village," said the Mole somewhat dubiously, slackening his pace, as the track, that had in time become a path and then had developed into a lane, now handed them over to the charge of a well-metalled road. The animals did not hold with villages, and their own highways, thickly frequented as they were, took an independent course, regardless of church, post office, or public-house. . . .

Once beyond the village, where the cottages ceased abruptly, on either side of the road they could smell through the darkness the friendly fields again; and they braced themselves for the last long stretch, the home stretch, the stretch that we know is bound to end, some time, in the rattle of the door-latch, the sudden firelight, and the sight of familiar things greeting us as long-absent travellers from far oversea. They plodded along steadily and silently, each of them thinking his own thoughts. The Mole's ran a good deal on supper, as it was pitch-dark, and it was all a strange country to him as far as he knew, and he was following obediently in the wake of the Rat, leaving the guidance entirely to him. As for the Rat, he was walking a little way ahead, as his habit was, his shoulders humped, his eyes fixed on the straight grey road in front of him; so he did not notice poor Mole when suddenly the summons reached him, and took him like an electric shock. . . .

Home! That was what they meant, those caressing appeals, those soft touches wafted through the air, those invisible little hands pulling and tugging, all one way! Why, it must be quite close by him at that moment, his old home that he had hurriedly for-saken and never sought again, that day when he first found the river! And now it was sending out its scouts and its messengers to capture him and bring him in. . . .

The call was clear, the summons was plain. He must obey it instantly, and go. "Ratty!" he called, full of joyful excitement, "hold on! Come back! I want you, quick!"

"O, come along, Mole, do!" replied the Rat cheerfully, still plodding along.

"Please stop, Ratty!" pleaded the poor Mole, in anguish of heart. "You don't understand! It's my home, my old home! I've just come across the smell of it, and it's close by here, really quite close. And I must go to it, I must, I must! O, come back, Ratty! Please, please come back!"

The Rat was by this time very far ahead, too far to hear clearly what the Mole was calling, too far to catch the sharp note of painful appeal in his voice. And he was much taken up with the weather, for he too could smell something—something suspi-ciously like approaching snow.

"Mole, we mustn't stop now, really!" he called back. "We'll come for it tomorrow, whatever it is you've found. But I daren't stop now—it's late, and the snow's coming on again, and I'm not sure of the way! And I want your nose, Mole, so come on quick, there's a good fellow!" And the Rat pressed forward on his way without waiting for an answer. . . .

The Mole subsided forlornly on a tree-stump and tried to con-trol himself, for he felt it surely coming. The sob he had fought with so long refused to be beaten. Up and up, it forced its way to the air, and then another, and another, and others thick and fast; till poor Mole at last gave up the struggle, and cried freely and helplessly and openly, now that he knew it was all over and he had lost what he could hardly be said to have found.

253

The Rat, astonished and dismayed at the violence of Mole's paroxysm of grief, did not dare to speak for a while. At last he said, very quietly and sympathetically, "What is it, old fellow? Whatever can be the matter? Tell us your trouble, and let me see what I can do."

Poor Mole found it difficult to get any words out between the upheavals of his chest that followed one upon another so quickly and held back speech and choked it as it came. "I know it's a—shabby, dingy little place," he sobbed forth at last, brokenly: "not like—your cosy quarters—or Toad's beautiful hall—or Badger's great house—but it was my own little home—and I was fond of it—and I went away and forgot all about it—and then I smelt it suddenly—on the road, when I called and you wouldn't listen, Rat—and everything came back to me with a rush—and I wanted it!—O dear, O dear!—and when you wouldn't turn back, Ratty—and I had to leave it, though I was smelling it all the time—I thought my heart would break.—We might have just gone and had one look at it, Ratty—only one look—it was close by—but you wouldn't turn back, Ratty, you wouldn't turn back! O dear, O dear!"

Recollection brought fresh waves of sorrow, and sobs again took full charge of him, preventing further speech.

The Rat stared straight in front of him, saying nothing, only patting Mole gently on the shoulder. After a time he muttered gloomily, "I see it all now! What a pig I have been! A pig—that's me! Just a pig—a plain pig!"

He waited till Mole's sobs became gradually less stormy and more rhythmical; he waited till at last sniffs were frequent and sobs only intermittent. Then he rose from his seat, and, remarking carelessly, "Well, now we'd really better be getting on, old chap!" set off up the road again, over the toilsome way they had come.

"Wherever are you (hic) going to (hic), Ratty?" cried the tearful Mole, looking up in alarm.

"We're going to find that home of yours, old fellow," replied the Rat pleasantly; "so you had better come along, for it will take some finding, and we shall want your nose."

"O, come back, Ratty, do!" cried the Mole, getting up and hurrying after him. "It's no good, I tell you! It's too late, and too dark, and the place is too far off, and the snow's coming! And—and I never meant to let you know I was feeling that way about it—it was all an accident and a mistake! And think of River Bank, and your supper!"

"Hang River Bank, and supper too!" said the Rat heartily. "I tell you, I'm going to find this place now, if I stay out all night. So cheer up, old chap, and take my arm, and we'll very soon be back there again." . . .

They moved on in silence for some little way, when suddenly the Rat was conscious, through his arm that was linked in Mole's, of a faint sort of electric thrill that was passing down that animal's body. Instantly he disengaged himself, fell back a pace, and waited, all attention.

The signals were coming through!

Mole stood a moment rigid, while his uplifted nose, quivering slightly, felt the air.

Then a short, quick run forward—a fault—a check—a try back; and then a slow, steady, confident advance.

The Rat, much excited, kept close to his heels as the Mole, with something of the air of a sleepwalker, crossed a dry ditch, scrambled through a hedge, and nosed his way over a field open and trackless and bare in the faint starlight.

Suddenly, without giving warning, he dived; but the Rat was on the alert, and promptly followed him down the tunnel to which his unerring nose had faithfully led him.

It was close and airless, and the earthy smell was strong, and it seemed a long time to Rat ere the passage ended and he could stand erect and stretch and shake himself. The Mole struck a match, and by its light the Rat saw that they were standing in an open space, neatly swept and sanded underfoot, and directly facing them was Mole's little front door, with "Mole End" painted, in Gothic lettering, over the bell-pull at the side.

Mole reached down a lantern from a nail on the wall and lit it, and the Rat, looking round him, saw that they were in a sort of fore-court. A garden-seat stood on one side of the door, and on the other, a roller; for the Mole, who was a tidy animal when at home, could not stand having his ground kicked up by other animals into little runs that ended in earth-heaps. On the walls hung wire baskets with ferns in them, alternating with brackets carrying plaster statuary—Garibaldi, and the infant Samuel, and Queen Victoria, and other heroes of modern Italy. Down one side of the fore-court ran a skittle-alley, with benches along it and little wooden tables marked with rings that hinted at overflowing mugs. . . .

Mole's face beamed at the sight of all these objects so dear to him, and he hurried Rat through the door, lit a lamp in the hall, and took one glance round his old home. He saw the dust lying thick on everything, saw the cheerless, deserted look of the long-neglected house, and its narrow, meagre dimensions, its worn and shabby contents—and collapsed again on a hall-chair, his nose in his paws. "O Ratty!" he cried dismally, "why ever did I do it? Why did I bring you to this poor, cold little place, on a night like this, when you might have been at River Bank by this time, toasting your toes before a blazing fire, with all your nice things about you!"

The Rat paid no heed to his doleful self-reproaches. He was running here and there, opening doors, inspecting rooms and cupboards, and lighting lamps and candles and sticking them up everywhere. "What a capital little house this is!" he called out cheerily. "So compact! So well planned! Everything here and everything in its place! We'll make a jolly night of it. The first thing we want is a good fire; I'll see to that—I always know where to find things. So this is the parlour? Splendid! Your own idea, those little sleeping-bunks in the wall? Capital! Now, I'll fetch the wood and the coals, and you get a duster, Mole—you'll find one in the drawer of the kitchen table—and try and smarten things up a bit. Bustle about, old chap!"

Encouraged by his inspiriting companion, the Mole roused himself and dusted and polished with energy and heartiness, while the Rat, running to and fro with armfuls of fuel, soon had a cheerful blaze roaring up the chimney. He hailed the Mole to come and warm himself; but Mole promptly had another fit of the blues, dropping down on a couch in dark despair and burying his face in his duster.

"Rat," he moaned, "how about your supper, you poor, cold, hungry, weary animal? I've nothing to give you—nothing—not a crumb!"

"What a fellow you are for giving in!" said the Rat reproachfully. "Why, only just now I saw a sardine-opener on the kitchen dresser, quite distinctly; and everybody knows that means there are sardines about somewhere in the neighbourhood. Rouse yourself! pull yourself together, and come with me and forage."

They went and foraged accordingly, hunting through every cupboard and turning out every drawer. The result was not so very depressing after all, though of course it might have been better; a tin of sardines—a box of captain's biscuits, nearly full—and a German sausage encased in silver paper.

"There's a banquet for you!" observed the Rat, as he arranged the table. "I know some animals who would give their ears to be sitting down to supper with us tonight!"

"No bread!" groaned the Mole dolorously; "no butter, no—"

257

"No pate de foie gras, no caviar!" continued the Rat, grinning. "And that reminds me—what's that little door at the end of the passage? Your cellar, of course! Every luxury in this house! Just you wait a minute."

He made for the cellar door, and presently reappeared, somewhat dusty, with a bottle of cider in each paw and another under each arm, "Self-indulgent beggar you seem to be, Mole," he observed. "Deny yourself nothing. This is really the jolliest little place I ever was in. Now, wherever did you pick up those prints? Make the place look so home-like, they do. No wonder you're so fond of it, Mole."

At last the Rat succeeded in decoying him to the table, and had just got seriously to work with the sardine-opener when sounds were heard from the fore-court without—sounds like the scuffling of small feet in the gravel and a confused murmur of tiny voices, while broken sentences reached them—"Now, all in a line—hold the lantern up a bit, Tommy—clear your throats first—no coughing after I say one, two, three.—Where's young Bill?—Here, come on, do, we're all a-waiting—"

"What's up?" inquired the Rat, pausing in his labours.

"I think it must be the field-mice," replied the Mole, with a touch of pride in his manner. "They go round carol-singing regularly at this time of the year. They're quite an institution in these parts. And they never pass me over—they come to Mole End last of all; and I used to give them hot drinks, and supper too sometimes, when I could afford it. It will be like old times to hear them again."

"Let's have a look at them!" cried the Rat, jumping up and running to the door.

It was a pretty sight, and a seasonable one, that met their eyes when they flung the door open. In the fore-court, lit by the dim rays of a horn lantern, some eight or ten little field-mice stood in a semi-circle, red worsted comforters round their throats, their fore-paws thrust deep into their pockets, their feet jigging for warmth. With bright beady eyes they glanced shyly at each other, sniggering a little, sniffing and applying coat-sleeves a good deal. As the door opened, one of the elder ones that carried the lantern was just saying, "Now then, one, two, three!" and forthwith their shrill little voices uprose on the air, singing one of the old-time carols that their forefathers composed in fields that were fallow and held by frost, or when snow-bound in chimney corners, and handed down to be sung in the miry street to lamp-lit windows at Yule-time.

Carol

Villagers all, this frosty tide,
Let your doors swing open wide,
Though wind may follow, and snow beside,
Yet draw us in by your fire to bide;
   Joy shall be yours in the morning!

Here we stand in the cold and the sleet,
Blowing fingers and stamping feet,
Come from far away you to greet—
You by the fire and we in the street—
   Bidding you joy in the morning! . . .

Goodman Joseph toiled through the snow—
Saw the star o'er a stable low;
Mary she might not further go—
Welcome thatch, and litter below!
   Joy was hers in the morning!

And then they heard the angels tell
"Who were the first to cry Nowell?

Animals all, as it befell,

In the stable where they did dwell!

Joy shall be theirs in the morning!"

The voices ceased, the singers, bashful but smiling, exchanged sidelong glances, and silence succeeded—but for a moment only. Then, from up above and far away, down the tunnel they had so lately travelled was borne to their ears in a faint musical hum the sound of distant bells ringing a joyful and clangorous peal.

"Very well sung, boys!" cried the Rat heartily. "And now come along in, all of you, and warm yourselves by the fire, and have something hot!"

"Yes, come along, field-mice," cried the Mole eagerly. "This is quite like old times! Shut the door after you. Pull up that settle to the fire. Now, you just wait a minute, while we—O, Ratty!" he cried in despair, plumping down on a seat, with tears impending. "Whatever are we doing? We've nothing to give them!"

"You leave all that to me," said the masterful Rat. "Here, you with the lantern! Come over this way. I want to talk to you. Now, tell me, are there any shops open at this hour of the night?"

"Why, certainly, sir," replied the field-mouse respectfully. "At this time of the year our shops keep open to all sorts of hours."

"Then look here!" said the Rat. "You go off at once, you and your lantern, and you get me—"

Here much muttered conversation ensued, and the Mole only heard bits of it, such as—"Fresh, mind!—no, a pound of that will do—see you get Buggins's, for I won't have any other—no, only the best—if you can't get it there, try somewhere else—yes, of course, home-made, no tinned stuff—well then, do the best you can!" Finally, there was a chink of coin passing from paw to paw, the field-mouse was provided with an ample basket for his purchases, and off he hurried, he and his lantern.

The rest of the field-mice, perched in a row on the settle, their small legs swinging, gave themselves up to enjoyment of the fire, and toasted their chilblains till they tingled; while the Mole, failing to draw them into easy conversation, plunged into family history and made each of them recite the names of his numerous brothers, who were too young, it appeared, to be allowed to go out a-carolling this year, but looked forward very shortly to winning the parental consent.

The Rat, meanwhile, was busy examining the label on one of the cider-bottles. "I perceive this to be Old Burton," he remarked approvingly. "Sensible Mole! The very thing! Now we shall be able to heat some cider! Get the things ready, Mole, while I open the bottles."

It did not take long to pour the cider and thrust the tin heater well into the red heart of the fire; and soon every fieldmouse was sipping and coughing and choking (for a little hot cider goes a long way) and wiping his eyes and laughing and forgetting he had ever been cold in all his life.

"They act plays too, these fellows," the Mole explained to the Rat. "Make them up all by themselves, and act them afterwards. And very well they do it, too! They gave us a capital one last year, about a field-mouse who was captured at sea by a Barbary corsair, and made to row in a galley; and when he escaped and got home again, his lady-love had gone into a convent. Here, you! You were in it, I remember. Get up and recite a bit."

The field-mouse addressed got up on his legs, giggled shyly, looked round the room, and remained absolutely tongue-tied. His comrades cheered him on, Mole coaxed and encouraged him, and the Rat went so far as to take him by the shoulders and shake him; but nothing could overcome his stage-fright. They were all busily engaged on him like water men applying the Royal Humane Society's regulations to a case of long submersion, when the latch clicked, the door opened, and the field-mouse with the lantern reappeared, staggering under the weight of his basket.

There was no more talk of play-acting once the real and solid contents of the basket had been tumbled out on the table. Under the generalship of Rat, everybody was set to do something or to fetch something. In a very few minutes supper was ready, and Mole, as he took the head of the table in a sort of a dream, saw a lately barren board set thick with savoury comforts; saw his little friends' faces brighten and beam as they fell to without delay; and then let himself loose—for he was famished indeed—on the provender so magically provided, thinking what a happy home-coming this had turned out, after all. As they ate, they talked of old times, and the field-mice gave him the local gossip up to date, and answered as well as they could the hundred questions he had to ask them. The Rat said little or nothing, only taking care that each guest had what he wanted, and plenty of it, and that Mole had no trouble or anxiety about anything.

They clattered off at last, very grateful and showering wishes of the season, with their jacket pockets stuffed with remembrances for the small brothers and sisters at home. When the door had closed on the last of them and the chink of the lanterns had died away, Mole and Rat kicked the fire up, drew their chairs in, heated themselves a last serving of cider, and discussed the events of the long day. At last the Rat, with a tremendous yawn, said, "Mole, old chap, I'm ready to drop. Sleepy is simply not the word. That your own bunk over on that side? Very well, then, I'll take this. What a ripping little house this is! Everything so handy!"

He clambered into his bunk and rolled himself well up in the blankets, and slumber gathered him forthwith, as a swath of barley is folded into the arms of the reaping-machine.

The weary Mole also was glad to turn in without delay, and soon had his head on his pillow, in great joy and contentment. But ere he closed his eyes he let them wander round his old room, mellow in the glow of the firelight that played or rested on familiar and friendly things which had long been unconsciously a part of him, and now smilingly received him back, without rancour. He was now in just the frame of mind that the tactful Rat had quietly worked to bring about in him. He saw clearly how plain and simple—how narrow, even—it all was; but clearly, too, how much it all meant to him, and the special value of some such anchorage in one's existence. He did not at all want to abandon the new life and its splendid spaces, to turn his back on sun and air and all they offered him and creep home and stay there; the upper world was all too strong, it called to him still, even down there, and he knew he must return to the larger stage. But it was good to think he had this to come back to, this place which was all his own, these things which were so glad to see him again and could always be counted upon for the same simple welcome.

HOW I SPENT MY MILLION

J. EDGAR PARK

I rubbed my eyes and looked at the letter a second time. Yes, I was not asleep, the thing had happened. There was my [drink] and the half-eaten doughnut just as I had left them when I went to the door for the mail. There was the other letter that had come, still unopened, and here was this one from a firm of lawyers I had never heard of before. And the sum and substance of it was this:—my old neighbor, John Doby, whose funeral I had just attended two days before, had made me the sole legatee of his entire estate, which, to quote the letter before me, "runs considerably over one million dollars."

My first act was [to accidentally knock my drink off the table in my exuberance]—but what did it matter?—I was a millionaire.

"Well," I said to myself "I can have anything I want now. I'm a millionaire." Then I thought to myself: "What in the world were those things I wanted so much? I remember thinking of them lately and wishing I could have them but knowing I couldn't have them. I shall be able to have them now. What in the world were they?" One by one they began to come back to me:—I had wished many a time that Mary's, my old housekeeper's, nose might be about an eighth of an inch shorter than it was. Perhaps that was the thing that had irritated me most in life. Then the other thing was the way my brother's wife was always praising up her children and the way she used the phrase, "though I say it as shouldn't," when she was relating some particularly extravagant judgment upon the miraculous endowments of her progeny. Oh, yes, I remember another thing I had often said to myself I desired more than anything else in the world. That was that my sister Jane might have a sense of humor. The way she always tried to explain my jokes to the rest of the company had always been one of my most exacting crosses.

Well, I was a millionaire now and could have anything I wanted so, of course, I would have these things attended to right off. Suddenly it struck me with a cold shock that after all, I was no better off than I was before. Even a million would not go any way at all towards reducing Mary's nose or changing the vulgar trait in Maria, or giving Jane a sense of humor—no nor in winning the other thing which, if the truth be told, I desired more than any of these—no, I sadly thought, even the possession of a million would not make me appear a whit more attractive or desirable in the eyes of someone who seemed to regard me now, as far as I could ascertain, as a mere object in her landscape. The fact was the million did not seem to help me to get the things I wanted most after all. Money tends to cushion you up among things and it was people I was most interested in. After all what did I want with a million?

One thing was clear. I'd give that million away and get done with it the first opportunity I could get. I said this to myself as I took up and opened the second letter which was lying unopened beside my plate.

"Ah, yes," I said, as I read it over quickly, "here is a chance right off to do some good with it." This was the other letter:

National Society for the Redemption of Christmas
23 Wail Street, New York

Dear Sir:

A number of public-spirited citizens have banded together for the purpose of redeeming Christmas from the many wasteful and useless features which cluster around it and of transforming it into an annual event which will be of real economic and moral value to the community. In the past the untrue legend of Santa Claus has made many young children liars; the destruction of thousands of young trees has robbed the future of many hundred dollars' worth of white pine and spruce lumber, a great amount of money is expended on absolutely useless illuminated cards, Christmas tree ornaments, candles, fancy wrapping paper, ribbon and house decorations, holly, mistletoe and other such extravagant and useless vanities.

If the money which runs to waste in these useless channels were only saved and put in the savings bank we calculate that every man, woman and child in the United States would have 53½ cents to his name in his bank book on January first.

Still more serious is this matter when we regard it from the point of view of what this money would do in providing strictly useful gifts for those who need them this year. It has actually been calculated that the amount thus wasted on fal-de-ral would purchase one warm, winter, flannel petticoat, two mittens and a chest protector for every worthy widow in the United States, and enough would be left over to provide 1¼ pairs of stout boots for each orphan in public institutions throughout the country.

In view of these facts we ask you to sign and send to us the enclosed pledge that you will spend this year an entirely rational and utilitarian Christmas, spending money only on useful and rational objects. We also ask you to enclose ten dollars as a membership fee to pay salary of secretary, treasurer, office expenses, etc., of this new organization. Larger donations are requested from those interested.

[Signed]
Bartimaeus Tintoes,
President

"What wonderful luck!" I said to myself, "to get a million and directions for the most useful method of spending it both in the same mail."

The street door bell rang, and in a moment Mary's nose appeared at the door, followed after the lapse of a moment by Mary to say Miss Helene Gracie wished to see me just for a moment. What a morning I was having! All the best things in the world were pouring in upon me:—money, directions for spending it, and now—the very beatific vision herself, who although the reader may not be aware of it has already been referred to in this narrative, was at my door to see me.

She came in and sat down in the brown plush armchair by the fire. She had never been to see me before, but somehow as she sat there I remembered having seen her in that very chair thousands of times in my day dreams.

"Won't you have a doughnut?" I said, handing her the plate.

She took one, saying she was quite hungry, as she had been out skating for an hour since an early breakfast.

"Take a lot," said I; "take two! Don't mind the expense. I'm a millionaire."

"I'm so glad to hear that," she said, "because I have called to ask you for a subscription."

Immediately I assumed that stony abstracted appearance so necessary a part of a rich man's defense against suggestion of attack by humanitarian bandits.

"I am sorry," I said, "but you could not have struck me at a worse time. I refer not merely to the shrinkage in my holdings which makes me feel rather poor this morning but also I have just arranged to give liberally to this cause," and I handed her the letter of Mr. Bartimaeus Tintoes.

"Oh, I am so sorry," she said, as she took it, "I wanted you to give half a dollar to help us to buy old Mrs. Gulpins a dicky-bird and a cage."

I gasped in amazement, but said nothing till she read the letter through. She read it without a word or sign, folded it carefully up into a very small size and then suddenly leaning forward stuck it into the reddest part of the fire, where it was burned in a moment.

"Oh, I have the address on the envelope all right," I said. "You're mad because you know it's perfectly true."

"Mrs. Gulpins—a dicky-bird—" I said in derision. "You know perfectly she has not enough to eat. She needs potatoes and mittens, instead of a dicky-bird. Now, it is quite true, Miss Gracie, what you took for a joke. Mr. Doby has made me his heir," and I handed her the lawyer's letter.

She read that through and returned it to me with these cabalistic words: "Well, that spoils you! No, I won't ask you even for fifty cents. You can't afford it, you poor man. They've robbed you of all the riches of life and given you instead another man's cast-off clothes." She rose to go. "It's all nonsense," she said. "It's all nonsense, this practical business. Mrs. Gulpins wants a dicky-bird in a gold cage. She has been dreaming of having one in her sunny bay window for the last forty years. You and I think she ought to have potatoes and mittens. Well, perhaps she ought to have them. If so, we ought to see she gets them some other time. But not at Christmas. For all the potatoes and mittens in the world would not make her one-millionth time so happy as this canary she has set her heart upon. Christmas is the time for giving people happiness, instead of giving them the things you think they need. Look at my small brother Tommy. Now, what I think he needs most of all is a sound spanking, but Christmas is not the time for giving him that. I'm going to give him the most useless toy telescope you ever saw because he wants it."

I sighed deeply, a safe-deposit vault sigh, and saw her into the hall. At the street door I said:

"Miss Gracie, I made two vows just before you came in this morning. One was to get rid of this entire million before Christmas Day, so as to be able to enjoy myself then. And the second was to spend it all on things that may be as frivolous and useless as they like, provided they give real pleasure to the people who get them. I want to blow it all in into a great bacchanalia of joy to other folk of the most unexpected and yet longed-for luxuries and happinesses, and I want you and your mother to help me to plan the whole thing out. Will you help me if I come round this evening?"

"Show me you are in earnest," she said, "by giving me that fifty cents."

I handed it to her, saying, "Now I have only $999,999.50 to spend, the burden is lightening."

"You have more sense than I thought," said she. "Come this evening."

In the evening I rang the bell at Mrs. Gracie's door. I found them both sitting at the dining-room table, which had been cleared. Each of them had a blank sheet of paper in front of her, and a pencil in her hand. As I came into the room the face of each was as blank as the paper. Miss Helene looked up as I entered. "Oh, I had no idea it was going to be such work," she said. "Mother and I sat down here after dinner gaily to spend your million for you as foolishly as we could and we can't think of a single useless way to make away with it that won't do more harm than good. Before I had one—I mean before you had one—to dispose of I knew lots of ways to spend it, but now I can't think of one."

We all sat round the table, appalled at the situation, blank paper, blank faces, hearts beating regularly blank, blank, blank—

Sadly I began to be convinced of the impossibility of doing any real good with my million. I could take away the self-respect of the students at the State University by paying their fees for them, or I could increase the bricks and mortar of a score of schools, but what those schools needed was more inspirational personalities in the teaching chairs and more ambitious students in the learners' desks, and that my money was powerless to give. I wanted something that would give at least a moment of glorious life to people that had never had the chance to feel that way before.

At last Helene broke the silence. "This won't do," she said. "Who are the people who most deserve to have the fun out of this million? We must all have the answer to that question on our papers before the clock strikes nine."

I looked up and saw it was five minutes to. The wheels in my brain began to buzz. Something must be thought, and thought immediately. Helene had her hands over her eyes, and the room seemed darkened thereby. Her mother's head was on the table.

Three minutes, four minutes passed, and just as the clock gave that whir, its warning that it was just getting up steam to strike, we all simultaneously took up our pencils and wrote something on our papers.

Now, you may believe in magic or not, as you please, but the fact remains that the word each of us had written was the same. The word we had all written down was this, the word "Mothers." At last we had something to start on. We were all agreed that the mothers of the world were those who denied themselves the things they wanted in order that they should give to others the things those others thought they needed.

"I have the whole scheme ready now," she said in a minute. "You get in touch with the teachers of the schools in the East Side wards and have them set this subject for a theme, that all the children are to write and bring this coming Monday, 'What Would Mother Like for Christmas.' You make the regulations, explain that it is not what Mother needs, but what Mother would like, and that it is not what Mother would like others to have, but what she would like for herself; and have it explained in each school that there are chances that a certain Santa Claus will do his best to help the child who writes the simplest and sincerest theme to give Mother just what she wants for Christmas."

"And," said I, "let's appoint ourselves the judges."

It seemed only a few days before we were gathered together around the same table with a pile of themes in front of us, several hundred in number. In addition, there was a list of several thousand articles costing less than one hundred dollars each, of none of which Mr. Bartimaeus Tintoes would have approved, but which the larger board of judges thought would bring genuine joy to the mothers whose children had suggested them.

Miss Helene had been granted a week's leave of absence from the school where she taught in order to go over the returns thoroughly. What a wonderful study they had been! First, there were a great many rejected suggestions in which our fallen human nature had played a great part, of which this is a specimen:

"I think the thing which would give my mother the greatest pleasure would be to see me riding round on one of those little cycles which are in the window of Tontine's store. She has often said that she would enjoy that more than anything else."

Some had to be rejected because they suggested things that no money could buy: that little children who had gone to the better land might come back into the mother's empty arms if it were only for a moment; that coarse, cruel, dissolute husbands might be transformed into the Sir Galahads they once seemed in the eyes of loving maidens—Oh, the pathos of that suggestion!— "the thing my mother would like most would be that my father should be the way he used to be."

The list of articles suggested included very many pieces of jewelry, and silk dresses, new hats, "stylish" baby carriages, pictures of all kinds, chiefly enlarged family photographs, rocking chairs for the parlor. One mother wanted enough to print a little book of poems she had written that she might give copies of it to her friends. Another wanted to be able to pay for prayers for the rest of the soul of her dead son. Another's longing was for a rosebud paper with ribbons on the parlor wall. Several dreamed of a season ticket to the winter's series of concerts; and for a great many the idea of being able to have some big yellow chrysanthemums on the table once in a while was perfectly intoxicating. Furs of various forms and shapes attracted many and Helene, who knew some of them, said they were those whom you would least expect to care for such finery. I chuckled as I thought how enraged Mr. Bartimaeus Tintoes would be to see me writing an order for a set of expensive furs for an Italian woman who supported her family by washing floors. But that was what little Angelina Maria said her mother wanted most of all, and I calculated it would give Mrs. Ferrari more of pleasure than anything anyone could dream of giving the wife of the man upon whose kitchen floor she worked Tuesday and Saturday. She probably would put them in a box and keep them there till the moths ate them, but in the meantime every morning she woke up she would feel the beatitude of the possession of those furs as a kind of glory in the back of her mind, and maybe take a glance at them in their box before she slipped out in the dark to wash floors till it grew dark again. It was great fun going over the pile of themes upon the table. "My mother would like most of all to see her old home in Sweden again and her old mother, who lives there still, but she cannot get anyone to look after us children when she's away." Helene knew how that could be arranged and I wrote out an order for the Swedish trip.

Gold-rimmed eyeglasses instead of steel spectacles attracted the soul of one Mrs. Moriarty, and a "piano to put ornaments on" was provided for Mrs. Stevaniski. Forty-two mothers were given orders for holidays at various longed-for summer resorts from Atlantic City to Coney Island, with free passes to all the shows, and provision made for a trained helper to look after their homes in the meantime. The way one of these suggestions was worded was very realistic. "Mother says what she would like most of all would be to get away from the sound of a baby or any of us children for about a week, so as she could sleep mornings and sit down once in a while daytimes."

We really spent a series of most delightful evenings together till at last the week before Christmas I began, with the aid of some experts, to total up just how much I had spent. Hard to spend a million? Why, it was the easiest thing in the world. How the figures did mount up! We were in the tens of thousands almost before we had started, and when you have spent $450,000 on the little things, with all the larger trips to Europe and such things before you, well, you begin to appreciate how small a sum of money a million really is.

Another happy afternoon we spent together, Helene, her mother and I, sorting out the labels which the children had written to accompany the presents. On the evening of the day before Christmas they were all distributed.

Never since the day when the voice was heard in Rama of Rachel weeping for her children was there ever heard so great a swelling of the voices of mothers, this time weeping for joy, singing for gladness, but most of all lost in transport at the thought that it was their little Alfredo, that it was their little Michael, that it was their own little Mary or Priscilla who had brought to them by their own skill at school these great gifts.

Early on that Christmas eve, Helene and I went out to bring Mrs. Gulpins the bird and cage she had contented herself to expect in heaven. As we walked home, house after house was illuminated and the sounds of greatest joy came often out of the smallest houses. "Things taste so much better and seem so much more heavenly in little houses," said Helene, as we stood outside one and heard the screams of delight and the enraptured huggings and kissings of some little mortal who was crying out at the top of her shrill voice, "I knew it all the time. It's a present from Me. Mamma, it's from Me."

There were tears in both our eyes and we went on down street after street—we could hardly tear ourselves away. "Well," I said, "I don't think a million ever gave such pleasure before, do you?"

"No" she said, "it has given at least one moment of crowded glorious life to the very mothers who thought their life was doomed to be drab for the rest of time, drabber every year. Only one thing I regret," she said; "you've gone and spent $50 more than your million and you haven't bought yourself a thing out of it. I wish I'd asked Mary, your housekeeper, what useless luxury you'd have liked and I could easily have slipped it into the accounts somehow without your knowing."

"I'll tell you exactly what I do want," I said; "it comes into our contract perfectly, because it is something absolutely useless and ornamental only."

We were coming in under the shade of the trees that fronted on her house and I took my life in my hand and told her just exactly what it was I wanted more than anything else in the world.

The clock struck nine as I came to her door and began to say good night, at ten-thirty she rang the bell in spite of me.

"Mother," she cried, as we got into the hall, "we forgot that you were a mother, too, and have come to ask you what you wanted for Christmas."

Her mother looked at us both, then, kissing me, she said, "My little girl told you, didn't she? that I wanted a son more than anything else in the world."

"No" I said, "I told her."

"A merry Christmas!" she said, kissing us both again.

THE STRANGERS

TED HARRISON

In the ninth month, of the twenty-third year, of Emperor Showa, the god of the harvest smiled on the rice fields of Honshu; and in that month, as in a hundred generations past, the people of our village heard the chill voice of the great cold. With each passing day it whispered louder through the twisted pines that guard our humble homes.

Ever since older brother returned from the war, we have worked together in the fields, and this year there would be more sweet potatoes and rice than ever before.

It was a good time of year in Narumi, and as Nobuo pumped the small flywheel pedal with his foot, I fed rice shocks into the grinding threshing machine's mouth. When the wheel suddenly stopped, I thought that Nobuo was tired, but the threshers in other fields were silent, too. Then I saw the strange procession: two foreign-looking people followed by a group of curious people, crossing the creaky bridge and entering our town.

"It is so, Father, I saw the two tall *Amerikajin* while I was returning from school. They were carrying their many possessions through the streets like harvest-time servants."

"Quiet, Daughter! Let Hideo finish speaking, and take care that the evening rice doesn't burn."

They didn't wear uniforms or carry rifles, and they paid Shimozato San, the landowner, much yen to stay at his guest house. He told everyone that they are Christian teachers from

America and will teach many strange and wonderful things to the villagers.

There was a sudden silence that filled our little home from the smoky rafters and straw roof thatching to the cracking plaster walls and worn straw-mat floors. The flickering lamplight chased deep shadows across our aging father's face, and there was a strange anger in his voice as he spoke.

"Hideo, your words are foolish, even for a second son. Since the Creator looked down from the rainbow of heaven, since Izunagi formed these islands with his jewel spear, this has been our land, our Japan! From the time our ancestors first came with the long sword and the rice plant, they found good earth and clear streams in this land of the pine tree hills. In those times our people planted the rice shoots with song till the Daimyo rulers saw the lands and treasures of other rulers. Then there were wars in the kingdom, with fear behind every door, and the rice pots no longer boiled in the huts of the villagers.

"But our great Kami heard the prayers of the silent hearts, and there was peace and song again—till—you have all heard how the same winds that brought the first followers of Buddha from Korea later blew across the inland sea with war from that 'Land of the morning freshness.' Each time the seeds of greed and anger have grown in the hearts of evil rulers, clever words and new false visions have led our people to sorrow.

"My sons, my daughter, can you soon forget how many nights we took shelter in the forest, and your own mother killed by a war plane's bombs? Have you forgotten hunger and cold when our crops were taken, and there was no charcoal to cook our poor rations? Certainly Nobuo remembers the islands of the great sunrise, where the youth of Japan's lost generation are buried, the islands where his arm was blown away. If these strangers must now stay in Narumi, let the family of Yamada Shotaro work hard in our fields and pay no heed to their foreign words."

In the days that followed, older brother and I saw the last bags of rice placed in storehouse, and found time to view more leisurely the season of turning leaves. People moved more rapidly through the narrow village streets now, winding their way through waves of children, noodle carts, and roast chestnut vendors.

By night, cheap fireworks fizzled over the muddy river at the edge of town, and the autumn festival was heralded by the sound of drums and bamboo flutes from the village square.

A flood of brightly colored kimonos surged out of sliding doors and down the narrow lantern-lighted streets. Nobuo and I were swept along with the crowd, with younger sister and her wooden Geta clogs clop-clopping along behind us. As is the manner of unmarried girls, Miyoko had again this year spent her small savings on an expensive new *obi* sash just for the festival.

In the village square the high, beribboned bamboo stage made its annual appearance. And the bright robes and chalk-whitened faces of actors and singers, milled around like a melting pot of colors on the high platform.

At one pause in the endless and unrehearsed program, the excited voices of the crowds chorused even louder than the previous drumbeat and chanting had been. Suddenly we felt a wave of silence sweep through the vast crowd. Surprised, I saw Nobuo unthinkingly try to spin himself around in the pressing throng with the arm he no longer had, and we both clearly heard the strange voice now.

"*Nihon No Minasoma,* (People of Japan), we have a great message for you!"

Standing on the stone steps of the old temple, the two *Amerikajin* towered over the crowd. The soft light of the lanterns cast a strange glow on their faces and seemed to flame up in the straw-colored hair of the speaker. The audience was silent; then, listening intently, we heard the words of our tongue oddly pronounced but startling clear.

"We are far from America and our people tonight," he began, "but we are glad to be here in Narumi. We are not great scholars or travelers of the world, but we are unpaid messengers with words of truth for this village and this nation. Our words sound strange to your ears, but the warm blood in our veins is just as yours. You look at our faces, but our feelings of hunger, of sorrow, and of joy are the same that you know.

"Your ancestors built this temple as a place of worship and prayer, and we have come these many thousands of miles to tell you that God does hear our prayers. We have come to say that this heavenly being is real, and he is surely the Heavenly Father of all nations, all peoples, and all tongues. Many hundreds of years ago God sent his son Jesus to this world with great teachings that could bring peace and joy to all who would hear. And Jesus who was born in a humble stable, went forth performing great miracles, but his faithful followers were not many. Going from place to place, he taught people the same eternal commandments of God that we come to bring you.

"But the people did not love one another as he had taught, and men who turned to their own wisdom, rather than asking of God, heard not his words. While he was yet young, Jesus was killed by people whose wickedness had blinded them to the great light of his message. But this message has gone forth to all peoples who would know the truth and find these blessings."

That's about all I remembered afterwards, but before departing, little sister with excited surprise pointed out something that our eyes had missed on the first stranger. Despite all the wealth of his faraway land, this youthful person most surely had large and poorly sewn patches on his trouser leg and coat.

Little sister Miyoko and I talked, as we hurried home, of the second teacher's words of the sacred history we could read, but older brother said nothing. One of the *Amerikajin* had talked of being in the war, and I wondered what Nobuo with the shot-away arm was thinking.

The winter winds rattled into the innermost sliding paper doors now, and the public bath became the only warm place in Narumi. Falling leaves huddled around the moss-covered stone lanterns in ancient gardens or fluttered down to the thin ice of lifeless goldfish ponds. This was the time of thankfulness for a good harvest, and each house echoed the thump of the wooden mallet beating the steaming rice into Mochi cakes. This was the time of ripe persimmon, tangerines, and sweetened bean cakes.

Perhaps things were going too well—till the angry voice of our father one day called us all to the forbidding silence of the guest room. "It is said," he began, "that little daughter is among those who gather in the meeting hall on the seventh day to hear the words of the foreigners."

There was a long silence as we stared at the straw mat floor, and finally father asked even more loudly, "Tell us, Miyoko, what is this foolishness that you do to bring sorrow to me?"

Holding back the tears, Miyoko pleaded, "The young men with the funny eyes came to our higher school, and they were very nice. All of the students were happy to hear about the customs of their country, and after singing a song they told us stories of a book they call the Bibo. Some of the girls even thought the visitors were handsome, but I don't think that they can see as well as we."

With a sharp nod father began to speak, and sister stopped as if she had suddenly lost her breath.

"It is written, 'A woman's heart is like the autumn skies; forever changing.' Little good does it do to send you to school when

279

a woman's real duty is to bless a man with sons and make his food taste good. You will probably even want to paint your lips soon or discard your slippers for the elevated shoes of tea house girls."

"Let no more be said, Daughter, till you reach the proper age, and I will then arrange for your marriage to a young man of good family. As for now, the sons and I will go to see these foreigners, and they will learn that the family of Yamada Shotaro will not hear their words."

Older brother and I quietly followed our father down the narrow streets, past the noodle shop, the carpenter, the fruit stands, and the sellers of cloth. Strangely enough the big sliding door was missing, and loud noises of hammering and sawing came from inside the yard.

Standing very formally at the outer gatepost, father rapped the heavy knocker in vain, said some unpleasant things about thoughtless laborers, and finally motioned us inside.

In old clothes and much perspiration the two *Amerikajin,* like poor craftsmen, were busily repairing the great door. We all bowed very low in surprise and embarrassment, but before father could officially introduce us, the two foreigners motioned for us to lift the other end of the door.

As we strained to raise this heavy thing into place, curious people began to gather outside, and father angrily avoided our glances. After much hammering the job was done, and our father, too winded to speak, slowly lowered himself onto a stone bench, like a man of great age.

Never had anyone dared treat father so shamefully, and certainly our sword-wielding samurai ancestors removed heads for less cause. The *Amerikajin,* however, calmly thanked us and after a short disappearance emerged from their house with steaming bowls of real milk. Sipping this wonderful drink, I waited for father to speak, but he just drank his milk and stared at the ground.

Finally he laid the empty bowl down, straightened the folds of his worn kimono, and arose majestically to his full five feet, six inches.

"I have a humble daughter," he began, "who is yet a child but has the thoughts of an old woman." The two tall listeners had given their respectful attention to this statement, but before father could go on they said, "yes" and hurried into the house again. When they returned this time, they handed us cans of milk, soap with a wonderful fragrance, and two brightly colored American dresses for younger sister. Of course father protested loudly, but they just said *"Nan demo Nai,"* (it is nothing). When he defiantly folded his arms across his chest, they carefully dumped several more cans into the long sleeves of his kimono.

All the way home father talked of the dangers of having such people in Narumi, but I admired their courage. In his anger, father had been caught unawares by the words of his opponents. In the ways of a city merchant, they had asked him which of two nights he could come to study their teachings, and without thinking he had made a promise.

For a time our family even returned to normal, but in the twelfth month there was a new excitement as the two teachers invited the whole village to a special party on the twenty-fifth day. Miyoko heard in the market that this was the festival which honored God's Son, and was called Kirisumasu.

On the cold afternoon of this eventful day, we watched the *Amerikajin* through their half-opened gate. In their spacious garden, to our surprise, they first propped up a large spruce tree and began to decorate it with all manner of beautiful things. As the day hurried on, many children gathered to watch. Their less forward parents waited expectantly behind bamboo shutters for whatever it was to happen. When curiosity finally overcame some of the ragged children, they returned noisily from behind the mystery of the gate with sacks of wondrous candies. The festival had indeed begun.

In a surprisingly short time the streets were full of children, farmers, fishermen, and merchants, and by the open gate, I saw fat Cho Cho San, the mayor, had made himself the official greeter, and was bowing low to beggars and landowners alike.

It was truly a remarkable evening, and all were impressed when a chorus of young people sang a beautiful song called "Silent Night." One of the foreigners then prayed very humbly that all people might seek to understand Jesus and his timeless teachings.

When the other teacher next told the audience of the kind old grandpa from the top of the world, the children got big eyes. Miyoko had whispered very seriously that he truly had a white beard and gave gifts to people in foreign lands. Some of the older people laughed at this story, but the speaker, with a flourish like a Kabuki actor, introduced us to Santa San himself. For one long minute there was silence in our ancient village of Narumi.

When the short fat man in the red suit began to speak, the words that came out through his thick beard were surprisingly good Japanese for a foreigner. "I am glad to come to your village," he said, "and although I have traveled far, I am refreshed by the friendship I find here. Japan has long been a land of many sorrows, but these two missionaries are truly your brothers, and they bring you the faith and love of their people and our God. If you will hear their words, you shall find peace and righteousness, and understanding shall grow in your hearts."

"Such wonderful words," the people around us said, "such an amazing person," but Santa San and the missionaries were busy now handing out small bundles of food and clothing to the most needy, and *Amerikajin* candies to all. There was another song, a farewell prayer, and there were tears in the eyes of many who filed out through the big gate. As the crowd slowly gathered outside, the charcoal maker's sooty hand caught my arm as he repentantly said: "And to think that I doubted the story of Santa San."

Miyoko, Nubuo, and I walked slowly home along the darkening road, greatly impressed by the things that we had learned. Even Nobuo told us of his thoughts: "My heart tells me that these things are true," he said, "but it is a great sorrow that our father will never listen."

"Why do you return so late?" Father questioned at the door, but in sleep we soon escaped answering.

In the charcoal heater's dim light, Yamada Shotaro walked through his quiet house to a small window overlooking the sleeping village of Narumi. Outside the moonlight outlined the ancient hills to the north, and a lonely wind sighed in the great pines. The old temple was a dark and silent silhouette.

But there was a new light in Yamada San's eyes, new faith and new strength to carry on. Yes, there would be typhoons, and earthquakes, and communism to fear, but spring would come, and the tender green rice shoots would be planted for a bigger harvest and a better future. There will be blessings for my good children, he thought, to himself; for this village, and for all of Japan. We have a new hope, and a new God to guide us. And then, carefully folding the bright red cloth, he wrapped Narumi's first Santa Claus suit in a silk cloth and tenderly put it away for the following year; for the twelfth month, of the twenty-fourth year, of the Emperor Showa.

THE WAYS OF PROVIDENCE

J .   A R T H U R   H O R N E

Attorney James Brown stood on the sidewalk of Sixth Avenue and gazed at the half-finished structure which was to be his home. Busy workmen were engaged with hammer and trowel on various parts of the building; while great piles of brick and stone, lumber, and shining slabs of marble were strewn about the grounds indicating the palatial nature of this modern dwelling. While the lawyer stood there enjoying this scene of activity, a smile overspread his handsome features. This was the fulfilment of one of his dreams—to have one of the finest homes in the city. Success was perching upon his banner now. In the early years of his struggle he had prayed for success. It had come slowly at first, but finally by patient effort and the influence of friends he had reached the goal at last. Providence, he concluded, had had nothing to do with it.

A man in a dark suit, evidently the architect in charge, came out of the building and joined the lawyer on the sidewalk.

"Billings, I have to leave for the coast this afternoon. The Oil Lands case has been called for the first week in October, and I'm not half ready. I will probably be gone all winter."

"We'll not be through here before the latter part of April, anyway, Mr. Brown, so you'll likely be back before we finish the interior," replied the architect. "The city department gave us the house number this morning. It is 914."

The lawyer took from his pocket a small notebook and jotted down the number.

"Don't slight anything, Billings, even if it goes a little over the estimate. A man builds only one house like this in a lifetime." And so saying the great lawyer turned and entered his waiting automobile and was driven away.

The same morning that this incident occurred another James Brown also stood on the sidewalk in front of his home. He, too, was going away to try his fortune in another state. Thus far success had not perched upon his banner. No automobile was to take him to the railroad station. No huge retaining fee had been sent him to insure the success of his venture. He was not thinking of the grandeur of his home, but of the sweet-faced, blue-eyed woman who stood in the doorway with a baby in her arms to have a final parting word with her husband ere he left for the mines in Nevada. "Don't take any risks, Jim," she said. "Better a whole skin than taking a chance on your life."

"Don't worry, Alice, I'll be back safe and sound, never fear. Kiss Jamie and Winnie and Ted for me when they come home from school and tell them Daddy expects some little letters to come along with yours." With a wave of his hand he turned and walked briskly away.

Alice turned to her household duties with a heavy heart. She loved her husband dearly and missed him when he went away. In their earlier married life she had accompanied him to several of the camps where he worked as an assayer, but since the children were old enough to attend school she had been compelled to stay at home. Jim was a steady worker and having no bad habits they had always had plenty for their needs, and had managed to lay aside a little in the bank with the hopes of someday buying a home of their own.

Jim's first letter from Nevada told of a change in his plans. "I've decided to take a lease," he wrote. "There's a fine fellow here named Bill Stauffer who will go with me. The mining company agrees to furnish transportation to the railroad for our ores at the same rate they pay for their own. I see no reason why we shouldn't clean up a bunch of money." Later letters confirmed this hopeful view, and under date of December 4, 1919, he wrote:

"We have found some more rich pockets of ore. We have about 15 tons on the dump that runs 160 ounces in silver and 45% lead. At present prices this should bring us nearly $2,000 apiece. As soon as we get 20 or 25 tons we'll make a shipment, and I'll come in with it."

The last few words thrilled Alice more than any thought of the money. Two thousand dollars sounded good, but the idea of soon seeing Jim again overshadowed everything else. She sang at her work, and when the children came home from school she took them in her arms one at a time and hugged them with delight.

"Papa's coming home soon, children," she told them. The little ones took hold of hands and circled about in high glee singing in their sweet, childish voices, "Daddy's coming home again! Daddy's coming home again!" Then Jamie stood on his head and Ted turned somersaults—all because daddy was coming home.

Just before Christmas, however, came the first letter of disappointment. "Well, dearie, I guess I can't come home for awhile yet, after all. We're snowed in for the winter. It started snowing Thursday and kept it up until last night. The dugway down to the camp is drifted level with the mountain. We'll have to store our ore in the tunnel until the road clears in the spring. This morning we struck another pocket that looks like it ought to be good for four or five tons.

"Christmas will be a bit lonesome, but maybe it'll be the last one I'll have to spend away from home."

By spring Jim figured they had nearly $20,000 worth of ore stored in the tunnel. Already the price of silver had begun to decline. A feeling of uncertainty pervaded the mining industry. Everywhere the high-grade orcs were rushed to the smelter.

"The snow is melting rapidly," Jim wrote in March. "We expect to get a wagon through within a week and start our ore to the railroad. Just think, dearie, nearly $10,000 for us. It means a home and maybe a small car. I don't care so much about the car if I can just see you in your own home with a nice bathroom, and a piano for Winnie to take lessons on."

Silver continued its downward course and lead began to follow. "We can't get the mining company to furnish us a single team to move our ore," he wrote in April. "They're so anxious to get their own ore to the smelter they don't give a hang about us. They keep promising but never do anything. This is terrible. Our ore has shrunk to half its value and still not a pound has been moved. I'm going to strike out for one of the ranches across the valley in the morning and see if I can get a team and wagon."

Later he wrote that he had secured the much-needed team for the trifling sum of $10 a day. "Had I known the mining company was going to treat us like this I would have hired this team a month ago. Well, never mind, sweetheart, the ore will still net us several thousand dollars. I guess we are not the only ones who are hard hit by the slump; the mines are closing down all around here."

A few days later Alice beheld a blue-coated messenger boy dismount from his bicycle in front of her house and come up the walk. With trembling fingers she signed for the telegram and hastened into her bedroom to read it:

Lone Pine Mountain, Nevada, May 19, 1920.
Mrs. James Brown
914 Sixth East St., City.
Jim injured hauling ore. Will reach city four-thirty today.
Wm. Stauffer.

Alice crushed the telegram in her hands and offered a silent prayer that Jim's injuries would not prove serious. She was nearly wild with uncertainty and dread. Why did telegrams have to be so cruelly brief? If she only knew the extent of his injuries it would not be so bad, but the uncertainty allowed her imagination to run riot, and she pictured him in all sorts of mangled conditions. One thought alone comforted her—she would see him soon again. At this thought she sprang up and began a hasty tidying of the rooms. She put clean sheets on the bed and made up the fire so that everything would be in readiness upon his arrival. As soon as the children came home from school she got them ready and took them with her to the depot, leaving the baby, however, in the care of a neighbor.

The first thing that caught her eye when she stepped off the street car at the depot was a white ambulance backed up before the doorway. The telegram had not said anything about providing such a thing for Jim; it must be for someone else. Just the same she felt irresistibly drawn toward the ambulance and approaching the driver she asked, "Are you waiting for someone coming in on the train?"

"Yes, a miner got hurt out in Nevada. He's comin' in on the 4:30." Her heart sank. Poor Jim! How he must be suffering! She turned to the driver with one more question.

"Do you happen to know the man's name?"

"No, they didn't tell me that. They just said to meet the 4:30 and bring back a miner that got hurt out in Nevada." He must have seen the look of apprehension on her face for he asked kindly, "Was you expectin' somebody sick on this train?"

"Yes," she said, "my husband. He was injured hauling ore, but I do not know how badly. I was not expecting this," indicating the ambulance. She had hard work to keep back the tears. The children must not see mother cry. By an effort she controlled herself, and taking a little hand in each of hers they went into the waiting room.

When the train pulled in, Alice was standing with the children on the platform, and when it came to a stop she eagerly scanned the car exits for sight of her husband. Presently she saw the white-coated driver of the ambulance approach one of the cars and she hurried over to him. A man on a stretcher was being carried down the car steps. One hand dangled limply over the edge of the stretcher, and Alice barely suppressed a cry. She stood beside the injured man as he was lowered to the platform. Yes, it was Jim, his face only half visible beneath the bandages. She almost flung herself on the stretcher. "O Jim, Jim, what has happened? Are you badly hurt?" He smiled wanly, and she tried to take his head in her arms. A groan escaped his lips as her hands went under his head and she quickly withdrew them. "Oh, did I hurt you? Forgive me, forgive me, I hardly know what I'm doing."

"It's his back, Mrs. Brown," said a kindly voice. She glanced up into the face of a stalwart man in the garb of a miner. "I'm Bill Stauffer; I guess you've heard of me. Them cuts on his face don't amount to nothin'. You see the rough-lock broke comin' down the steep road; he had to turn the horses up the mountain an' the load tipped over. If it wasn't for his back he'd be fit as any man in a few days."

The children began to cry when they saw their father lying there so limp and helpless. The injured man raised his right hand and patted Winnie's dark curls. His voice was low—almost a whisper. "Don't you cry, children, Daddy'll be all right pretty soon." This comforted them. Thus strong is the faith of childhood. Not so with Alice; his grave words only added to her grief.

The big miner and the chauffeur carried Jim to the waiting ambulance and he was driven away to the hospital. Half an hour later Alice was seated beside her husband's cot in the hospital awaiting the arrival of the doctor.

And the next morning's paper which contained among the local items a brief account of Jim Brown's accident had blazoned forth on the front page a picture of the state's noted lawyer James Brown and an accompanying article telling of his success in winning the first of his Oil Land cases in California.

We need not follow Jim and Alice throughout the long, hot days of summer while Jim lay in his plaster cast at the hospital, hoping and praying for the return of his health. In a way they were happy days, for not since their honeymoon had they been so much in each other's company. They were lovers once more with four additional knots binding their hearts together.

At last the day came when the cast was removed and Jim once more stood upon his feet free from its hateful pressure. He turned and twisted his body about to make sure that his cure was complete. "Thank God there's no pain now," he said fervently.

"Maybe it's all for the best, Jim," Alice returned with shining, tear-stained eyes as she watched him walk about the little room. "Providence has queer ways of doing things sometimes, you know."

"Yes," he said, and he stopped to look intently into the blue eyes, "Providence did me a good turn when it led me to your father's door, for no man ever had a sweeter wife than you have been to me, dear."

Throughout all this trying period Alice's faith and trust in God had never wavered, but now it seemed as if all things conspired together to break her spirit. When Jim left the hospital, he entered the great army of unemployed who walked the streets of our cities from the fall of 1920 until the spring of 1922. Mines were closing down or running only part time; stores and factories were cutting their forces; building was almost at a standstill; and gaunt poverty and distress were on every hand. The twelve hundred dollars which Jim had received as his portion of the mining venture was about exhausted when his hospital and doctor bills were paid. Still their hearts were brave when they returned to their humble home on Sixth East, and Jim set out early the next morning to try and find employment.

The first person he encountered was Joe Sanders, a brother assayer. "Still with the King Company, Joe?" Jim asked.

"No, they closed down two months ago. Didn't you know?"

"I hadn't heard. I've been in the hospital, so I guess I'm not up on the latest news. What are you driving at now?"

"Hunting another job," Joe answered. "And you?"

"Same thing. Are jobs really that scarce?"

"I'll say they are." They wished each other luck and passed on. Jim called in at several assay offices where he was well known and in each of them he found men seeking employment. At first he was not discouraged. He was a good assayer and had never before experienced any difficulty getting a position. As the days wore on, however, the full extent of the mining collapse became apparent.

"I guess I'll have to find some other kind of work," he told Alice when he returned after the third day's trial. "There seems to be more assayers than the market requires." Poor Jim! In the next few days he was to learn that there were more men in every line of work than the market required. Night after night, footsore and weary, he dragged his way homeward. Their small savings dwindled rapidly and were finally wiped out. Not once in all this trying period did his brave little wife fail to greet him with a smile and whisper words of encouragement when he left the door.

The first work he got was helping a man clean out a store that had just been vacated by a shoe company. For this he received fifty cents. Then he got three days' work helping unload coal at one of the coal yards and was paid a ton of coal, which he was thankful to get. His grocer, Mr. Gibson, gave him a job cleaning out the back room and basement of the store and cutting up a pile of boxes into kindling wood. For this work he was given credit for twelve dollars on account. In six weeks he had received in actual cash in hand the total sum of fifty cents.

"Things will soon take a turn for the better, I am sure," Alice said when he reviewed these little items to her one evening in November. He was going over his accounts while she sat mending a pair of Ted's trousers. "Did you see Mr. Shultz about that work at the smelter?"

"Yes, he's going out in a few days, and if anything turns up he'll let me know."

On December 10 Jim received a note from Mr. Gibson asking him to call at his earliest convenience. "I know what that means," Jim remarked grimly. "It means no more groceries on credit." He was right. When he called to see Mr. Gibson, he was told that the store was carrying so many unpaid bills that it would be ruinous to increase them.

"I'm sorry to have to do this, Brown, but it would soon come to the same thing anyway. The wholesalers will cut me off if I get in much deeper. I will carry your account as it now stands until you can get work, but that is the best I can do."

"Mr. Gibson, I appreciate all you have done for me, and I hope I can soon pay you every dollar I owe you." The kindhearted grocer leaned across the counter and laid a hand on Jim's arm.

"I know you do, Brown, and as soon as you get in work again I shall be glad to re-open your account until you draw your first pay."

"Thanks, Mr. Gibson." And with that Jim turned and walked out of the store. Life seemed a little less joyous to him as he wended his way homeward. Who would have thought a year ago that today would find him in such a plight?

"We still have some flour and coal," Alice said when he

reported the interview to her, and added, "and a Father above, don't forget that, Jim."

He threw his arms about her and held her close. "And the bravest little wife that God ever sent to earth."

A few days later, a snowstorm netted Jim several dollars cleaning sidewalks, and on December 21 a letter came from Shultz telling him to come out to the smelter and see if he could not get on there, as he had heard some talk of them putting on another man. A dollar was enclosed to pay his fare there and back.

The next day Jim was at the plant seeking an interview with Superintendent MacIntyre. For three days he persisted, staying at night with his friend Shultz. On the morning of the twenty-fourth he was informed, rather gruffly, that they would not put on another man before the first of the year, if at all. "We'll keep you in mind and if we need anyone we'll let you know," the foreman said more kindly as he noted the look of pain come into Jim's face at this blow to his hopes. For some time Jim wandered about the plant not caring to meet anyone. His tongue was dry and parched, and he quenched his thirst repeatedly at the little fountain near the furnace room. At four o'clock he boarded the train for home.

He entered the first car he came to, which happened to be the smoker. He had barely sunk down into the seat when he heard a voice behind him say, "Well, Brown, this is providential to find you here." He turned at the sound of his name and beheld Superintendent MacIntyre shaking hands with the man in the next seat back of him. He recognized the man instantly as the great lawyer who had gone to California to plead the famous Oil Land cases.

"I don't know whether it was Providence or not that put me on this train, but I'm surely glad to see you, Mac," the lawyer returned laughing.

"Same old atheist, eh?" the superintendent rejoined. "Anyway

I've a letter here for you from Edith which arrived from Butte this morning. She wanted me to be sure you received it before night."

"Hasn't Edith returned from Butte yet?" There was evident disappointment not unmixed with annoyance in his tone.

"No, she'll be down on the 10:30 tonight. Go ahead and read the letter—read it to me if you like." There was the sound of tearing paper as the envelope was torn open and then Jim heard the following:

"Your telegram came as a great surprise. I had just received your letter saying you could not be home before the first of the year. I'm so glad we can spend Christmas together. The kiddies are wild with delight. The house is all ready for us, everything was moved before I left, only I let Mrs. McGregor go home for the holidays. Never mind, I can cook a better Christmas dinner than she can. I can't bear to think of spending Christmas in a hotel, and there won't be room at Will's—Florence and the children are coming down with me—so we'll just have to go to our own home. Jim, it's the grandest thing I ever looked at, even our best pieces of furniture look shabby among such brilliant settings. Oh, I wouldn't miss spending Christmas there for worlds, now that you are going to be with us.

"I've made out a list of groceries and some things for the children's Christmas which I will enclose. If you'll order them sent up to the house we'll have the finest Christmas ever. The house number is 914, don't forget that. Meet us at the train, sure."

More rattling of paper and then, "Just look at this list will you, Mac, it's as long as your arm." They both laughed heartily.

"Trust a woman to think of the details." This from the superintendent.

To the lone man in the seat ahead all this seemed staged to mock his poverty. "Some men have everything and some nothing," Jim said to himself bitterly. "This fellow will spend his Christmas literally in the lap of luxury, while I have not a penny to take home to my wife and children." A spirit of rebellion arose in his soul at the scurvy trick fate had played him. Alice always credited things to Providence, but this man who reveled in wealth and groceries had no faith in Providence. Perhaps it was simply that some men knew how to make money and others didn't and Providence cared not a whit. This thought was gall to his soul.

When their train reached the city, Jim felt too depressed to go home, and he wandered about the streets for some time. Loads of good things stared at him from the store windows, and on the streets crowds of people were hurrying along carrying bulging bags and bundles that foretold a happy Christmas on the morrow. He alone of all that vast throng seemed penniless and forsaken. Surely Providence would not pass his family by so cruelly. Just then a paper bag burst in the arms of a woman, scattering potatoes over the sidewalk. She gathered them up hastily. One she missed. Jim picked it up and put it in his pocket. "This will be our Christmas dinner," he said, and laughed bitterly. It grew colder, and he turned his footsteps homeward.

Alice tried to greet him with a smile when he opened the door, but when she saw the drawn look on his face she burst into tears. He put his arm about her and led her to a chair in the kitchen. The children had placed the broom across the backs of two chairs and hanging suspended from it were four stockings of varying lengths. "It wouldn't be so bad for us," Alice sobbed on his shoulder, "we could stand it, but the children—not a thing in the house for their Christmas. Whatever in the world are we going to do, Jim? Do you think God doesn't care?" What could he say? It was the echo of his own thought. He was about to speak when their attention was arrested by a quick step on the back porch and a hurried thump on the door. Jim got up and opened the door.

295

A young fellow in overalls and jumper smeared with flour confronted them.

"Is this number 914?" he asked. Jim nodded assent. "We've brought your groceries; where'll we put 'em?"

"I didn't order any groceries," Jim answered. "You must have the wrong number."

"Ain't your name Brown, James Brown?" the young fellow persisted, looking at a paper in his hand.

"Yes," Jim answered, puzzled.

"This is the place all right. We'll back in." He dashed off into the darkness, and the next moment they heard the chug of a motor. The rear end of a big truck loomed out of the darkness and bumped into the porch. Two men began piling things onto the porch. Sacks of flour, potatoes, and sugar; cases of soap, canned milk, fruit, and vegetables; boxes, bundles, and packages of every description were unceremoniously dumped onto the porch or carried into the kitchen, while the bewildered family stood about in utter amazement. When a pretty Christmas tree appeared, the silence was suddenly broken by cries and exclamations of delight from the children, and the tree was carried triumphantly into the front room.

"Who sent all this?" Jim finally asked one of the men.

"I dunno, Mister; Santa Claus, I reckon." The next minute the two men climbed into their truck and rode off into the night.

Jim and Alice looked into each other's faces questioningly. Jim was the first to speak. "Who in the world could have sent them?"

"It must have been Bill Stauffer," she answered. "He sent a card saying he would see us at Christmastime. You see he had twelve hundred dollars from the lease, the same as we did."

Jim shook his head. "No, Alice, the check he sent us was the total received from our ore. I saw a copy of the account while I was out at the smelter. The bighearted fellow kept not one cent for himself. No, it must have been someone else."

Still mystified, they began to look over the things. A box of brilliant-colored trimmings came first into view. These were seized upon by the children and carried into the front room where Jamie was already setting up the tree. Alice next uncovered two beautiful dolls and hastily hid them in her bedroom. Doll carriages, a tricycle, books, games, and toys were quickly hidden away. Candies, nuts, oranges, and apples followed. A turkey she laid on the table. By this time Alice was in a perfect fever of delight. "I just knew the Lord would not forsake us!" she said.

But Jim still felt that all was not right. At first he had been stunned by this sudden change from poverty to affluence, but now he began to collect his scattered wits. He went out onto the porch and looked the things over. With a sickening sensation the truth suddenly dawned on him; this was undoubtedly the supply Attorney Brown had ordered for his own home. Someone at the store had blundered. Instead of delivering the things to Sixth Avenue they had been brought to Sixth East. He remembered now the house number the lawyer had read from the letter was 914—the same as his. An error such as this would probably not occur in any other city in the United States. "Of course the mistake will be discovered as soon as Attorney Brown reaches his home and finds the things have not been delivered. He'll call the store, and the things will be traced to us. Anyway, I'll have to notify the store. These things are not meant for us at all."

Shouts of joyous laughter came to him from the house and pierced his heart like knife thrusts. "My poor, little kiddies!" he exclaimed, "I'm afraid your joy will be short-lived." With a groan he sat down on one of the boxes and covered his face with his hands. "And Alice, my dear, sweet, angel wife! It will nearly break her heart when she learns the truth." O God in heaven, avert the blow!" Tears welled up into his eyes, and in the darkness his chin quivered.

How long he sat thus he did not know. He was roused by the sound of an automobile stopping in front of the house. He got up and walked over beyond the edge of the building and peered out. In the darkness he made out the figure of a man just stepping from an automobile. "It's all over," he said to himself in a choking voice, "all over." He leaned against the porch post to steady himself for a minute or two, and then went slowly into the house.

When he reached the door that opened into the front room, he swung it open unnoticed and stopped within the shadow. Just inside the front door, hat in hand, stood Attorney Brown. Ted had evidently let him in, for Alice with flushed face and shining eyes was coming out from behind the gaily decorated tree. She stared in astonishment at sight of the unexpected visitor. "Well, how-do-you-do?" she greeted him cheerily.

"I ordered some things sent—sent—," the lawyer began awkwardly. Alice advanced toward him.

"Are you the one who so generously sent us these things?" she asked in amazement. He winked his eyes a couple of times and appeared to swallow something.

"A—a—, yes, ma'am." Alice went to him and took his hand in both of hers.

"God bless your kind heart," she said fervently, and there were tears in her eyes when she said it. "I don't know who you are, but I know that Providence sent you to us in our time of need. You cannot know what it means to go day after day, month after month without employment, never knowing one day what you will have to eat the next. Surely God put it in your heart to do this noble deed." She released his hand, and he shifted his weight awkwardly from one foot to the other.

"I'm afraid you are giving me more credit than I deserve," he replied. Then a merry twinkle came into his eyes and he smiled good-humoredly. "I thought I'd just take a run down and see if the things were delivered all right."

Jim was struggling to adjust himself to the unexpected turn the case had taken. He advanced into the room, extending his hand which the other took in a hearty handshake. "I don't know how to thank you, but I'll repay you as soon as I can get to earning again." The attorney laid his hand on Jim's shoulder.

"Now, don't talk about paying me, nor thanking me, either, or you'll spoil it all. This is the first time in my life I've ever been a real Santa Claus." He looked at the children playing about the tree, talking in suppressed, excited tones, their little hearts almost bursting with joy. Never had they dreamed of a Christmas like this. The scene evidently touched the heart of the great lawyer, for he took the chair Alice offered him and sat for some time gazing at them in silence. "My!" he finally exclaimed, "I wouldn't have missed this for a thousand dollars." He arose and turned to Jim.

"Let's see, you say you are out of employment, Mr.—Mr.—."

"Brown, the same as yours," Jim answered. The lawyer looked startled for a moment.

"Oh—, oh yes, I see. What is your occupation, Mr. Brown?" Jim told him. "Assayer? Good! My brother-in-law is superintendent of the smelter." He took a card from his pocket and handed it to Jim. "If you'll call at my office any time after tomorrow I'll give you a letter to him. He'll find a place for you. Well, I must be going. I've a few purchases to make before the stores close." He bowed gracefully to Alice. "Goodnight," he said, then sweeping the room with his glance added, "and a Merry Christmas to everyone."

"Merry Christmas! Merry Christmas!" chorused after him as he closed the door.

The parents looked at each other in silence for a moment, then Alice put her arms around her husband's neck and drew his face down to hers. "Now, will you say the Lord isn't watching over us?" she challenged.

And he answered, "I wouldn't dare."

TO SPRINGVALE FOR CHRISTMAS

ZONA GALE

When President Arthur Tilton of Briarcliff College, who usually used a two-cent stamp, said, "Get me Chicago, please," his secretary was impressed, looked for vast educational problems to be in the making, and heard instead:

"Ed? Well, Ed, you and Rick and Grace and I are going out to Springvale for Christmas. . . . Yes, well, I've got a family too, you recall. But mother was seventy last fall and—Do you realize that it's eleven years since we all spent Christmas with her? Grace has been every year. She's going this year. And so are we! And take her the best Christmas she ever had, too. Ed, mother was seventy last fall—"

At dinner, he asked his wife what would be a suitable gift, a very special gift, for a woman of seventy. And she said: "Oh, your mother. Well, dear, I should think the material for a good wool dress would be right. I'll select it for you, if you like—" He said that he would see, and he did not reopen the subject.

In town on December twenty-fourth he timed his arrival to

allow him an hour in a shop. There he bought a silver-gray silk of a fineness and a lightness which pleased him and at a price which made him comfortably guilty. And at the shop, Ed, who was Edward McKillop Tilton, head of a law firm, picked him up.

"Where's your present?" Arthur demanded.

Edward drew a case from his pocket and showed him a tiny gold wristwatch of decent manufacture and explained: "I expect you'll think I'm a fool, but you know that mother has told time for fifty years by the kitchen clock, or else the shield of the black-marble parlor angel who never goes—you get the idea?—and so I bought her this."

At the station was Grace, and the boy who bore her bag bore also a parcel of great dimensions.

"Mother already has a feather bed," Arthur reminded her.

"They won't let you take an automobile into the coach," Edward warned her.

"It's a rug for the parlor," Grace told them. "You know it *is* a parlor—one of the few left in the Mississippi Valley. And mother has had that ingrain down since before we left home—"

Grace's eyes were misted. Why would women always do that? This was no occasion for sentiment. This was a merry Christmas.

"Very nice. And Ricky'd better look sharp," said Edward dryly.

Ricky never did look sharp. About trains he was conspicuously ignorant. He had no occupation. Some said that he "wrote," but no one had ever seen anything that he had written. He lived in town—no one knew how—never accepted a cent from his brothers, and was beloved of everyone, most of all of his mother.

"Ricky won't bring anything, of course," they said.

But when the train pulled out without him, observably, a porter came staggering through the cars carrying two great suitcases and following a perturbed man of forty-something who said, "Oh, here you are!" as if it were they who were missing, and squeezed himself and his suitcases among brothers and sister and rug. "I had only a minute to spare," he said regretfully. "If I'd had two, I could have snatched some flowers. I flung 'em my card and told 'em to send 'em."

"Why are you taking so many lugs?" they wanted to know.

Ricky focused on the suitcases. "Just necessities," he said. "Just the presents. I didn't have room to get in anything else."

"Presents! What?"

"Well," said Ricky, "I'm taking books. I know mother doesn't care much for books, but the bookstore's the only place I can get trusted."

They turned over his books: fiction, travels, biography, a new illustrated edition of the Bible—they were willing to admire his selection. And Grace said confusedly but appreciatively: "You know, the parlor bookcase has never had a thing in it excepting a green curtain *over* it!"

And they were all borne forward, well pleased.

Springvale has eight hundred inhabitants. As they drove through the principal street at six o'clock on that evening of December twenty-fourth, all that they expected to see abroad was the popcorn wagon and a cat or two. Instead they counted seven automobiles and estimated thirty souls, and no one paid the slightest attention to them as strangers. Springvale was becoming metropolitan. There was a new church on one corner and a store building bore the sign "Public Library." Even the little hotel had a rubber plant in the window and a strip of cretonne overhead.

The three men believed themselves to be a surprise. But, mindful of the panic to be occasioned by four appetites precipitated into a Springvale ménage, Grace had told. Therefore the parlor was lighted and heated; there was in the air of the passage an odor of brown gravy which, no butler's pantry ever having inhibited, seemed a permanent savory. By the happiest chance,

Mrs. Tilton had not heard their arrival nor—the parlor angel being in her customary eclipse and the kitchen grandfather's clock wrong—had she begun to look for them. They slipped in, they followed Grace down the hall, they entered upon her in her gray gingham apron worn over her best blue serge, and they saw her first in profile, frosting a lemon pie. With some assistance from her, they all took her in their arms at once.

"Aren't you surprised?" cried Edward in amazement.

"I haven't got over being surprised," she said placidly, "since I first heard you were coming!"

She gazed at them tenderly, with flour on her chin, and then said: "There's something you won't like. We're going to have the Christmas dinner tonight."

Their clamor that they would entirely like that did not change her look.

"Our church couldn't pay the minister this winter," she said, "on account of the new church building. So the minister and his wife are boarding around with the congregation. Tomorrow's their day to come here for a week. It's a hard life and I didn't have the heart to change 'em."

Her family covered their regret as best they could and entered upon her little feast. At the head of her table, with her four "children" about her, and father's armchair left vacant, they perceived that she was not quite the figure they had been thinking her. In this interval they had grown to think of her as a pathetic figure. Not because their father had died, not because she insisted on Springvale as a residence, not because of her eyes. Just pathetic. Mothers of grown children, they might have given themselves the suggestion, were always pathetic. But here was mother, a definite person, with poise and with ideas, who might be proud of her offspring, but who, in her heart, never forgot that they *were* her offspring and that she was the parent stock.

"I wouldn't eat two pieces of that pie," she said to President Tilton; "it's pretty rich." And he answered humbly: "Very well, Mother." And she took with composure Ricky's light chant:

"Now, you must remember, wherever you are,

That you are the jam, but your mother's the jar."

"Certainly, my children," she said. "And I'm about to tell you when you may have your Christmas presents. Not tonight. Christmas Eve is no proper time for presents. It's stealing a day outright! And you miss the fun of looking forward all night long. The only proper time for the presents is after breakfast on Christmas morning, *after* the dishes are washed. The minister and his wife may get here any time from nine on. That means we've got to get to bed early!"

President Arthur Tilton lay in his bed looking at the muslin curtain on which the street lamp threw the shadow of a bare elm which he remembered. He thought: "She's a pioneer spirit. She's the kind who used to go ahead anyway, even if they had missed the emigrant party, and who used to cross the plains alone. She's the backbone of the world. I wish I could megaphone that to the students at Briarcliff who think their mothers 'try to boss' them!"

"Don't leave your windows open too far," he heard from the hall. "The wind's changed."

In the light of a snowy morning the home parlor showed the cluttered commonplace of a room whose furniture and ornaments were not believed to be beautiful and most of them known not to be useful. Yet when—after the dishes were washed—these five came to the leather chair which bore the gifts, the moment was intensely satisfactory. This in spite of the sense of haste with which the parcels were attacked—lest the minister and his wife arrive in their midst.

"That's one reason," Mrs. Tilton said, "why I want to leave part of my Christmas for you until I take you to the train tonight. Do you care?"

"I'll leave a present I know about until then too," said Ricky. "May I?"

"Come on now, though," said President Arthur Tilton. "I want to see mother get her dolls."

It was well that they were not of an age to look for exclamations of delight from mother. To every gift her reaction was one of startled rebuke.

"Grace! How could you? All that money! Oh, it's beautiful! But the old one would have done me all my life. . . . Why, Edward! You extravagant boy! I never had a watch in my life. You ought not to have gone to all that expense. Arthur Tilton! A silk dress! What a firm piece of goods! I don't know what to say to you—you're all too good to me!"

At Ricky's books she stared and said: "My dear boy, you've been very reckless. Here are more books than I can ever read—now. Why, that's almost more than they've got to start the new library with. And you spent all that money on me!"

It dampened their complacence, but they understood her concealed delight and they forgave her an honest regret of their modest prodigality. For, when they opened her gifts for them, they felt the same reluctance to take the hours and hours of patient knitting for which these stood.

"Hush, and hurry," was her comment, "or the minister'll get us!"

The minister and his wife, however, were late. The second side of the turkey was ready and the mince pie hot when, toward noon, they came to the door—a faint little woman and a thin man with beautiful, exhausted eyes. They were both in some light glow of excitement and disregarded Mrs. Tilton's efforts to take their coats.

"No," said the minister's wife. "No. We do beg your pardon. But we find we have to go into the country this morning."

"It is absolutely necessary that we go into the country," said the minister earnestly. "This morning," he added impressively.

"Into the country! You're going to be here for dinner."

They were firm. They had to go into the country. They shook hands almost tenderly with these four guests. "We just heard about you in the post office," they said. "Merry Christmas—oh, Merry Christmas! We'll be back about dark."

They left their two shabby suitcases on the hall floor and went away.

"All the clothes they've got between them would hardly fill these up," said Mrs. Tilton mournfully. "Why on earth do you suppose they'd turn their back on a dinner that smells so good and go off into the country at noon on Christmas Day? They wouldn't do that for another invitation. Likely somebody's sick," she ended, her puzzled look denying her tone of finality.

"Well, thank the Lord for the call to the country," said Ricky shamelessly. "It saved our day."

They had their Christmas dinner; they had their afternoon—safe and happy and uninterrupted. Five commonplace-looking folk in a commonplace-looking house, but the eye of love knew that this was not all. In the wide sea of their routine they had found and taken for their own this island day, unforgettable.

"I thought it was going to be a gay day," said Ricky at its close, "but it hasn't. It's been heavenly! Mother, shall we give them the rest of their presents now, you and I?"

"Not yet," she told them. "Ricky, I want to whisper to you."

She looked so guilty that they all laughed at her. Ricky was laughing when he came back from that brief privacy. He was still laughing mysteriously when his mother turned from a telephone call.

"What do you think?" she cried. "That was the woman that brought me my turkey. She knew the minister and his wife were to be with me today. She wants to know why they've been eating a lunch in a cutter out that way. Do you suppose—"

They all looked at one another doubtfully, then in abrupt conviction. "They went because they wanted us to have the day to ourselves!"

"Arthur," said Mrs. Tilton with immense determination, "let me whisper to you, too." And from that moment's privacy he also returned smiling, but a bit ruefully.

"Mother ought to be the president of a university," he said.

"Mother ought to be the head of a law firm," said Edward.

"Mother ought to write a book about herself," said Ricky.

"Mother's mother," said Grace, "and that's enough. But you're all so mysterious, except me."

"Grace," said Mrs. Tilton, "you remind me that I want to whisper to you."

Their train left in the late afternoon. Through the white streets they walked to the station, the somber little woman, the buoyant, capable daughter, the three big sons. She drew them to seclusion down by the baggage room and gave them four envelopes.

"Here's the rest of my Christmas for you," she said. "I'd rather you'd open it on the train. Now, Ricky, what's yours?"

She was firm to their protests. The train was whistling when Ricky owned up that the rest of his Christmas present for his mother was a brand new daughter, to be acquired as soon as his new book was off the press. "We're going to marry on the advance royalty," he said importantly, "and live on—" The rest was lost in the roar of the express.

"Edward!" shouted Mrs. Tilton. "Come here. I want to whisper—"

She was obliged to shout it, whatever it was. But Edward heard, and nodded, and kissed her. There was time for her to slip something in Ricky's pocket and for the other good-byes, and then the train drew out. From the other platform they saw her brave, calm face against the background of the little town. A mother of "grown children" pathetic? She seemed to them at that moment the one supremely triumphant figure in life.

They opened their envelopes soberly and sat soberly over the contents. The note, scribbled to Grace, explained: Mother wanted to divide up now what she had had for them in her will. She would keep one house and live on the rent from the other one, and "here's all the rest." They laughed at her postscript:

"Don't argue. I ought to give the most—I'm the mother."

"And look at her," said Edward solemnly. "As soon as she heard about Ricky, there at the station, she whispered to me that she wanted to send Ricky's sweetheart the watch I'd just given her. Took it off her wrist then and there."

"That must be what she slipped in my pocket," said Ricky.

It was.

"She asked me," he said, "if I minded if she gave those books to the new Springvale Public Library."

"She asked me," said Grace, "if I cared if she gave the new rug to the new church that can't pay its minister."

President Arthur Tilton shouted with laughter.

"When we heard where the minister and his wife ate their Christmas dinner," he said, "she whispered to ask me whether she might give the silk dress to her when they get back tonight."

All this they knew by the time the train reached the crossing where they could look back on Springvale. On the slope of the hill lay the little cemetery, and Ricky said:

"And she told me that if my flowers got there before dark, she'd take them up to the cemetery for Christmas for father. By night she won't have even a flower left to tell her we've been there."

"Not even the second side of the turkey," said Grace, "and yet I think—"

"So do I," her brothers said.

WHICH OF THE NINE?

A U T H O R   U N K N O W N

Once upon a time in the city of Budapest there lived a poor shoemaker who simply couldn't make ends meet. Not because the people had suddenly decided to give up wearing shoes, nor because the city council had passed an ordinance directing that his shoes be sold at half price, nor even because his work was not satisfactory. Indeed, the good man did such excellent work that his customers actually complained that they couldn't wear out anything he had once sewed together. He had plenty of customers who paid him promptly and well enough; not one of them had run away without paying his bill. And yet Cobbler John couldn't make ends meet.

The reason was that the good Lord had blessed him all too plentifully with nine children, all of them healthy as acorns.

Then one day, as if Cobbler John hadn't trouble enough, his wife died. Cobbler John was left alone in this world with nine children. Two or three of them were going to school; one or two of them were being tutored; one had to be carried around; gruel had to be cooked for the next; another one had to be fed; the next one dressed, yet another washed. And on top of all this he had to earn a living for them all. As you can imagine this was a big job—just in case you doubt it.

When shoes were made for them, nine had to be made all at once; when bread was sliced, nine slices had to be cut all at one time. When beds were made ready, the entire room between the window and door became one single bed, full of little and big blonde and brunette heads.

"Oh my dear Lord God, how Thou hast blessed me," the good artisan often sighed. And even after midnight he still worked and hammered away at his lasts in order to feed the bodies of so many souls, stopping occasionally to chide now one, now another tossing restlessly in a dream. Nine they were—a round number, nine. But thanks to the Lord, there was no cause for complaint because all nine were healthy, obedient, beautiful and well-behaved, blessed with sound bodies and stomachs.

On Christmas Eve, Cobbler John returned late from his many errands. He had delivered all sorts of finished work and had collected a little money which he had used to buy supplies and pay for their daily needs. Hurrying homeward he saw stands on every street corner, laden with golden and silver lambs and candy dolls which push-cart women were selling as gifts for well-behaved children. Cobbler John stopped before one or two of the carts . . . Maybe he ought to buy something . . . but what? For all nine? That would cost too much. Then just for one? And make the others envious? No, he'd give them another kind of present: a beautiful and good one, one that would neither break nor wear out, and which all could enjoy together and not take away from each other.

"Well, children! One, two, three, four . . . are you all here?" he

310

said when he arrived home within the circle of his family of nine. "Do you know it is Christmas Eve? A holiday, a very special holiday. Tonight we do no work, we just rejoice!"

The children were so happy to hear that they were supposed to rejoice that they almost tore down the house.

"What now! Let's see if I can't teach you that beautiful song I know. It's a very beautiful song. I have saved it to give you all a Christmas present."

The little ones crawled noisily into their father's lap and up on his shoulders, and waited eagerly to hear the lovely song.

"Now what did I tell you? If you are *good* children . . . just stand nicely in line . . . there . . . the bigger ones over here and the smaller ones next to them." He stood them in a row like organ pipes, letting the two youngest ones stay on his lap.

"And now—silence! First I'll sing it through, then you can join in." Taking off his green cap and assuming a serious, pious expression, Cobbler John began to sing the beautiful melody: "On the blessed birth of Our Lord Jesus Christ . . ."

The bigger boys and girls learned it very quickly, but the smaller ones found it a bit more difficult. They were always off key and out of rhythm. But after a while they all knew it. And there could be no more joyous sound than when all the nine thin little voices sang together that glorious song of the angels on that memorable night. Perhaps the angels were still singing it when the melodious voices of the nine innocent souls prayed for an echo from above. For surely there is gladness in heaven over the song of children.

But there was less gladness immediately above them. There was a bachelor living all by himself in nine rooms. In one he sat, in another he slept, in the third one he smoked his pipe, in the fourth he dined, and who knows what he did in the others? This man had neither wife nor children but more money than he could count. Sitting in room number eight that night, the rich man was wondering why life had lost its taste. Why did his soft, springy bed give him no peaceful dreams? Then, from Cobbler John's room below, at first faintly but with ever increasing strength, came the strains of a certain joy-inspiring song. At first he tried not to listen, thinking they would soon stop. But when they started all over for the tenth time, he could stand it no longer. Crushing out his expensive cigar, he went down in his dressing-gown to the shoe-maker's flat.

They had just come to the end of a verse when he walked in. Cobbler John respectfully got up from his three-legged stool and greeted the great gentleman.

"You are John, the cobbler, aren't you?" the rich man asked.

"That I am, and at your service, Your Excellency. Do you wish to order a pair of patent-leather boots?"

"That isn't why I came. How very many children you have!"

"Indeed I have, Your Excellency—little ones and great big ones. Quite a few mouths to feed!"

"And many more mouths when they sing! Look here, Master John, I'd like to do you a favour. Give me one of your children. I'll adopt him, educate him as my own son, take him travelling abroad with me, and make him into a gentleman. One day he'll be able to help the rest of you."

Cobbler John stared when he heard this. These were big words—to have one of his children made a gentleman! Who wouldn't be taken by such an idea? Why, of course he'd let him have one! What good fortune! How could he refuse?

"Well then, pick out one of them quickly, and let's get it over with," said the gentleman. Cobbler John started to choose.

"This one here is Alex. No, him I couldn't let go. He is a good student and I want him to become a priest. The next one? That's a girl and, of course, Your Excellency doesn't want a girl. Little

Ferenc? He already helps me with my work. I couldn't do without him. Johnny? There, there—he is named after me. I couldn't very well give him away! Joseph? He's the image of his mother—it's as if I saw her every time I look at him. This place wouldn't be the same without him. And the next one is another girl—she wouldn't do. Then comes little Paul: he was his mother's favorite. Oh my poor darling would turn in her grave if I gave him away. And the last two are small—they'd be too much trouble for Your Excellency. . . . "

He had reached the end of the line without being able to choose. Now he started all over; this time beginning with the youngest and ending with the oldest. But the result was always the same: he couldn't decide which one to give away because one was as dear to him as the other, and he would miss them all.

"Come, my little ones—you do the choosing," he finally said. "Which of you wants to go away and become a gentleman and travel in style? Come now, speak up! Who wants to go?"

The poor shoemaker was on the verge of tears as he asked them. But while he was encouraging them, the children slowly slipped behind their father's back, each taking hold of him; his hand, his arm, his leg, his coat, his apron, all hanging on to him and hiding from the gentleman. Finally, Cobbler John couldn't control himself any longer. He knelt down, gathered all into his arms and let his tears fall on their heads as they cried with him.

"It can't be done, Your Excellency! It can't be done. Ask of me anything in the world, but I can't give you a single one of my children so long as the Good Lord has given them to me."

The rich gentleman said that he understood, but that the shoemaker should do at least one thing for him: would he and his children please not sing any more? And for this single sacrifice he asked Cobbler John to accept one thousand florins.

Master John had never heard the words "One thousand

florins" spoken in all his life. Now he felt the money being pressed into his hand.

His Excellency went back to his room and to his boredom. And Cobbler John stood staring incredulously at the oddly-shaped bank note. Then he fearfully locked it away in the wooden chest, put the key in his pocket, and was silent. The little ones were silent too. Singing was forbidden. The older children slumped moodily in their chairs, quieting the smaller ones by telling them they weren't allowed to sing any more because it disturbed the fine gentleman upstairs. Cobbler John himself was silently walking up and down. Impatiently he pushed aside little Paul, the one who had been his wife's favourite, when the boy asked that he be taught that beautiful song because he had already forgotten how it went.

"We aren't allowed to sing any more!"

Then he sat down angrily at his bench and bent intently over his work. He cut and hammered and sewed until suddenly he caught himself singing: "On the blessed birth of Our Lord Jesus Christ . . ." He clapped his hand over his mouth. But then, all at once he was very angry. He banged the hammer down on the work-bench, kicked his stool from under him, opened the chest, took out the thousand florin note and ran upstairs to His Excellency's apartment.

"Good kind Excellency, I am your most humble servant. Please take back your money! Let it not be mine, but let us sing whenever we please, because to stop me and my children is worth much more than a thousand florins."

With that, he put the note down on the table and rushed breathlessly back to his waiting children. He kissed them, one after the other, and, lining them up in a row, just like organ pipes, he sat himself on a low stool, and together they began to sing again with heart and soul: "On the blessed birth of Our Lord Jesus Christ . . ."

They couldn't have been happier if they had owned the whole of the great big house.

But the one who owned the house was pacing up and down through his nine rooms, asking himself how it was that people down below could be so happy and full of joy in such a tiresome boring world as this!

THE CANDLE IN THE FOREST

TEMPLE BAILEY

The Small Girl's mother was saying, "The onions will be silver, and the carrots will be gold—" "And the potatoes will be ivory," said the Small Girl, and they laughed together.

The Small Girl's mother had a big white bowl in her lap, and she was cutting up vegetables. The onions were the hardest because one cried a little over them.

"But our tears will be pearls," said the Small Girl's mother, and they laughed at that and dried their eyes and found the carrots much easier, and the potatoes the easiest of all.

Then the Next-Door Neighbor came in and said, "What are you doing?"

"We're making a beefsteak pie for our Christmas dinner," said the Small Girl's mother.

"And the onions are silver, and the carrots gold, and the potatoes ivory," said the Small Girl.

"I'm sure I don't know what you are talking about," said the Next-Door Neighbor. "We are going to have turkey for Christmas, and oysters and cranberries and celery." The Small Girl laughed and clapped her hands.

"But we are going to have a Christmas pie—and the onions are silver and the carrots gold—"

"You said that once," said the Next-Door Neighbor, "and I should think you'd know they weren't anything of the kind."

"But they are," said the Small Girl, all shining eyes and rosy cheeks.

"Run along, darling" said the Small Girl's mother, "and find poor Pussy-Purr-Up; he's out in the cold. And you can put on your red sweater and red cap."

So the Small Girl hopped away like a happy robin, and the Next-Door Neighbor said, "She is old enough to know that onions aren't silver."

"But they are," said the Small Girl's mother, "and the carrots are gold and the potatoes are—"

The Next-Door Neighbor's face was flaming. "If you say that again, I'll scream. It sounds silly to me."

"But it isn't the least silly," said the Small Girl's mother, and her eyes were as blue as sapphires and as clear as the sea; "it is sensible. When people are poor, they have to make the most of little things. And we'll have only a pound of steak in our pie, but the onions will be silver—"

The lips of the Next-Door Neighbor were folded in a thin line. "If you had acted like a sensible creature, I shouldn't have asked you for the rent."

The Small Girl's mother was silent for a moment; then she said: "I am sorry—but it ought to be sensible to make the best of things."

"Well," said the Next-Door Neighbor, sitting down in a chair with her back held very stiff, "a beefsteak pie is a beefsteak pie. And I wouldn't teach a child to call it anything else."

"I haven't taught her to call it anything else. I was only trying to make her feel that it was something fine and splendid for Christmas day, so I said that the onions were silver—"

"Don't say that again," snapped the Next-Door Neighbor, "and I want the rent as soon as possible." With that she flung up her head and marched out of the front door, and it slammed behind her and made wild echoes in the little house.

And the Small Girl's mother stood there alone in the middle of the floor, and her eyes were like the sea in a storm. But presently the door opened, and the Small Girl, looking like a red robin, hopped in. And the Small Girl said, out of the things she had been thinking, "Mother, why don't we have turkey?"

The clear look came back into the eyes of the Small Girl's mother, and she said, "because we are content."

And the Small Girl said, "What is 'content'?"

And her mother said, "It is making the best of what God gives us. And our best for Christmas day, my darling, is a beefsteak pie." So she kissed the Small Girl, and they finished peeling the vegetables, and then they put them with the pound of steak to simmer on the back of the stove. After that the Small Girl had her supper of bread and milk, and Pussy-Purr-Up had milk in a saucer on the hearth, and the Small Girl climbed up in her mother's lap. "Tell me a story."

But the Small Girl's mother said, "Won't it be nicer to talk about Christmas presents?"

And the Small Girl sat up and said, "Let's."

317

And the mother said, "Let's tell each other what we'd rather have in the whole wide world—"

"Oh let's." said the Small Girl. "And I'll tell you first that I want a doll—and I want it to have a pink dress—and I want it to have eyes that open and shut—and I want it to have shoes and stockings—and I want it to have curly hair . . . " She had to stop because she didn't have any breath left in her body, and when she got her breath back, she said, "Now, what do you want, Mother, more than anything else in the whole wide world?"

"Well," said her mother, "I want a chocolate mouse."

"Oh," said the Small Girl, "I shouldn't think you'd want that."

"Why not?"

"Because a chocolate mouse—why, a chocolate mouse isn't anything."

"Oh, yes, it is," said the Small Girl's mother. "A chocolate mouse is 'Hickory Dickory Dock'; and 'Pussy Cat, Pussy Cat Where Have you Been'; and it's 'Three Blind Mice'; and it's 'A Frog He Would a Wooing Go'; and it's—"

The Small Girl's eyes were dancing. "Oh, tell me about it."

And her mother said, "Well, the mouse in Hickory Dickory Dock ran up the clock, and the mouse in 'Pussy Cat, Pussy Cat' was frightened under the chair, and the mice in 'Three Blind Mice' ran after the farmer's wife, and the mouse in 'A Frog He Would a Wooing Go' went down the throat of the crow—"

And the Small Girl said, "Could a chocolate mouse do all that?"

"Well," said the Small Girl's mother, "we could put him on the clock and under a chair and cut his tail off with a carving knife, and at the very last we could eat him up like a crow—"

"And he wouldn't be a real mouse?"

"No, just a chocolate one with cream inside."

"Do you think I'll get one for Christmas?"

"I'm not sure." The Small Girl's mother hesitated, then told the truth, "My darling—Mother saved up the money for a doll, but the Next-Door Neighbor wants the rent."

"Hasn't Daddy any more money?"

"Poor Daddy has been sick for so long."

"But he's well now."

"I know. But he has to pay money for doctors and for medicine and money for your red sweater and money for milk for Pussy-Purr-Up and money for our beefsteak pie."

"The Boy Next Door says we're poor, Mother."

"We are rich, my darling. We have love and each other and Pussy-Purr-Up—"

"His mother won't let him have a cat," said the Small Girl, with her mind still on the Boy Next Door, "But he's going to have a radio."

"Would you rather have a radio than Pussy-Purr-Up?"

The small girl gave a cry of derision. "I'd rather have Pussy-Purr-Up than anything else in the whole wide world." At that, the great cat, who had been sitting on the hearth with his paws tucked under him and his eyes like moons, stretched out his satin-shining length and jumped upon the arm of the chair beside the Small Girl and her mother and began to sing a song that was like a mill-wheel away off. He purred so long and loud that at last the Small Girl grew drowsy. "Tell me some more about the chocolate mouse," she said, and she nodded and slept. The Small Girl's mother carried her into another room, put her to bed, and came back to the kitchen—and it was full of shadows.

But she did not let herself sit among them. She wrapped herself in a great cape and went out into the cold dusk. There was a sweep of wind, heavy clouds overhead, and a band of dull orange showing behind the trees where the sun had burned down. She went straight from her little house to the big house of the Next-

Door Neighbor, and she rang the bell at the back entrance. A maid let her into the kitchen, and there was the Next-Door Neighbor and the two women who worked for her and a Daughter-in-Law who had come to spend Christmas. The great range was glowing, and things were simmering, and things were stewing, and things were steaming, and things were baking, and things were boiling, and things were broiling, and there was a fragrance of a thousand delicious dishes in the air.

And the Next-Door Neighbor said, "We are trying to get as much done as possible tonight. We are having twelve people for Christmas dinner tomorrow." And the Daughter-in-Law, who was all dressed up and had an apron tied about her, said in a sharp voice, "I can't see why you don't let your maids work for you."

And the Next-Door Neighbor said, "I have always worked. There is no excuse for laziness."

And the Daughter-in-Law said, "I'm not lazy, if that's what you mean. And we'll never have any dinner if I have to cook it," and away she went out of the kitchen with tears of rage in her eyes.

And the Next-Door Neighbor said, "If she hadn't gone when she did, I should have told her to go," and there was rage in her eyes but no tears. She took her hands out of the pan of bread crumbs and sage, which she was mixing for the stuffing, and said to the Small Girl's mother: "Did you come to pay the rent?"

The Small Girl's mother handed her the money, and the Next-Door Neighbor went upstairs to write a receipt. Nobody asked the Small Girl's mother to sit down, so she stood in the middle of the floor and sniffed the enticing fragrance and looked at the mountain of food, which would have fed her small family for a month. While she waited, the Boy Next Door came in and said, "Are you the Small Girl's mother?"

"Yes."

"Are you going to have a tree?"

"Yes."

"Do you want to see mine?"

"It would be wonderful." So he led her down a long passage to a great room, and there was a tree which touched the ceiling, and on the very top branches and on all the other branches were myriads of little lights which shown like stars, and there were gold balls and silver ones and red and blue and green balls, and under the tree and on it were toys for boys and toys for girls, and one of the toys was a doll in a pink dress! At that the heart of the Small Girl's mother tightened, and she was glad she was not a thief, or she would have snatched at the pink doll when the boy wasn't looking and hidden it under her cape and run away with it.

The Boy Next Door was saying: "It's the finest tree anybody has around here. But Dad and Mother don't know that I've seen it."

"Oh, don't they?" said the Small Girl's mother. "Now do you know, I should think the very nicest thing in the whole wide world would be not to have seen the tree."

The Boy Next Door stared and said, "Why?"

"Because the nicest thing in the world would be to have somebody tie a handkerchief around your eyes tight as tight and then to have somebody take your hand and lead you in and out and in and out, until you didn't know where you were, and then to have them untie the handkerchief—and there would be the tree—all shining and splendid." She stopped, but her singing voice seemed to echo and re-echo in the great room.

The boy's staring eyes had a new look in them. "Did anyone ever tie a handkerchief over your eyes?"

"Oh, yes—"

"And lead you in and out and in and out?"

"Yes."

"Well nobody does things like that in our house. They think it's silly."

"Do you think it's silly?" asked the Small Girl's mother.

"No, I don't."

She held out her hand to him. "Will you come and see our tree?"

"Tonight?"

"No, tomorrow morning—early."

"Before breakfast?" She nodded yes. "Oh, I'd like that." So that was a bargain, with a quick squeeze of their hands on it.

Then the Small Girl's mother went back to the kitchen, and the Next-Door Neighbor came down with the receipt, and the Small Girl's mother went out of the back door and found that the orange band which had burned on the horizon was gone, and there was just the wind and the sighing of trees. Two men passed her on the brick walk which led to the house, and one of the men said: "If you'd only be fair to me, father."

And the other man said, "All you want of me is money."

"You taught me that, father."

"Blame it on me—" Their angry voices seemed to beat against the noise of the wind and the sighing trees so that the Small Girl's mother shivered and drew her cape around her and ran on as fast as she could to her little house. There were all the shadows to meet her, but she did not sit among them. She made a dish of milk toast and set the toast in the oven to keep it hot, and then she stood at the window watching. At last she saw through the darkness what looked like a star, low down, and she knew that the star was a lantern, and she ran and opened the door wide. And the young husband set the lantern down on the threshold and took her in his arms and said, "The sight of you is more than food and drink."

When he said that, she knew that he had had a hard day, but her heart leaped because she knew that what he said to her was true. Then they went into the house together, and she set the food before him. And that he might forget his hard day, she told him of her own. And when she came to the part about the Next-Door Neighbor and the rent, she said, "I'm telling you this because it has a happy ending."

And he put his hand over hers and said, "My dear, everything with you has a happy ending."

"Well, this is a happy ending," said the Small Girl's mother, with all the sapphire in her eyes emphasizing it. "Because when I went over to pay the rent, I was feeling how poor we were and wishing that I had a pink doll for baby and books for you, and—and—a magic carpet to carry us away from work and worry. And then I went into the kitchen of the big house, and there was everything delicious, and then I went into the parlor and saw the tree—with everything hanging on it that was glittering and gorgeous—and then I came home," her breath was quick and her lips smiling, "I came home—and I was glad I lived in my little house."

"What made you glad, dearest?"

"Because love is here; and hate is there and a boy's deceit and a man's injustice. They were saying sharp things to each other—and—and their dinner will be nothing. And in my house is the faith of a child in the goodness of God and the bravery of a man who fought for his country—" She was in his arms now.

"And the blessing of a woman who has never known defeat." His voice broke on the words. In that moment it seemed as if the wind stopped blowing and as if the trees stopped sighing and as if there was the sound of a heavenly host singing. The Small Girl's mother and the Small Girl's father sat up very late that night. They popped a great bowl of crisp snowy corn and made it into balls. They boiled sugar and molasses and cracked nuts and made candy of them.

They cut funny little Christmas Fairies out of paper and

painted their jackets bright red, with round silver buttons of the tinfoil that came on a cream cheese. And they put the balls and candy and the painted fairies and a long red candle in a big basket and set it away. And the Small Girl's mother brought out the chocolate mouse. "We will put this on the clock," she said, "where her eyes will rest on it the first thing in the morning." And the Small Girl's mother said, "She was lovely about giving up the doll, and she will love the tree."

"We'll have to get up very early." said the Small Girl's father. "And you'll have to run ahead and light the candle." They got up before the dawn the next morning, and so did the Boy Next Door. He was there on the step, waiting, blowing his hands, and beating them quite like the poor little boys in a Christmas story, who haven't any mittens. But this wasn't a poor little boy, and he had many pairs of fur-trimmed gloves, but he had left the house in such a hurry that he had forgotten to put them on. So there he stood on the front step of the little house, blowing on his hands and beating them. And it was dark, with a sort of pale shine in the heavens, which didn't seem to come from the stars or to herald the dawn; it was just a mystical silver glow that set the boy's heart to beating.

Then suddenly someone came around the corner—someone tall and thin, with a cap on his head and an empty basket in his hands. "Hello," he said, "A Merry Christmas." It was the Small Girl's father, and he put the key in the lock and they went in and turned on a light, and there was a table set for four. And the Small Girl's father said, "You see we have set a place for you. We must eat something before we go out."

And the Boy Next Door said, "Are we going out? I came to see the tree."

"We are going out to see the tree."

Before the Boy Next Door could ask any more questions, the

Small Girl's mother appeared with her finger on her lips and said: "Sh-sh," and then she began to recite in a hushed voice, "Hickory Dickory Dock—" There was a little cry and the sound of dancing feet, and the Small Girl in a red dressing gown came flying in.

"Oh mother, the mouse is on the clock—the mouse is on the clock!" Well, it seemed to the Boy Next Door that he had never seen anything so exciting as the things that followed. The chocolate mouse went up the clock and under the chair—and would have had its tail cut off except the Small Girl begged to save it. "I want to keep it as it is, Mother." And playing this game as if it were the most important thing in the whole wide world were the Small Girl's mother and the Small Girl's father, all laughing and flushed and chanting the quaint old words to the quaint old music. The Small Girl absolutely refused to eat the mouse. "He's my darling Christmas mouse, Mother."

So her mother said, "We'll put him on the clock again, where Pussy-Purr-Up can't get him while we are out."

"Oh are we going out?" said the Small Girl, round-eyed.

"Yes."

"Where are we going?"

"To find Christmas." That was all the Small Girl's mother would tell. So they had breakfast, and everything tasted perfectly delicious to the Boy Next Door. But first they bowed their heads, and the Small Girl's father said, "Dear Christchild, on this Christmas morning, bless these children, and help us all to keep our hearts young and full of love for Thee." The Boy Next Door, when he lifted his head, had a funny feeling as if he wanted to cry, and yet it was a lovely feeling—all warm and comfortable.

For breakfast they each had a baked apple and great slices of sweet bread and butter and great glasses of milk, and as soon as they were finished, away they went out of the door and down into the woods back of the house, and when they were deep in the woods, the Small Girl's father took out of his pocket a little flute and began to play, and he played thin piping tunes that went fluttering around among the trees, and the Small Girl hummed the tunes until it sounded like singing bees, and their feet fairly danced, and the boy found himself humming and dancing with them.

Then suddenly the piping ceased, and a hush fell over the woods. It was so still that they could almost hear each other breathe—so still that when a light flamed suddenly in the open space, it burned without a flicker. The light came from a red candle that was set in the top of a living tree. It was the only light on the tree, but it showed the snowy balls and the small red fairies whose coats had silver buttons. "It's our tree, my darling," he heard the Small Girl's mother saying.

Suddenly it seemed to the boy that his heart would burst in his breast. He wanted someone to speak to him like that. The Small Girl sat high on her father's shoulder, and her father held her mother's hand. It was like a chain of gold, their holding hands like that and loving each other. The boy reached out and touched the woman's hand. She looked down at him and drew him close. He felt warmed and comforted. The red candle burning there in the darkness was like some sacred fire of friendship. He wished that it would never go out, that he might stand there watching it with his small cold hand in the clasp of the Small Girl's mother.

It was late when the Boy Next Door got back to his own home. But he had not been missed. Everybody was up, and everybody was angry. The Daughter-in-Law had declared the night before that she would not stay another day beneath that roof, and off she had gone with her young husband and her little girl, who was to have had the pink doll on the tree. And the Next-Door Neighbor kept saying, "Good riddance—good riddance," and not once did she say, "A Merry Christmas." But the Boy Next Door held something warm and glowing like the candle in the forest, and so he came to his mother and said, "May I have the pink doll?"

She spoke frowningly. "What does a boy want of a doll?"

"I'd like to give it to the little girl next door."

"Do you think I buy dolls to give away in charity?"

"Well, they gave me a Christmas present."

"What did they give you?" He opened his hand and showed a little flute tied with a gay ribbon; he lifted it to his lips and blew on it, a thin piping tune.

"Oh, that," said the mother scornfully, "Why, that's nothing but a reed from the pond!" But the boy knew that it was more than that. It was a magic pipe that made you dance and made your heart warm and happy. So he said again, "I'd like to give her the doll," and he reached out his hand and touched his mother's— and his eyes were wistful.

His mother's own eyes softened—she had lost one son that day—and she said, "Oh, well, do as you please."

The Boy Next Door ran into the great room and took the doll from the tree and wrapped her in paper and flew out of the door and down the brick walk and straight to the little house. When the door was opened, he saw that his friends were just sitting down to dinner—and there was the beefsteak pie all brown and piping hot, with a wreath of holly,—and the onions were silver and the carrots gold. The Boy-Next-Door went up to the Small Girl and said, "I've brought you a present." With his eyes all lighted up, he took off the paper in which it was wrapped, and there was the doll, in rosy frills, with eyes that opened and shut and shoes and stockings and curly hair that was bobbed and beautiful.

And the Small Girl, in a whirlwind of happiness, said, "Is it really my doll?"

And the Boy Next Door felt very shy and happy and said, "Yes."

And the Small Girl's mother said, "It was a beautiful thing to do," and she bent and kissed him.

Again that bursting feeling came into the boy's heart, and he lifted his face to hers and said, "May I come sometimes and be your boy?"

And the Small Girl's mother said, "Yes." And when at last he went away, she stood in the door and watched him, such a little lad, who knew so little of loving. And because she knew so much of loving, her eyes filled to overflowing. But presently she wiped the tears away and went back to the table. And she smiled at the Small Girl and the Small Girl's father. "And the potatoes were ivory," she said. "Oh, who would ask for turkey, when you can have a pie like this?"

CHRISTMAS STORIES IN POETRY

UPON JUDEA'S PLAINS

BRUCE R. McCONKIE

I stood upon Judea's plains
And heard celestial sounds and strains;
I heard an angel, free from sin,
Announce the birth of David's kin.

On shepherds watching sheep by night
There came a shining, glorious light,
As holy choirs from heaven's dome
Saw God's own Son make clay his home.

And voices sweet sang this reprise:
"To God on high, let praise arise;
And peace, good will to men on earth;
This is the day of Jesus' birth."

To me there came this witness sure:
He is God's Son, supreme and pure,
To earth he came, my soul to save,
From sin and death and from the grave.

THE FRIENDLY BEASTS

AUTHOR UNKNOWN

Jesus, our brother, strong and good,
Was humbly born in a stable rude;
And the friendly beasts around Him stood,
Jesus, our brother, strong and good.

"I," said the sheep with curly horn,
"I gave Him my wool for His blanket warm.
"He wore my coat on Christmas morn,
"I," said the sheep with curly horn.

"I," said the dove from rafters high.
"I cooed Him to sleep so He would not cry,
"We cooed Him to sleep, my mate and I;
"I," said the dove from rafters high.

"I," said the cow, all white and red.
"I gave Him my manger for His bed;
"I gave Him my hay to pillow His head;
"I," said the cow, all white and red.

"I," said the donkey, shaggy and brown.
"I carried His mother uphill and down;
"I carried her safely to Bethlehem town,
"I," said the donkey, shaggy and brown.

And every beast, by some good spell,
In the stable dark was glad to tell,
Of the gift he gave Emmanuel,
The gift he gave Emmanuel.

THE HOLY NIGHT

ELIZABETH BARRETT BROWNING

We sate among the stalls at Bethlehem;
The dumb kine from their fodder turning them,
   Softened their hornèd faces
   To almost human gazes
   Toward the newly Born:
The simple shepherds from the star-lit brooks
   Brought visionary looks,
As yet in their astonied hearing rung
   The strange sweet angel-tongue:
The magi of the East, in sandals worn,
   Knelt reverent, sweeping round,
   With long pale beards, their gifts upon the ground,
   The incense, myrrh, and gold
These baby hands were impotent to hold:
So let all earthlies and celestials wait
   Upon thy royal state.
   Sleep, sleep, my kingly One!

THE LAMB

WILLIAM BLAKE

Little Lamb, who made thee?
Dost thou know who made thee?
Gave thee life, and bid thee feed
By the stream and o'er the mead;
Gave thee clothing of delight,
Softest clothing, woolly, bright;
Gave thee such a tender voice,
Making all the vales rejoice?
Little Lamb, who made thee?
Dost thou know who made thee?

Little Lamb, I'll tell thee,
Little Lamb, I'll tell thee,
He is called by thy name,
For he calls himself a Lamb;
He is meek, and he is mild;
He became a little child.
I a child, and thou a lamb,
We are called by His name.
Little Lamb, God bless thee!
Little Lamb, God bless thee!

IN THE BLEAK MID-WINTER

CHRISTINA ROSSETTI

In the bleak mid-winter
   Frosty wind made moan,
Earth stood hard as iron,
   Water like a stone;
Snow had fallen, snow on snow,
   Snow on snow,
In the bleak mid-winter
   Long ago.

Our God, Heaven cannot hold him
   Nor earth sustain;
Heaven and earth shall flee away
   When he comes to reign:
In the bleak mid-winter
   A stable-place sufficed
The Lord God Almighty
   Jesus Christ. . . .

What can I give him,
   Poor as I am?
If I were a shepherd
   I would bring a lamb,
If I were a Wise Man
   I would do my part,—
Yet what I can I give him,
   Give my heart.

WHILE SHEPHERDS WATCHED

NAHUM TATE

While shepherds watch'd their flocks by night,
All seated on the ground,
The angel of the Lord came down,
And glory shone around.
"Fear not!" said he; for mighty dread
Had seized their troubled minds;
"Glad tidings of great joy I bring
To you and all mankind."

"To you, in David's town this day,
Is born of David's line
The Savior who is Christ the Lord,
And this shall be the sign:
The heav'nly Babe you there shall find
To human view displayed,
All meanly wrapped in swathing bands,
And in a manger laid."

Thus spake the seraph; and forthwith
Appeared a shining throng
Of angels praising God who thus
Addressed their joyful song:
"All glory be to God on high
And on the earth be peace.
Goodwill henceforth from heaven to man,
Begin and never cease."

YE SIMPLE MEN

CHARLES WESLEY

Ye simple men of heart sincere
Shepherds, who watch your flocks by night,
Start not to see an angel near,
Nor tremble at his glorious light

An herald from the heavenly king,
I come your every fear to chase;
Good tidings of great joy I bring,
Great joy to all the fallen race.

To you is born on this glad day,
A Saviour, by our host adored,
Our God in Bethlehem survey,
Make haste to worship Christ the Lord.

By this the Saviour of mankind,
The incarnate God shall be displayed
The Babe ye wrapped in swathes shall find,
And humbly in a manger laid.

A CHRISTMAS IDYL

ORSON F. WHITNEY

A stranger star o'er Bethlehem
Shot down its silver ray
Where, cradled in a manger's fold,
A sleeping infant lay.
Whilst, guided by that finger bright,
The Orient sages bring
Rare gifts of myrrh and frankincense
To hail the new-born King.

Oh wondrous grace! Will Gods go down
Thus low that men may rise?
Imprisoned here that Mighty One
Who reigned in yonder skies?
E'en so. Time's trusty horologe
Now chimes the hour of Noon—
A dying world is welcoming
The Godhead's gracious boon.

He wandered through the faithless world,
A Prince in shepherd's guise;
He called his scattered flock, but few
The Voice would recognize;
For minds upborne by hollow pride,
Or dimmed by sordid lust,
Ne'er look for kings in beggar's garb—
For diamonds in the dust.

He wept o'er doomed Jerusalem,
Her temples, walls and towers;
O'er palaces where recreant priests
Usurped unhallowed powers.
"I am the Way of Life and Light!"
Alas! twas heeded not—
Ignored Salvation's message, spurned
The wondrous truths He taught.

O bane of damning unbelief!
Thou source of lasting strife!
Thou stumbling-stone, thou barrier 'thwart
The gates of Endless Life!
O love of self and Mammon's lust!
Twin portals to Despair—
Where Bigotry, the blinded bat,
Flaps through the midnight air!

Through these, gloom-wrapt Gethsemane!
Thy glens of guilty shade
Wept o'er the sinless Son of God,
By gold-bought kiss betrayed;
Beheld him unresisting dragged—
Forsaken, friendless, lone,
To halls where dark-browed Hatred sat
On Judgment's lofty throne.

As sheep before His shearers, dumb,
Those patient lips were mute;
The clamorous charge of taunting tongues
He deigned not to dispute.
They smote with cruel palm His face—
Which felt, but scorned the sting—
They crowned with thorns His quivering brow,
Then, mocking, hailed Him "King!"

On Calvary's hill they crucified
The God whom worlds adore!
"Father, forgive!"—the pang was past—
Immanuel was no more.
No more where thunders shook the earth,
Where lightnings, 'thwart the gloom,
Beheld that deathless Spirit spurn
The shackles of the tomb!

Far flashing on its wings of light—
A falchion from its sheath—
It cleft the realms of Darkness, and
Dissolved the bands of Death.
Hell's dungeons burst! Wide open swung
The everlasting bars,
Whereby the ransomed soul shall win
Those heights beyond the stars.

I Heard the Bells on Christmas Day

HENRY WADSWORTH LONGFELLOW

I heard the bells on Christmas day
Their old familiar carols play,
And wild and sweet the words repeat
Of peace on earth, good will to men.

I thought how, as the day had come,
The belfries of all Christendom
Had rolled along th' unbroken song
Of peace on earth, good will to men.

And in despair I bowed my head:
"There is no peace on earth," I said,
"For hate is strong and mocks the song
Of peace on earth, good will to men."

Then pealed the bells more loud and deep:
"God is not dead, nor doth he sleep;
The wrong shall fail, the right prevail,
With peace on earth, good will to men."

Till, ringing, singing, on its way,
The world revolved from night to day,
A voice, a chime, a chant sublime,
Of peace on earth, good will to men!

BEFORE THE PALING OF THE STARS

CHRISTINA ROSSETTI

Before the paling of the stars,
　　Before the winter morn,
Before the earliest cockcrow,
　　Jesus Christ was born:
Born in a stable,
　　Cradled in a manger,
In the world His hands had made
　　Born a stranger.

Priest and king lay fast asleep
　　In Jerusalem,
Young and old lay fast asleep
　　In crowded Bethlehem;
Saint and Angel, ox and ass,
　　Kept a watch together
Before the Christmas daybreak
　　In the winter weather.

Jesus on His mother's breast
　　In the stable cold,
Spotless Lamb of God was He,
　　Shepherd of the fold:
Let us kneel with Mary maid,
　　With Joseph bent and hoary,
With Saint and Angel, ox and ass,
　　To hail the King of Glory.

CHILD JESUS

HANS CHRISTIAN ANDERSEN

When the Christ Child to this world came down,
He left for us His throne and crown,
He lay in a manger, all pure and fair,
Of straw and hay His bed so bare.
But high in heaven the star shone bright,
And the oxen watched by the Babe that night.
Hallelujah! Child Jesus!

Oh, come, ye sinful and ye who mourn,
Forgetting all your sin and sadness,
In the city of David a Child is born,
Who doth bring us heav'nly gladness.
Then let us to the manger go,
To see the Christ who hath loved us so.
Hallelujah! Christ Jesus!

GOD REST YOU MERRY, GENTLEMEN

A U T H O R U N K N O W N

God rest you merry, gentlemen,
Let nothing you dismay,
Remember Christ our Saviour
Was born on Christmas Day;
To save us all from Satan's power
When we were gone astray.
O tidings of comfort and joy, comfort and joy,
O tidings of comfort and joy.

In Bethlehem, in Jewry,
This blessed Babe was born,
And laid within a manger,
Upon this blessed morn;
To which His mother Mary
Did nothing take in scorn.
[*Refrain*]

From God our Heavenly Father,
A blessed angel came;
And unto certain Shepherds
Brought tidings of the same:
How that in Bethlehem was born
The Son of God by Name.
[*Refrain*]

"Fear not," then said the angel,
"Let nothing you afright,
This day is born a Saviour
Of a pure Virgin bright,
To free all those who trust in him
From Satan's power and might."
[*Refrain*]

The shepherds at those tidings
Rejoiced much in mind,
And left their flocks a-feeding,
In tempest, storm and wind:
And went to Bethlehem straightway
The Son of God to find.
[*Refrain*]

And when they came to Bethlehem
Where our dear Saviour lay,
They found him in a manger,
Where oxen feed on hay;
And with each other kneeling down,
Unto their God did pray.
[*Refrain*]

Now to the Lord sing praises,
All you within this place,
And with true love and brotherhood
Each other now embrace;
This holy tide of Christmas
Let nothing now deface.
O tidings of comfort and joy, comfort and joy,
O tidings of comfort and joy.

CHRISTMAS AT SEA

ROBERT   LOUIS   STEVENSON

The sheets were frozen hard, and they cut the naked hand;
The decks were like a slide, where a seaman scarce could stand;
The wind was a nor'-wester, blowing squally off the sea;
And cliffs and spouting breakers were the only things a-lee.

They heard the surf a-roaring before the break of day;
But 'twas only with the peep of light we saw how ill we lay.
We tumbled every hand on deck instanter, with a shout,
And we gave her the maintops'l, and stood by to go about.

All day we tacked and tacked between the South Head and the
    North;
All day we hauled the frozen sheets, and got no further forth;
All day as cold as charity, in bitter pain and dread,
For very life and nature we tacked from head to head.

We gave the South a wider berth, for there the tide-race roared;
But every tack we made we brought the North Head close
    aboard.
So's we saw the cliff and houses and the breakers running high,
And the coastguard in his garden, with his glass against his eye.

The frost was on the village roofs as white as ocean foam;
The good red fires were burning bright in every longshore home;
The windows sparkled clear, and the chimneys volleyed out;
And I vow we sniffed the victuals as the vessel went about.

The bells upon the church were rung with a mighty jovial cheer;
For it's just that I should tell you how (of all days in the year)
This day of our adversity was blessèd Christmas morn,
And the house above the coastguard's was the house where I
    was born.

O well I saw the pleasant room, the pleasant faces there,
My mother's silver spectacles, my father's silver hair;
And well I saw the firelight, like a flight of homely elves,
Go dancing round the china plates that stand upon the shelves.

And well I knew the talk they had, the talk that was of me,
Of the shadow on the household and the son that went to sea;
And O the wicked fool I seemed, in every kind of way,
To be here and hauling frozen ropes on blessèd Christmas Day.

They lit the high sea-light, and the dark began to fall.
"All hands to loose topgallant sails," I heard the captain call.
"By the Lord, she'll never stand it," our first mate, Jackson, cried.
. . . "It's the one way or the other, Mr. Jackson," he replied.

She staggered to her bearings, but the sails were new and good,
And the ship smelt up to windward just as though she understood;
As the winter's day was ending, in the entry of the night,
We cleared the weary headland, and passed below the light.

And they heaved a mighty breath, every soul on board but me,
As they saw her nose again pointing handsome out to sea;
But all that I could think of, in the darkness and the cold,
Was just that I was leaving home and my folks were growing old.

How the Great Guest Came

E D W I N   M A R K H A M

Before the cathedral in grandeur rose
At Ingelburg where the Danube goes;
Before its forest of silver spires
Went airily up to the clouds and fires;
Before the oak had ready a beam,
While yet the arch was stone and dream—
There where the altar was later laid,
Conrad, the cobbler, plied his trade.

* * *

It happened one day at the year's white end—
Two neighbors called on their old-time friend;
And they found the shop, so meager and mean,
Made gay with a hundred boughs of green.
Conrad was stitching with face ashine,
But suddenly stopped as he twitched a twine:
"Old friends, good news! At dawn today,
As the cocks were scaring the night away,
The Lord appeared in a dream to me,
And said, 'I am coming your Guest to be!'
So I've been busy with feet astir,
Strewing the floor with branches of fir.
The wall is washed and the shelf is shined,
And over the rafter the holly twined.
He comes today, and the table is spread
With milk and honey and wheaten bread."

His friends went home; and his face grew still
As he watched for the shadow across the sill.
He lived all the moments o'er and o'er,
When the Lord should enter the lowly door—
The knock, the call, the latch pulled up,
The lighted face, the offered cup.
He would wash the feet where the spikes had been,
He would kiss the hands where the nails went in,
And then at the last would sit with Him
And break the bread as the day grew dim.

While the cobbler mused there passed his pane
A beggar drenched by the driving rain.
He called him in from the stony street
And gave him shoes for his bruisèd feet.
The beggar went and there came a crone,
Her face with wrinkles of sorrow sown.
A bundle of fagots bowed her back,
And she was spent with the wrench and rack.
He gave her his loaf and steadied her load
As she took her way on the weary road.
Then to his door came a little child,
Lost and afraid in the world so wild,
In the big, dark world. Catching it up,
He gave it the milk in the waiting cup,
And led it home to its mother's arms,
Out of the reach of the world's alarms.

The day went down in the crimson west
And with it the hope of the blessed Guest,
And Conrad sighed as the world turned gray:
"Why is it, Lord, that your feet delay?
Did You forget that this was the day?"
Then soft in the silence a Voice he heard:
"Lift up your heart, for I kept my word.

Three times I came to your friendly door;
Three times my shadow was on your floor.
I was the beggar with bruisèd feet;
I was the woman you gave to eat;
I was the child on the homeless street!"

WHEN CHRIST WAS BORN IN BETHLEHEM

HENRY WADSWORTH LONGFELLOW

When Christ was born in Bethlehem,
'Twas night, but seemed the noon of day;
The stars, whose light
Was pure and bright,
Shone with unwavering ray;
But one, one glorious star
Guided the Eastern Magi from afar. . . .

As shepherds watched their flocks by night,
An angel, brighter than the sun,
Appeared in air,
And gently said,
"Fear not, be not afraid.
For lo! beneath your eyes,
Earth has become a smiling paradise."

IN MEMORIAM*

ALFRED, LORD TENNYSON

From the poem in memory of Tennyson's friend, Arthur Henry Hallam, who died in September 1833.

28

The time draws near the birth of Christ.
    The moon is hid; the night is still;
    The Christmas bells from hill to hill
Answer each other in the mist. . . .

This year I slept and woke with pain,
    I almost wished no more to wake,
    And that my hold on life would break
Before I heard those bells again.

But they my troubled spirit rule,
    For they controlled me when a boy;
    They bring me sorrow touched with joy,
The merry merry bells of Yule.

29

With such compelling cause to grieve
    As daily vexes household peace,
    And chains regret to his decease,
How dare we keep our Christmas Eve;

Which brings no more a welcome guest
 To enrich the threshold of the night
 With showered largess of delight
In dance and song and game and jest?

30

With trembling fingers did we weave
 The holly round the Christmas hearth;
 A rainy cloud possessed the earth,
And sadly fell our Christmas Eve.

At our old pastimes in the hall
 We gamboled, making vain pretense
 Of gladness, with an awful sense
Of one mute Shadow watching all.

We paused. The winds were in the beech,
 We heard them sweep the winter land;
 And in a circle hand-in-hand
Sat silent, looking each at each.

Then echo-like our voices rang;
 We sung, though every eye was dim,
 A merry song we sang with him
Last year, impetuously we sang.

We ceased, a gentler feeling crept
 Upon us: surely rest is meet.
 "They rest," we said, "their sleep is sweet,"
And silence followed, and we wept.

Our voices took a higher range;
 Once more we sang: "They do not die

Nor lose their mortal sympathy,
Nor change to us, although they change;

"Rapt from the fickle and the frail
  With gathered power, yet the same,
  Pierces the keen seraphic flame
From orb to orb, from veil to veil."

Rise, happy morn, rise, holy morn,
  Draw forth the cheerful day from night,
  O Father, touch the east, and light
The light that shone when hope was born.

106

Ring out, wild bells, to the wild sky,
  The flying cloud, the frosty light,
  The year is dying in the night;
Ring out, wild bells, and let him die.

Ring out the old, ring in the new,
  Ring, happy bells, across the snow,
  The year is going, let him go;
Ring out the false, ring in the true.

Ring out the grief that saps the mind,
  For those that here we see no more;
  Ring out the feud of rich and poor,
Ring in redress to all mankind.

Ring out a slowly dying cause,
  And ancient forms of party strife;
  Ring in the nobler modes of life,
With sweeter manners, purer laws.

Ring out the want, the care, the sin,
   The faithless coldness of the times;
   Ring out, ring out my mournful rimes,
But ring the fuller minstrel in.

Ring out false pride in place and blood,
   The civic slander and the spite;
   Ring in the love of truth and right,
Ring in the common love of good.

Ring out old shapes of foul disease;
   Ring out the narrowing lust of gold;
   Ring out the thousand wars of old,
Ring in the thousand years of peace.

Ring in the valiant man and free,
   The larger heart, the kindlier hand;
   Ring out the darkness of the land,
Ring in the Christ that is to be.

ON THE MORNING OF CHRIST'S
NATIVITY

JOHN MILTON

I

This is the month, and this the happy morn,
Wherein the Son of Heaven's eternal King,
Of wedded Maid and Virgin Mother born,
Our great redemption from above did bring;
For so the holy sages once did sing,
    That he our deadly forfeit should release,
And with his Father work us a perpetual peace.

II

That glorious form, that light unsufferable,
And that far-beaming blaze of majesty,
Wherewith he wont at Heaven's high council-table
To sit the midst of Trinal Unity,
He laid aside; and here with us to be,
    Forsook the courts of everlasting day,
And chose with us a darksome house of mortal clay. . . .

V

But peaceful was the night
Wherein the Prince of Light

His reign of peace upon the earth began:
The winds with wonder whist,
Smoothly the waters kissed,
    Whispering new joys to the mild ocĕan,
Who now hath quite forgot to rave,
While birds of calm sit brooding on the charmed wave.

VI

The stars with deep amaze
Stand fixed in steadfast gaze,
    Bending one way their precious influence,
And will not take their flight
For all the morning light,
    Or Lucifer that often warned them thence;
But in their glimmering orbs did glow,
Until their Lord himself bespake, and bid them go.

SMALL SHEPHERD

ANOBEL ARMOUR

Starlight lay softly on the fold,
And huddled sheep turned palely gold
While one small, startled shepherd stood
At the hill's edge, by the olive wood.

He had seen angels, heard their song,
And though Bethlehem's road had seemed too long
To shepherds who had left him there,
The small boy knew that everywhere,
Through all his life and down the years
Angels would sing for his dreaming ears,
And that where he went, near or far,
He would walk under a Christmas star!

THE OXEN

THOMAS HARDY

Christmas Eve, and twelve of the clock.
"Now they are all on their knees,"
An elder said as we sat in a flock
By the embers in hearthside ease.

We pictured the meek mild creatures where
They dwelt in their strawy pen,
Nor did it occur to one of us there
To doubt they were kneeling then.

So fair a fancy few would weave
In these years! Yet, I feel,
If someone said on Christmas Eve,
"Come; see the oxen kneel,

"In the lonely barton by yonder coomb
Our childhood used to know,"
I should go with him in the gloom,
Hoping it might be so.

THE SHEPHERD LEFT BEHIND

MILDRED PLEW MERRYMAN

"The hour is late," the shepherds said,
"And the miles are long to wind;
Do you stay here with the sheep, instead!"
And they left the lad behind.

He heard their feet in the dark ravine,
The drop of the sheepfold bars,
And then blue stillness flowed between
The huddled sheep and stars.

He sat him down to wait for dawn,
His crook across his knees,
And thought of the shepherds moving on
Under the olive trees.

Herding his flocks in Palestine,
He thought, that lad of old,

How some must follow the Angel's sign
And some must tend the fold.

And as he mused he took his pipe—
'Twas a shepherd's pipe he had—
And there, while the frosty stars grew ripe
And shone on the shepherd lad,

The first sweet Christmas carol twined
From the willow's slender stem—
Blown by the shepherd left behind—
To a Babe in Bethlehem.

THE THREE KINGS

**HENRY WADSWORTH
LONGFELLOW**

Three Kings came riding from far away,
　　Melchior and Gaspar and Baltasar;
Three Wise Men out of the East were they,
And they travelled by night and they slept by day,
　　For their guide was a beautiful, wonderful star.

The star was so beautiful, large, and clear,
　　That all the other stars of the sky
Became a white mist in the atmosphere,
And by this they knew that the coming was near
　　Of the Prince foretold in the prophecy.

Three caskets they bore on their saddlebows,
    Three caskets of gold with golden keys;
Their robes were of crimson silk with rows
Of bells and pomegranates and furbelows,
    Their turbans like blossoming almond-trees.

And so the Three Kings rode into the West,
    Through the dusk of night, over hill and dell,
And sometimes they nodded with beard on breast,
And sometimes talked, as they paused to rest,
    With the people they met at some wayside well.

"Of the child that is born," said Baltasar,
    "Good people, I pray you, tell us the news;
For we in the East have seen his star,
And have ridden fast, and have ridden far,
    To find and worship the King of the Jews."

And the people answered, "You ask in vain;
    We know of no king but Herod the Great!"
They thought the Wise Men were men insane,
As they spurred their horses across the plain,
    Like riders in haste, and who cannot wait.

And when they came to Jerusalem,
    Herod, the Great, who had heard this thing,
Sent for the Wise Men and questioned them;
And said, "Go down unto Bethlehem,
    And bring me tidings of this new king."

So they rode away; and the star stood still,
    The only one in the gray of morn;
Yes, it stopped,—it stood still of its own free will,
Right over Bethlehem on the hill,
    The city of David, where Christ was born.

And the Three Kings rode through the gate and the guard,
 Through the silent street, till their horses turned
And neighed as they entered the great inn yard;
But the windows were closed, and the doors were barred,
 And only a light in the stable burned.

And cradled there in the scented hay,
 In the air made sweet by the breath of kine,
The little child in the manger lay,
The child, that would be king one day
 Of a kingdom not human but divine.

His mother Mary of Nazareth
 Sat watching beside his place of rest,
Watching the even flow of his breath,
For the joy of life and the terror of death
 Were mingled together in her breast.

They laid their offerings at his feet:
 The gold was their tribute to a King,
The frankincense, with its odor sweet,
Was for the Priest, the Paraclete,
 The myrrh for the body's burying.

And the mother wondered and bowed her head,
 And sat as still as a statue of stone;
Her heart was troubled yet comforted,
Remembering what the Angel had said
 Of an endless reign and of David's throne.

Then the Kings rode out of the city gate,
 With a clatter of hoofs in proud array;
But they went not back to Herod the Great,
For they knew his malice and feared his hate,
 And returned to their homes by another way.

'TWAS THE NIGHT BEFORE CHRISTMAS

CLEMENT C. MOORE

'Twas the night before Christmas, when all through the house
Not a creature was stirring, not even a mouse;
The stockings were hung by the chimney with care,
In hopes that ST. NICHOLAS soon would be there;
The children were nestled all snug in their beds,
While visions of sugar-plums danced through their heads;
And Mamma in her 'kerchief, and I in my cap,
Had just settled our brains for a long winter's nap
When out on the lawn there arose such a clatter,
I sprang from my bed to see what was the matter;
Away to the window I flew like a flash,
Tore open the shutters and threw up the sash.
The moon on the breast of the new-fallen snow
Gave the lustre of midday to objects below;
When, what to my wondering eyes should appear,
But a miniature sleigh, and eight tiny reindeer,
With a little old driver, so lively and quick,
I knew in a moment it must be Saint Nick.
More rapid than eagles his coursers they came,
And he whistled, and shouted, and called them by name:
"Now, Dasher! now, Dancer! now, Prancer and Vixen!
On, Comet! on, Cupid! on, Donder and Blitzen!
To the top of the porch! to the top of the wall!
Now, dash away! dash away! dash away all!"

As dry leaves that before the wild hurricane fly,
When they meet with an obstacle, mount to the sky,
So up to the house-top the coursers they flew,
With a sleigh full of toys—and St. Nicholas too!
And then, in a twinkling, I heard on the roof,
The prancing and pawing of each little hoof.
As I drew in my head, and was turning around,
Down the chimney St. Nicholas came with a bound.
He was dressed all in fur, from his head to his foot,
And his clothes were all tarnished with ashes and soot!
A bundle of toys he had flung on his back,
And he looked like a pedlar just opening his pack;
His eyes—how they twinkled! his dimples, how merry!
His cheeks were like roses, his nose like a cherry!
His droll little mouth was drawn up like a bow,
And the beard of his chin was as white as the snow.
The stump of a pipe he held tight in his teeth,
And the smoke, it encircled his head like a wreath.
He had a broad face, and a little round belly,
That shook, when he laugh'd, like a bowlful of jelly.
He was chubby and plump; a right jolly old elf;
And I laughed, when I saw him, in spite of myself.
A wink of his eye, and a twist of his head,
Soon gave me to know I had nothing to dread.
He spoke not a word, but went straight to his work,
And filled all the stockings—then turned with a jerk,
And laying his finger aside of his nose,
And giving a nod, up the chimney he rose.
He sprang to his sleigh, to his team gave a whistle,
And away they all flew, like the down off a thistle.
But I heard him exclaim, ere he drove out of sight,
"Happy Christmas to all! and to all a good night!"

TRUE STORIES OF CHRISTMAS PRESENT

PAPA'S SONG

NETTIE HUNSAKER

I don't think I will ever forget that Christmas. There was little snow that year. It was as if the world couldn't quite decide whether or not winter had really come. Such were the conditions as I drove home from college to spend the Christmas holidays with my family.

I suspected it would be the last Christmas I would spend at home. We all knew that soon after Christmas I would leave on my mission. Then would come marriage, and Christmases from then on would be spent with my own little family. Oh, I knew there would be years when I would spend Christmas Day with my family, but never again would I be there for the "season," the days of baking, nights spent caroling, the stockings to be hung, and other activities which filled the weeks before Christmas. I was growing up. I was leaving home, and the thought scared me.

I had anticipated that last Christmas at home for months. My family had many holiday traditions which we celebrated together for years, and each held a special meaning for me. I was the second of eleven children, and my nine younger brothers and sisters also added to the excitement.

That week before Christmas was wonderful. I savored every minute of the gingerbread houses, the stockings hanging in the living room, wreaths in our windows, acting out the Nativity, decorating our tree, and all the secrets and surprises which seemed to invade every corner of our warm house. It was everything I could want my last Christmas at home to be like. Yet, despite the happy feelings, I kept being reminded that this would be the last year things would be the same.

One of the Christmas traditions which we children looked forward to the most took place on Christmas Eve. Starting with the youngest, Papa would take each child downstairs to the living room. Then, holding him or her in the old rocking chair, Papa would sing us a special Christmas song. It was the same song every year, and we all knew it by heart. The song talked about angels and dancing toys on Christmas morning. Sitting there in Papa's arms with the Christmas tree lights shining in the dark room, you couldn't help but feel secure. Somehow you knew you were still a child, and tomorrow would reveal all the joys that Christmas morning could bring. No matter how old we were or how big we grew, Papa always rocked us on Christmas Eve.

As I lay in my bed that night, I watched each of my sisters and brothers in turn be taken down the stairs. I was the oldest child at home that year since my older sister had left on her mission. Below me in the living room, I heard the song over and over as each child was sung to. Then it was my turn. I followed Papa down the stairs into the living room. He sat in the big chair and opened his arms.

"Do you still want me to sit on your lap?" I asked.

"Of course," he smiled. Gratefully, I climbed onto his lap and pulled my knees up to my chin, snuggling up next to him.

"This is my last night to be rocked," I said.

"I know," came his quiet reply.

As the first few strains of the familiar tune began in the tape recorder next to us, I thought back to all the years I had heard this song on Christmas Eve. Suddenly something in me wanted to stay. I was so warm and comfortable, and I had no idea what the future months and years would hold. I started to cry.

Don't let this song end, I thought.

Papa began to sing.

Heaven bless you, little one, while you're fast asleep.
You'll awake to dancing toys,
Candy canes, Christmas joys.
And I pray your whole life through,
Angels will watch over you,
Loving you the way I do,
My little one, sleep well.

Each year before this night, the song had reminded me of Christmas and what the next morning would bring. But on this last time, I knew Papa was singing about life and the years ahead—not toys that would break or wear out, but eternal joys I would find on my journey through life, joys I was not even aware of now. On this night I heard the emotion of his voice as he sang for angels to watch over me, not just for tonight but for tomorrow night and all the nights that would follow when he wouldn't be there.

I let my tears flow, as the last strains of music faded away. Papa and I watched the lights of the tree in the darkness, and we rocked and rocked, long after the song had ended.

As we rocked, I thought what our last night in heaven must have been like, the night before each of us came to earth to be born. Did Heavenly Father hold us close and tell us of the joys and dancing toys which we would find on the morrow? Did we cry and wish we could stay with him forever, even though we knew earth life would bring us more joys than we could imagine? He must have held us long after his song to us had ended, asking that angels would watch over us in our earthly journey, that our years away from him would be filled with happiness and would eventually lead us back to his presence.

I found comfort as I thought of my Heavenly Father that night, while my earthly father rocked me. Even though Papa couldn't be there every day in the future to help me with each struggle I would face, my Father in Heaven would be there. No matter what the years ahead would bring, I would not only have the support of an earthly father but of my Heavenly Father. And he would guide my paths and bring me home for good. That night I felt he too was singing, "Loving you the way I do, my little one, sleep well."

THE BROKEN PICTURE

JODY SHIELDS

We were not, as my brother Fred used to say, "exactly the poorest family in the community," then he would add, "but it's for certain we aren't the richest, either!" We had most of the necessities, but the extras were few and spaced far between. So it was that, by average comparison, our Christmases were rather lean.

I remember we used to stare wide-eyed with awe and wonder at the stacks of packages under the Christmas trees at our cousins' homes. All around the bases of their trees would be richly and fashionably wrapped presents—and it wouldn't even be Christmas for another week.

At our house, Santa brought everything on Christmas Eve. There just weren't any other presents to be had, except what we gave each other. They were usually things we made ourselves, and we kept them secreted away until Christmas Eve. Then we would get them out and place them in a chair near the tree so Santa could distribute them with the bounty he brought when he came.

On Christmas Day we would open our presents, wild with excitement and delight. As soon as everything had been opened, inspected, and given an initial breaking-in, we were off for our cousins' houses to see how they had fared. Somehow, looking at all their treasures made ours seem pale by comparison.

We always took fruitcakes, homemade candy and cookies to them. Almost always they gave us grocery boxes of oranges, nuts, and canned goods.

The Christmas I remember best was just before I turned eight. My older sister, Marcia, was ten, and she had learned to crochet during the summer. She announced with a great deal of pride that she was going to crochet Mom a pair of hot pads made like little girls' dresses. She had been saving her allowance for the thread, and she had asked her Primary teacher to help her with the pattern.

I was really impressed and wished I knew how to do something really beautiful like that. All I could do was some embroidery, but I didn't really enjoy doing it. Besides, I didn't have the kind of money it would take for a scarf or a pair of pillow slips to work.

Christmas was drawing closer, and we were busy getting things ready. Almost every night we would shut ourselves in our bedroom and work on the gifts we were making for everyone. Marcia would be crocheting as swiftly as she could, being very careful to keep her stitches even and not to miss any. I would sit on our bed and watch her and wish I had something special for Mom, but I could think of nothing.

One day I had gone through some boxes on the back porch to see if I could find some odds and ends to trim the book tote I was making for Marcia. Mom had said she would help me sew them on if I could find some scraps and cut out the designs.

In one of the boxes I found an old picture frame. The glass had been broken out, but there were still the backing pieces of cardboard and a torn, yellowing piece of paper in it. I recognized it immediately, and it gave me a sharp twinge of regret when I remembered how it had come to be hidden away in the scrap box.

On the paper was a poem, surrounded with drawings of flowers, birds, a small house, clouds, and grass. It had hung in the kitchen ever since I could remember, and we children had read and reread the poem so many times we all had it memorized. Then, one day, we had been fighting and chasing each other with the broom, and I had accidentally knocked the picture to the floor. The glass broke into a hundred pieces, and some of them had torn the paper on which the poem was written.

Mom had come quickly. At first she didn't say anything. She just stood there for a minute with a strange look on her face. Then she quietly shooed us out of the room so we wouldn't get cut on the broken glass. It was so unusual for her not to say something that we went in a hurry but lingered at the doorway.

We looked back to see her on her knees picking up the broken pieces of glass, and we could tell that she was crying.

She never said anything about it. Not even when Daddy got home from work that night. He didn't seem to notice its absence from the wall, either. All during dinner we could not keep from stealing guilty glances at the spot where it had hung, all the time expecting Mother to mention it and Father to take proper disciplinary measures. But nothing was said, and the frame and torn paper had just disappeared as if it had never existed.

Now, as I held them in my hands with a wave of memories sweeping over me, I knew what I was going to do for my gift to Mom this year. Very carefully I wrapped the frame in the scraps I had picked out for the book tote and carried it to my room. I hid it in the bottom of my drawer, underneath my pajamas, until I could assemble the materials I would need.

I would have to have Daddy or Wayne, my oldest brother, cut a new glass for me. In order to get the right size, I would have to measure the cardboard backing. I made a mental note to do that first thing. Then I would have to have a piece of paper to do the printing and drawings on. It had to be special paper, heavier than most, with a silky finish. It never occurred to me to doubt if I could copy the printing and the drawing accurately enough to be acceptable. I just knew that this was what I had to do for my mother for Christmas.

The next time we went to town for groceries, I went away from the family and hurried to the dime store where Mom did much of her shopping. I knew they had a stationery department, and I was sure that was where I would find the paper I needed. The clerk was very helpful and together we found just the right piece of paper. But it came in a package, and if I bought the whole package, I would not have enough money for the gold ink I would need. I had to have gold ink, because that is what was on the other one. It was such a good idea that only to do it halfway would be worse than not to do it at all. I would just have to get more money. But, how, this close to Christmas?

A fat, wet tear slipped from my eye and ran down my cheek.

"What's wrong?" asked the kindly clerk. "Isn't this paper what you wanted?"

"Yes, yes," I replied, trying vainly to hold back the other tears that were pushing to spill out after the first, "only—only I don't have enough money to buy the whole package and gold ink, too," I sobbed.

"Hmm." The clerk tapped her chin with a forefinger. "Would

it help if you bought only one sheet?" She smiled. "I could sell you one sheet for a nickel."

"Oh, yes!" I breathed happily, wiping my tears on the sleeve of my coat. I handed her my money, and she took one sheet of paper from the package and put the rest of the package in a special place under the counter. She got a small jar of gold ink and rang up the sale on her cash register.

Clutching the sack she had handed me, I hurried back to the grocery store just as the family was about to launch an all-out search for me.

"Where have you been?" they asked. "We were terribly worried about you!"

"I was just doing some shopping," I said.

Since everyone was feeling the spirit of Christmas, no one said any more about it, and we went home.

I went straight to the bedroom where I had been assembling all the things I would need. I had only two days left until Christmas. I would have to hurry. I would also have to be very careful in my haste to keep from spoiling it. To make mistakes would be worse than not to do it at all, I told myself as I got out pencil, pen, and scrap paper. School was out for the Christmas holiday, so I would be able to spend most of the day working on my gift. Marcia had finished her hot pads and had them wrapped and hidden away until Christmas. She was free to play in the snow, or ice skate, or whatever her fancy dictated. And her fancy certainly did not relish watching me prepare my gift. She did not know what it was going to be, and I did not want her to know. I didn't want anyone to know. I wasn't sure they wouldn't laugh and say it was silly.

Very carefully I practiced each drawing over and over until I felt I could do it well enough to set it down on the silk-surfaced sheet. I drew them lightly in pencil and then outlined them in

India ink. The gold would provide accents and be the finishing touch.

The next day I began the lettering. First I practiced copying each line over and over until my fingers hurt. Then I rested for awhile before I started lightly penciling the letters on the sheet with the drawings.

I had had some doubt about my ability to print the letters small enough and neatly enough, but as I stared at the torn original, I realized that it, too, had been printed by hand, and I felt that if they (whoever "they" may have been) could do it, so could I.

I dipped the pen in the ink and sent up a silent prayer, "Dear, dear God, please let it be neat. Please don't let me spoil it now." I drew the first letter with its fancy curlicues and thicker lines, and sighed audibly as it came out perfect. The other letters were plainer, but smaller, and they must be kept of uniform size. I paused to rest, dipped the pen, uttered my prayer silently in my mind, and set down the other two letters in the first word, then the rest of the letters in the first line, and so on. Very carefully and cautiously I drew over each letter with black ink, praying that it wouldn't smear; praying that it wouldn't drip; praying that the lines wouldn't waver; praying that it would be a worthy gift.

At last it was finished. I put on the touches of gold and left it to dry for a minute while I got out the frame and the new glass and the wrapping paper. Then, I slipped the glass into the frame, set the sheet with the poem against the glass, placed the cardboard backing in place, and tapped the small nails into the holes to hold it all in place.

I wrapped tissue paper around it, then placed it in an emptied Christmas card box and wrapped it. It was Christmas Eve and my fingers hurt, my shoulders ached, and my eyes burned from the strain, but my gift for Mom was ready, and my heart was light as I left the bedroom and closed the door softly behind me.

The next morning I could hardly open my presents, I was so excited and somewhat apprehensive. I kept a close watch on Mom as she opened her gifts. She smiled a big smile and gave Marcia a special hug when she unwrapped the hot pads. They were really something, I thought, with a twinge of uncertainty.

At last she was opening the package that held my gift. My breath caught in my throat. It seemed everyone was watching, and I couldn't help wishing they wouldn't pay any attention. Mom carefully drew aside the tissue paper and looked at the framed poem, the crude drawings, the rough printing. For a long moment she sat staring at it, then she slowly threw back her head and I sensed, more than heard, a sob catch in her throat.

I was intently avoiding looking at her. My full attention was concentrated on the new pair of ice skates I had received for Christmas, yet I knew that she threw me a look out of the corner of her eye as she rose and carried the gift, box and all, into the kitchen.

"She's crying," Marcia said softly. "Why?"

"I don't know," Fred answered easily, not bothering to take his eyes off the electric train set he was trying to assemble around the base of the Christmas tree.

I assiduously avoided answering, and I looked the other way as I wiped a tear from my own cheek. Suddenly, I couldn't stay there any longer. I grabbed my new skates and my coat and ran outside. Everyone would think I had gone to try the skates out. I ran through the snow with tears blinding my eyes. My precious, rotten, horrible gift had been rejected, and it served me right! I collapsed, sobbing on the tree trunk where we sat to change our skates, the image of Mother throwing my gift into the trash, box and all, vivid in my mind.

Daddy found me there. He had followed Mom into the kitchen, then had followed me outside.

"What's wrong, Kitten?" he asked gently, as he pressed my head against his shoulder so the rough weave of his jacket could absorb my tears.

"She didn't like it!" I sobbed in my misery.

"Nonsense!" he replied quickly. "Honey, she loved it. Believe me, Kitten. I don't think she has ever received a gift that pleased her more."

"Then why is she crying?"

"I doubt you'd understand." He paused so long I was afraid he wasn't going to try to explain. After a long minute, which I spent drying my eyes and blowing my nose, he went on, "You see, Kitten, that poem was given as a gift to your grandmother many years ago. When our first baby was born, Grandma gave it to your Mom. She said that Mamma should always remember the message of the poem and that, if she did, it would help and inspire her as much as it had helped and inspired Grandma. Mamma had me hang it in the kitchen where she would be able to see it and read its message. She loved it very much."

"Then, why didn't she get it fixed when we broke it?" I asked, not yet convinced.

"Well, it bothered Mamma to love that particular picture so much. She hated to make a big fuss over it. You see, Kitten, she was the one who gave it to Grandma in the first place."

He took my hand, and together we walked slowly to the house. Inside it was cozy and warm, and the Christmas turkey was beginning to spread its fragrance from the oven. There was Mamma, her eyes shining as she stood against the sink peeling potatoes. Marcia was gathering the wrapping paper and ribbon from the living room floor. Fred and Wayne were arguing (quietly yet) over the electric train, and there was my gift, hanging on the wall in the exact spot it had hung for so long, ever since I could remember.

THE CHRISTMAS WE GAVE AWAY

FAE ELLSWORTH

The Christmas I remember best began with tragedy. It happened at six a.m. on one of those crisp Idaho Falls mornings the day before Christmas. Our neighbors, the Jessee Smith family slept peacefully in their two-story home. The baby, barely six months old, was in a crib next to her parents' room, and three older children were upstairs.

Suddenly something jarred Jessee from his sleep. He thought he smelled smoke. Could a spark from the torch he'd defrosted the frozen winter pipes with the day before have started a fire in the basement? Still half asleep, he stumbled to the bedroom door and flung it open. Clouds of black smoke poured into the room. "Lorraine!" he yelled. "Get the baby!" He ran toward the stairs and his sleeping children. The smoke was thicker as he gasped for breath. "Rick! Tom! Wake up!" The boys scrambled out of their beds. "Run, boys!" Tom grabbed his younger brother's hand and they raced down the smoke-filled stairway to safety. His daughter's room was next. As Jessee groped through the heavy shroud of grey, he called, "Cindy! Cindy! Where are you?"

"Here, Daddy, here!" He followed the frightened cries, scooped up his daughter in his arms, and with his hand over her face, felt his way out the room and down through a narrow path of searing flames. They coughed, choked, gasped for breath, until they at last stumbled out the door where a relieved wife and three children stood shivering in the snow.

Now the family looked to the smoke and flames pouring out

the roof of their home, the home that the night before had held all their earthly treasures. It had also held a promise of Christmas, mulled cider, homemade candy, and stockings waiting to be filled. They stood huddled in their nightclothes, barefoot in the biting cold and watched their Christmas burn up along with their house.

The spell was broken by the sound of sirens piercing the icy air. Firemen leaped from the huge red trucks and turned their powerful hoses on the blaze. Seconds later, the bishop of the Smith's ward drove up, bundled the family into his car, and took them to a home the ward elders quorum had just completed as a fundraising project. They were not to witness the firemen's hopeless battle with the flames. For when the trucks finally pulled away, this time in silence, nothing stood of their house but its charred skeleton against the sky.

And tomorrow was Christmas. At our house we were putting the last secret wrappings on the presents, making the last batch of popcorn for popcorn balls to go in our Christmas stockings. We three children were attempting dubious harmony with our favorite carols and breaking into giggles at the results.

Then Dad came in with the news. We sat with serious faces listening to him tell of the fire, the narrow escape, the house where the Smiths were spending Christmas Eve.

"Why?" Mother said. "Why did this happen, just at Christmas? It isn't fair. They had children, just the same ages as ours," she said. Jessee and Dad were the closest friends; they even joked that they were so close they wore the same size shirt. The same size shirt! "Bill," Mother began hesitantly, "would you mind terribly if we gave Jessee one of the shirts I bought you for Christmas? You wear the same size . . ." A hush fell on us all. We all seemed to be thinking the exact same thing. "I've got it!" my ten-year-old brother shouted. "We'll give the Smiths a Christmas! A Christmas for Christmas!"

"Where could we get one?" my inquisitive little sister asked. "We'll give them ours," the others chorused in.

"Of course! We'll give them ours!" The house rang with excited voices, until Dad's stern command silenced us. "Hold it! Let's make sure we all want to do this. Let's take a vote. All in favor say aye."

"AYE!" chorused back at him. "All opposed?" was met with silence.

The hours that followed are ones we will never forget. First we sat around the tree and handed out presents. Instead of opening them, the giver would divulge their contents so the label could be changed to the appropriate Smith family member. My heart fell when Dad handed Kevin a box wrapped in gold foil and green ribbon. "It's a baseball glove, son," Dad told him, and a flash of disappointment crossed Kevin's face. I knew how he'd longed for that glove, and Dad wanted to say, "You keep it, son," but Kevin smiled as if he'd read our thoughts. "Thanks, Dad. It's just what Stan wanted, too," he replied.

"Look, here's the recipe holder I made for you, that is, for Sister Smith." We signed all the tags "From Santa," and the activity that followed would have put his workshop elves to shame.

They had presents, but what about a Christmas dinner? The turkey was cooked, pies baked, the carrots and celery prepared, then all packed in a box. The Christmas stockings must be stuffed. Dad got a length of clothesline and some clothespins to hang the stockings with, but what about a tree? We looked at ours. Could we really part with it? "I know," Dad volunteered. "Let's decorate it with things they'll need." And so more things were added to the tree: a tube of toothpaste tied with red ribbon, a razor, comb, bars of soap nestled in the branches. Finally it was all ready.

It was a strange procession that silently paraded through the dark streets of Idaho Falls that night. Father led the way carrying a completely decorated tree. Mother followed with a complete Christmas dinner, down to the last dish of cranberry sauce. The three of us children pulled wagons and a sled piled with boxes of gifts. We waited until the last light was out in the Smiths' borrowed home, and then Mom and Dad stealthily carried each item in the door. When the last stocking had been hung, we turned again toward home.

All the way home I worried about what waited for my family at our home. What if the others were disappointed? All that was left were a few pine needles and paper scraps. I couldn't have been more wrong. The minute we were back inside we were more excited than ever. Every pine needle and paper scrap was a reminder of the magic of the evening, and we hadn't taken that to the Smiths. It was in our home as real as if you could see it. A happier family never went to bed on a Christmas Eve, and the next morning the magic was still there. For our celebration we wrote a promise to each person on a card and presented it around a spruce branch tied in a red ribbon.

"One shoe shine. To Father. Love, Kevin." "This is good for two turns doing the evening dishes. Love, your husband, Bill." And so it went.

Our Christmas dinner consisted of scrambled eggs and bacon, toast and sliced oranges. Somehow, I don't remember a better one. And I know we sang our carols that night with the same unconventional harmony, but they sounded sweeter than angels to me.

"Oh, Mommy," said my small sister as she snuggled up for her bedtime Christmas story, "I like to give Christmases away." Tears blurred the book in mother's hands, because she knew that none of us would ever forget this Christmas; the one when we gave our best gift. As she read the story of the Baby born in a manger, it seemed our gift was but a small tribute to him who gave his best gift, his Son, to us.

THE JOY THEY SHARED

JUANITA SADLER

Ever notice how sometimes those who have the least are the most grateful and the most giving?

Christmas Eve in the Philippines was a bright, sun-drenched day. The evidence that it was Christmas boomed from the jeepney radios as we made our way along the crowded streets to the barrio where our investigators, the Juguilons, lived.

They were not only our investigators; they were our friends. We were going to share Christmas Eve with them. They didn't have much, but they wanted to share what they did have. We found that the Filipinos were very generous: you could never give them something without them wanting to give you much more. As missionaries in the Philippines we were always receiving from the kindly people we served. The Juguilons were such a family. Their home was modest, but it was filled with love, love they were always willing to give away.

Their home was one of the smallest in the barrio; its one room was clean and tidy. All of the family's belongings were tied in neat little bundles which hugged the walls. When we came to teach the gospel we sat on the floor with the family.

Our meetings with the family were wonderful and productive. Brother and Sister Juguilon worked hard to understand all that we were telling them. They read the Book of Mormon we gave them. They had to read from our Bible because they could not afford to buy their own. They were diligent; they listened and studied and prayed so they could become a part of the Lord's true church.

When we arrived on Christmas Eve, the room was almost filled by two borrowed, king-sized wooden chairs. We were invited to sit while our friends sat at our feet.

Sitting in the middle of the circle of children was a scraggly little Christmas tree which had been delivered anonymously to the Juguilon home that evening. Underneath it was a gift for each of the children. With beaming faces our friends shared their joy with us. The small, green symbol of Christmas was, to this family, the world's most beautiful. It boasted of widely spaced branches draped with candy-filled ornaments and a popcorn garland which hung lazily from its limbs.

Six pairs of children's eyes focused lovingly on the tiny tree. A small hand lifted to touch a branch, as if to confirm its reality. Another softly coaxed a hanging ornament into gentle movement. We all enjoyed watching the children until the Christmas festivity began. This festivity was a quiet, yet joyful one.

With grateful reverence, Sister Juguilon placed a white box in front of her. Each of us waited in anticipation as she knelt and carefully began to unfold the sides of the box. Even the Christmas tree could not hold the children's attention now. Inside were swirls of snow-white frosting that blanketed the enticing Christmas feast—it was a cake, a beautiful, store-bought cake. For the Juguilon family this was a most unusual and rare treat.

All eyes were turned upon us as we received the first pieces.

No one else ate, just us. We were their guests; they waited to eat until they were certain that we desired no more. Their joy came in giving.

Together we celebrated the birth of our Savior. We left filled with the joy they shared. However, their story continued in our absence on Christmas Day.

Mealtime on that Christmas Day was attended by Brother Juguilon, but not partaken of. Finally Sister Juguilon asked her husband why he would not eat that day. He quietly answered that this day was, for him, a day of fasting, and a day of thanksgiving. Knowing that it was Christmas she agreed that it was a day for thanksgiving. "But fasting?" she asked.

Quietly he answered. "This year was different. This year each of our children received a gift for Christmas." This, to him, was cause to return thanks to God.

SEVEN THOUSAND DOLLARS BY CHRISTMAS

ANNE CASTLETON BUSATH

The talent auction where my sister Sue impulsively bid $20 to hear our own mother do an imitation of Jessie Evans Smith's singing was my earliest memory of our building fund projects. Several years later, I baked over one thousand cornmeal muffins for another project. Large building fund projects were just a part of being an active member of the Church before other methods of financing building projects were established.

By 1970, when I was seventeen, we'd built the first phase of our building (font, kitchen, classrooms, and multipurpose area), nearly depleting the building fund even though many hours of labor had been donated. The multipurpose area was too small almost as soon as we moved in. So even with our depleted fund, we started on the second phase, a chapel.

By the end of October the chapel was completed, but $7,000 was still outstanding. The ward leaders decided not to use it until it was paid for, set Christmas as the goal for occupancy, and bolted the doors.

One Sunday dad stayed long after Sunday School. By the time we sat down to dinner, our stomachs were growling in unison. Dad and mother, Haydn, Laird, and Brandt sat on one side of the table, with Sarah, Sydney, Sue, and me on the piano bench. McCune was away at college. Then dad prayed, alluding mysteriously to goals and a new opportunity. As we fell to eating, dad announced that a family council would convene when the meal was over.

He began it with an announcement in his I'm-not-saying-this-twice voice. "The ward council has met and settled on a plan to pay for the chapel by Christmas. If we make it, we're planning a special service in the chapel on Christmas morning. Part 1 is to raise $2,000 at a $20-a-plate Thanksgiving dinner. Elaine, I wonder if you'd consider accompanying me? We'd love any of you children to join us, but you must pay your own way. Part 2 is to raise the other $5,000 by giving all the money we would ordinarily spend on Christmas to the building fund."

Five-year-old Sydney broke the silence. "How will Santa Claus know not to come?" After that, it didn't seem appropriate to ask "if," and we voted unanimously to support the plan.

As Thanksgiving got closer, the aroma in our home was as enticing as ever because Mother had been assigned to make the pumpkin pies. Haydn, at thirteen, was the only one of us to go to the dinner with mother and dad, and was the youngest in the branch to pay for his own meal.

When McCune came home from college, he spearheaded a family pep rally and brainstorming session. Brandt thought of ingenious ways to get money from mother and dad for jobs we ordinarily did for free. Mother suggested that we hire out as neighborhood odd-jobbers. McCune volunteered to write our relatives about our project, suggesting they send money in place of gifts. Laird thought we could still make gifts for each other using household materials and scraps. Sue thought we should give gifts of love by doing things that the receiver would ordinarily have to do, such as taking out the garbage for Brandt, practicing the drums for Laird, or trying to get a date for me. It began to look like we could have a semblance of Christmas after all.

Within the next few days, I noticed Laird and Brandt disappearing into the basement to emerge hours later wearing secretive smiles. Laird declared, "No one can make me tell what I've been doing in the basement with wood, glue, and raw kidney beans." Sarah and Syd invaded the scrap drawer, pirating ribbons, bows, and scrap paper, while Sue and I secluded ourselves in the sewing room.

It must have been McCune who first thought of the dollhouse for Sarah and Syd. Dad came up with the wood scraps, the know-how, the paint, and the patience. Mother provided the blueprint and artistic vision. When we got started, the girls' bedtime got earlier as everyone else's got later. Their complaints competed with the boys' pounding in the garage. Mother taught Sue and me to be meticulous as we made drapes, lamps, and bedspreads to scale.

Meanwhile we collected money from babysitting, odd jobs, newspaper routes, housecleaning, and snow shoveling. We never knew how the building fund drive was progressing, and until Christmas Day we didn't know if we'd raised enough. But I remember putting my $40 in a donation envelope and proudly giving it to our branch president, satisfied that I would never have spent quite that much on Christmas.

Christmas Eve, always a night filled with family traditions, found us acting out the Nativity story. After reading the second chapter of Luke, we had family prayer and unceremoniously hustled Sarah and Syd off to bed, with sad predictions about how tomorrow would be different from all other Christmases because there wouldn't be any presents.

Dad and the boys carried in the dollhouse and placed it on the window seat where they would see it first thing from the stairs. It was two stories high with a flight of stairs, wallpaper in the bedrooms, furniture varnished and upholstered, and a bright red roof. Mother stood back, directing us on the exact placement of the tiny furnishings. We proudly surveyed our handiwork and unanimously decided that a more wonderful dollhouse couldn't be found in any store. Dad wryly concurred: "I can't think of any store that would sell a dollhouse like ours either!"

Our Christmas Eve sleep was deep, undisturbed by extravagant expectations.

We awoke to "Joy to the World" and dad marshalling the boys out of their bunks. In bathrobes and in order, youngest to oldest, we pranced around at the top of the stairs, while downstairs dad made an elaborate and noisy pretense of checking the living room and making sure that each string of lights on the tree was lit. While coming slowly back up the stairs, dad admonished us to be sure that each gift had our name on it before we ripped it open. Then he led us, very deliberately, down the stairs, stopping every step or two to give additional advice designed, we knew, to drive us crazy.

When the little girls caught sight of the dollhouse, they squealed and established immediate ownership of a bedroom each and ran back upstairs to get their dolls.

With great effort, we persuaded them to join us in our living room so we could open presents, an amazing abundance of them in homey, homely birthday wrappings.

Between each round of presents, we sang a Christmas carol—picking the shortest songs and accelerating the tempo. The basement mystery was solved when I opened Laird's six-sectioned letter holder (with four sections for all the free things I sent for) decorated with a background of glued-on kidney beans and my name traced in white rice. Brandt had made a wood-on-wood wall plaque.

If I would but take the trouble to paint the wood butterfly blue, it would blend nicely in my yellow and orange bedroom.

By the time the mound of used and reused wrapping paper was over Sydney's head, it was time for church. I dressed with care and then combed the girls' hair, while they pranced with excitement and bombarded me with questions. "Could I take a doll's bed to church? I won't look at it once, I promise." "Will Reagan feel bad if I tell her we got a dollhouse?" "What if the church is all locked up?" "Do you think they'd let us in even if there was only $6,999.50?"

In the car, we urged dad to hurry and insisted that the trees outside just weren't going by fast enough. By the time the fifteen-minute trip was over we fairly burst out of the car and raced to the doors.

There was the chapel—doors wide open, shiny, beautiful, and

ours. Members of the branch greeted each other like the brothers and sisters we had truly become. Even with all the excitement, it wasn't hard to be reverent as we left the foyer and entered the spacious chapel.

During the service we all took turns expressing our feelings and experiences. From the eighty-year-old grandmothers down to the five-year-old boys, we all had had a wonderful Christmas. We had given ourselves, in honor of our Elder Brother, the best Christmas ever.

A CHOCOLATE CHRISTMAS

RICHARD R. SCHAAR

It was during the war years. We landed in New Guinea on Dec. 24th and it was raining and hot and muggy. Trucks took us 22 miles inland and oh! what a lonely, lost, forsaken feeling we had—only jungle, heat, swamp and bugs. We pitched our tents and our only light was a piece of tent rope about 4 inches long stuck in a tin can of kerosene.

Already on board ship I struck up an acquaintance with a lonesome G.I. and we became fast buddies. His tent was next to mine.

I was unpacking my duffel bag and wondering what I could give him at least, for Christmas tomorrow. We each had the same

G.I. equipment so there was nothing in that line to give him and beyond that there was nothing you could buy. But I did remember seeing a scrawled sign on a tree back on the road that simply said "PX." This I must investigate. I made an excuse to my buddy that I was going to look around a bit. Since trucks were coming and going all the time, it was no job to simply hang onto the sides of one and the fellows inside would pull you in.

The roads were bad so the trucks had to go slow anyway. I asked them about this PX and they said, "Well, they call it that for want of a better name—they don't have any PX supplies yet—just a few candy bars." They told me when to jump off and, sure enough, a few candy bars were all they had and all of them took up only the space inside the lid of a footlocker. A sign said: "Only one bar to a customer—Leave some for the others." All bars were 4 cents each. I picked out a Hershey milk chocolate bar and hitched a ride back to camp.

I took a piece of waxed-bread-wrapping paper that I found near the PX and wrapped the candy bar. At least the paper had some colored lettering on it from a San Francisco bread company. Then I took an empty ration can and put some fern leaves in it. I then took a piece of stationery and made a Christmas card out of it with some sketches of eight water buffaloes pulling an Army truck (representing Santa's reindeer and sled), added a serious four-line jingle I made up and then placed them all together on top of an ammunition box and thus my Christmas shopping was done. I covered it all with the end of my tent flap so my buddy couldn't see it.

Christmas morning came and I was already up—I couldn't sleep much anyway because my mind was across thousands of miles most of the night. I went to my buddy's tent and he also was up and puttering around. I wished him a Merry Christmas and told him Santa had come—to come over to my tent and take a look. I threw back the tent flap and he just stood there with tears in his eyes.

Finally he said to come back to his tent, because Santa had been there, too. We walked back and he threw back the cover of his bunk and there also was a Hershey milk bar and a homemade card. That is why he was puttering around when I came the first time. I almost choked with feelings. Then when he unwrapped my "present" and saw that we had each given the other the same thing, we both just stood there and shook our heads and laughed and cried. I asked where he got it from and he said, "Well, do you remember that PX sign we passed back on the road as we were coming in . . . ? Well, after you took off yesterday . . ." and the rest he didn't have to tell me. We both had the same idea and did the same thing.

We sat down together and sparingly nibbled on our chocolate bars and talked about the folks at home and hoped next year things would be different.

So simple, but how can anyone forget it?

A GIFT OF FRIENDSHIP

LARUE H. SOELBERG

This Christmas had begun like any other. The laughter of our happily excited children was evidence that Santa had indeed been able to decipher the hastily scrawled notes mailed weeks before.

As was our custom, LeRoy and I would wait until the children had sufficient time to inspect, test, compare and segregate their new treasures before we would open our gifts.

The similarity of this Christmas, to any other, ended here.

The loud knock on the front door demanded immediate answer.

"Come quick!" There was urgency in our friend's voice. "I think you have a fire at your store!"

Fears flooded my mind as I ran through the vacant lot to the store—a small grocery business, which was not yet half paid for.

There were no flames rising from the building, but the windows were solid black!

A fireman came running up and put his hand against the window.

"No heat!" he seemed relieved, "and there's no fire now—let's open it up."

Our hopes were raised. Perhaps we had not lost everything!

He turned the key and pushed open the door. The dense, choking smoke that had filled every minute space of the small building drifted out into the street.

My heart sank! It was like looking at the inside of a coal-black furnace. Not a crack, not a corner, not one can stacked beneath another, had escaped the ugly black filth!

LeRoy, with the help of some of the firemen, removed the motor that had burned itself out. We stood gazing in disbelief at the result.

True, the store had not burned, but was it salvageable? Perhaps the building and equipment could be cleaned, but what about the thousands of bottles, cans and cartons? Even if they could be saved, how could we possibly survive the closing of business for even a few days?

"Only one thing to do." The voice was surprisingly cheerful. "Let's see if we can clean it up."

We were reluctant to accept this offer of help. After all, wasn't this Christmas? A day to be spent with family and loved ones.

"Come on," he joked, "my son will be glad to get me out of the house so that he can play with his electric train. Get me a bucket and some soap."

No sooner would we equip one volunteer with cleaning items, when another would appear at the door, demanding, as one neighbor put it, "A chance to participate in this joyful, holiday project."

Each person who came to the door uttered an astonished, "Oh, no!" and then, "Where do you want me to start?"

By 11 A.M. there were more than forty people—friends, neighbors, firemen, patrons and new acquaintances, scrubbing away at the terrible black goo. Still they kept coming! We were overwhelmed!

The men had taken over the cleaning of the ceiling, the most stubborn and difficult task of all. The women were working in twos, taking items off the shelves, cleaning what they could and boxing the rest.

One young lad, who was recuperating from a broken leg, made trips to the cafe to get hamburgers and potato chips to feed the workers. Another brought turkey and rolls, which, I'm certain, were to have been the biggest part of their Christmas dinner.

An energetic teenager must have run twenty miles emptying buckets and refilling them with clean hot water.

A service station operator brought hundreds of old cleaning rags.

An electrician worked on a motor replacement and soon had the refrigerator case operating again. This was no ordinary cleaning job. Every inch had to be scrubbed, scoured, washed and rinsed. Sometimes this procedure had to be repeated seven times before the white of the walls and ceiling would show through. Yet everyone was laughing and joking, as though they were having a good time!

"Actually, I only dropped by to supervise," came a comment from behind the bread rack.

"I bet this cures you of following fire trucks," a fireman chided his wife.

We all laughed when an attractive blonde woman, who was perched on top of the vegetable case, and now bore a striking resemblance to a chimney sweep, burst out with a chorus of "Chim Chim Cheree."

It was shortly after 2 A.M. when we locked the front door. Everyone had gone. As they finished their jobs, they just slipped out—not waiting for a word of thanks or a smile of appreciation.

We walked home hand in hand. Tears flowed freely down my cheeks. Not the tears of frustration and despair that had threatened earlier, but tears of love and gratitude. Business would open as usual tomorrow—because fifty-four kind people had the true spirit of Christmas in their hearts.

Our children had left the tree lights burning and our presents lay unopened in a neat pile on the floor. They would wait until morning. Whatever those gaily wrapped packages contained would be dwarfed, indeed, by the great gift of friendship given to us that Christmas Day.

A SOLDIER'S CHRISTMAS IN ITALY

GEORGE I. CANNON

The notice read: "Christmas Eve Services Tonight; 6:00 to 7:00 P.M. Conducted in the Group Chapel (Barn located in front of the large white building and to the left of the well). If possible please bring a candle."

As the fellows bunched around the bulletin board a few aired their feelings:

"What a Christmas this is going to be without any mail!"

"Remember last year when we were in Africa, we said that next Christmas we would be home?"

"Yeah, and if you ask me, Italy ain't home."

"How can a guy have the Christmas spirit over here?"

The fellows had reason to feel gloomy. We had just arrived in Italy and were encountering the rain, wind, and mud typical of "sunny Italy" in December. We hadn't received any letters for weeks——Christmas packages weren't even discussed—the mess sergeant was feeding us "C" rations three times a day—our tents leaked. Yes, we were a cheerless group.

As time for the Christmas Eve services drew near, the fellows started towards the barn, and by six o'clock the bomb stools were occupied. Observing the fellows, I couldn't see any trace of the dissatisfaction which was evidenced at the bulletin board. Their faces shone from heartless scrubbing, and they seemed to glow inside as well. Taking in the surroundings I could understand why the transition.

An old adobe barn with huge wooden doors and iron locks was our makeshift chapel. Overhead were two wooden arches with the gabled ceiling shrouded in darkness. The walls, once white, were turning gray, and here and there silhouettes danced as the flickering candles threw off their light. The floor of cement slabs was firm and cold. The air was still pungent with traces of livestock and rusty farm machinery. As I walked between the row of candles and took my seat, I noticed the rude altar decorated with pine boughs and a candle at each end casting light upon a closed Bible. Over in a corner the strains of time-old carols emerged from the midget reed organ. Here was the natural setting for the Christmas story. How simple it was to visualize standing at the manger and seeing a "babe wrapped in swaddling clothes."

The men's voices rang through the chapel as they sang the carol, "Joy to the world, the Lord is come." Then the chaplain rose and read from the scriptures, "Behold, a virgin shall be with child, and shall bring forth a son, and they shall call his name Emmanuel which being interpreted is, God with us." (Matthew 1:23.) How meaningful were these words! Among such surroundings with tinsel discarded and forgotten, thousands of miles from loved ones, the verity of this prophecy was felt—"God [was] with us." As we bowed our heads that Christmas Eve, a united prayer was offered silently that all men could know the real spirit of Christmas.

ONE SHINY DIME
AND THREE PENNIES

CHERYL KELLER

The K-Tom Cafe didn't look very impressive that first day—a small, yellow, box-like structure with a pop sign in the window. I was to find, however, that it communicated exactly what they took pride in: a working man's cafe and a "decent place to bring the wife and kids."

I can still see the bored young man at the employment office peering over his horn-rimmed spectacles. "Hmmm, sorry, Ma'am, we haven't any openings for graduate home economists . . . perhaps in a few months? We'll keep your name on file."

"What do you have *now*? I need a *job*!"

"Oh." Again the drumming fingers shuffled the pitifully small pile of job cards: "waitress, short-order cook, housekeeping—"

"What do they pay?" I interrupted. The pay, as could be expected, was minimum wage—but anything was better than nothing. The short-order cook paid 10¢ an hour more than the others and allowed Sundays off, so I put it at the top of my list.

The card for the K-Tom read: "Wanted: short-order cook, manage grill and other duties as assigned; morning shift, 4 A.M. to 1 P.M.; experience preferred." I was good at interviews, I had cooked all my life for a family of ten kids (I was second to the oldest and the first girl), and I had worked in the dorm kitchen. When the K-Tom called me back to report to work Monday morning at four A.M., little did I realize that the card should have read: "Wanted: short-order cook with eight arms, dexterity of circus

397

acrobat, memory of elephant, and ears of an owl—can distinguish rustling of mouse in dry grass at one hundred yards."

It started out bad and got worse.

I think everyone else who worked there must have been at least six feet tall. The other employees seemed to enjoy watching me push the closest canister over to the shelf and stand tiptoe on top of it to reach something. Then they would slowly shake their heads and chuckle, "I do believe you're a little short on one end, but for the life of me, can't tell which end. . . ."

And there was this whole ghastly thing about eggs—one must *never* break the customer's egg. (Odd how one expects—and demands—the perfect egg in a cafe.) I would awaken trembling in the middle of the night from dreams of a huge, black grill reaching out long black arms to burn me; or leering three-foot eggs, breaking and running across the grill, cackling with laughter.

No matter how hard I tried, it seemed I couldn't get all the orders straight nor get them fast enough. As December rolled around, things didn't seem to be getting any better.

I think my employers sensed how hard I was trying: I arrived early, worked hard and cheerfully at any project, and struggled earnestly with the grill and orders. At least they didn't fire me.

Two weeks before Christmas, and only one week before our first anniversary, my husband and I put our total cash assets on the couch between us: thirteen cents—one shiny dime and three pennies. It had all seemed so easy: we married, I finished my last year of college, and LaMar was promised a good job with a new furniture store starting as soon as we could move. We moved—only to find construction was behind schedule and his job wouldn't be available for a month. He went to work at another job. Then came eye surgery and the verdict that he would probably be unable to work for two years. He was flat on his back with excruciating pain in his head. Our savings lasted through the first month as I nursed him, but were soon gone; only his patience and love kept us going. That's when I became a fry cook.

My journal entries for that Christmas tell the story best:

December 18—Our first anniversary, and the weather is miserable. Between the grey skies, sleety snow, and tears, I could hardly see the road on my way home. When I got there, LaMar was actually out of bed and had made it to the door. His face was pale with bright spots of color burning in his cheeks—I fear a fever. He was eager to get me over to the couch. I sat down quickly so he would—he still cannot stand without trembling. Like a mischievous schoolboy, he pulled a candy cane from behind the pillow. Laughing and crying, we fed each other little bites. Gradually he told me how, resting every two or three steps, he had walked two blocks to get it for me for our anniversary. Two blocks! It probably seemed like a thousand miles with the pain he has been fighting, the pain that even now makes him tremble.

December 24—One of the waitresses told me that Kay and Tom usually give everyone a small Christmas surprise. I told myself it wouldn't include me—the newest employee. I hadn't even been there a month, and I was doing a terrible job. Surely they wouldn't include me. But on the way to work my hands gripped the steering wheel so tightly I noticed the whiteness of my knuckles. With every swish of the windshield wipers I prayed, "Let it be some little thing I can give him. Please don't let it be some girl thing, for I've nothing for him. Oh, Father, I can bear anything, only give me a gift to take home to my man."

Kay and Tom, the owners of the cafe, gathered all the employees together. "Will everyone step out front, please." I hesitated.

"Come on, let's get moving, so we can get home a few minutes early tonight."

At the doorway, I gasped. It couldn't be—for us! I was almost in shock when they started passing things out: a huge basket of fruit and nuts, a box of chocolates, a five dollar bill, and some girl-ish trinket—I've forgotten what. I know I must have cried, and I know I said thanks.

But how do you truly thank someone who has given you, not only a gift, but *Christmas*?

Ten years have come and gone, and there have been many times we have wondered how we'll ever get by. But in the back of our minds we always see one shiny dime and three pennies and taste again that crunchy candy cane and ripe fruit.

Thanks, Kay and Tom, not only for Christmas . . . but also for courage.

FOOD FOR SANTA

ANNA MARIE SCOW,
AS TOLD TO JACK M. LYON

Afew years ago, we wondered if we were even going to have a Christmas. We were struggling financially and hardly had enough money to buy food, let alone buy presents. Our cupboards were actually bare. When our bishop announced the ward Christmas party in sacrament meeting, our children were really excited. They especially looked forward to visiting with Santa, who would be there to give them some candy. We thought that candy might be the only present they would receive. Then the bishop said the party would also be a chance to help the poor.

Each child who wanted to talk to Santa would first have to donate a can of food. Our hearts sank—with our seven children, we couldn't afford a can of food for each one.

At first we thought we would just stay home and not go to the party. But as the days passed, I prayed about what to do. I felt that I should act in faith and things would work out. Acting on my impression, I went to the grocery store to see what food items I might buy, although I really didn't know what I would be able to afford. On one aisle was a display of Chinese noodles, and they were on sale: eight packages for a dollar. And I had a dollar! I bought seven packages, which our children took to the party and happily added to the large pile of food near Santa's chair. This may not seem like much, but in our position even that was a sacrifice.

After the party, we went home. We were preparing for bed when someone pulled into our driveway. It was the bishop—and he was bringing all that food to us. In the following days, we thanked the Lord over and over for his love and goodness to us during that Christmas season.

THE ANONYMOUS BENEFACTOR

SUSAN   EASTON   BLACK

With a Cadillac, a maid, and a gardener, my family always had a Christmas with the best gifts from Santa's sleigh. The days my parents struggled to survive the Great Depression were only whispers of yesteryear when I was born. Mink had replaced wool and the country club societal whirl had captured my parents' fancy. In the 1950s they had become the American dream, and Christmas was merely an excuse to lavish each child with a fairyland of unrestrained wants.

My anticipation of opening gifts on Christmas Day was boundless, for I knew my mother was an uncontrolled shopper when it came to my whims. Being the only girl in a family of boys, I fared better than any at Christmas. My want list seemed to be surpassed only by my presents. After opening one gift after another, I toted my new acquisitions up and down the street so all the neighbors would know that Santa loved me best and that my parents were spoiling me to my complete satisfaction.

From such a worldly background of material prosperity, it seemed only natural for me to fantasize that when I had children of my own, the established tradition of wealth and abundant giving at Christmas would continue—and that it would be even more lavish. If that had been the case, I would not have had one memorable Christmas—just more of the same. Stuffed animals may have been bigger and clothes fancier and gadgets more sophisticated, but ho-hum can be found even in the abundant life.

It was in 1977 . . . that my Christmas took a strange twist.

Circumstances had changed. I was no longer the little girl await-ing the parental handout, but was an adult attempting to make my own way in life. I was a graduate student in 1977, completing a doctoral degree and raising three small sons alone. Like several other graduate students, I had obtained university employment as a research writer for a professor; and like most of the students, I was struggling to meet my financial obligations.

Having more "month than money" had become my norm, but never more so than in December 1977. Five days before Christ-mas, I realized that my mismanagement of funds would prevent any ostentation in gift buying for my children. In fact, it seemed to prevent much gift buying of any kind. It seemed unbearable to me—a young mother who knew all too well how to selfishly flaunt Christmas treasures before less fortunate neighbors, but not how to graciously be one of the less fortunate.

Cuddling my sons, I reluctantly explained my abhorrence of debt and the specter of our economic plight. My emotions sur-faced as the children attempted to comfort me by nodding assuredly, "Don't worry! Santa Claus will give us gifts."

Cautiously I explained, "I think Santa Claus is also having a bad year."

With certainty my firstborn son, Brian, announced, "But on television his sleigh is still filled with toys. With five days left till Christmas, he'll have plenty for us." His younger brother Todd interjected, "Besides, Santa won't forget us. We've been good this year."

As all three nodded in agreement, I did too. My sons had been good. They had found happiness and friendship in our family; we all were unusually close. Perhaps it was our circumstance. Yet, despite their goodness, they would soon be disappointed because neither Santa nor mother would bring the desired presents on Christmas Day.

That night I cried and pled with the Lord for relief, for a glimmer of hope that Christmas in our home would be better than I anticipated. My verbal prayers awakened the children. They seemed to intuitively know what was causing my unhappiness. "Don't worry about presents. It doesn't matter," said Brian. I knew it didn't matter on December 20th, but I knew it would be *all*-important on December 25th.

The next morning I could not hide the despair and self-pity that had marred my face through the night. "What is wrong?" I was asked again and again at the university. My trite reply was "Nothing." Unconvinced friends pried and seemed in their own way to make matters worse. I snapped at the extended hand of friendship and grimaced at their undue interest in my personal life.

Arriving home, I methodically pulled the mail from the mailbox as I entered the house. A curious, unstamped envelope caught my attention. "To a very, very, very, very, very special lady" was typewritten on the envelope. I gazed at the envelope and wondered if it were meant for me. Hoping it was, I tore it open. To my surprise I found several dollars inside, but not a note of explanation.

"Come quickly," I beckoned my children. Together we counted the money, examined the envelope, and expressed wonder at the anonymous gift. This was a direct answer to my prayer. There was enough money in the envelope to buy an extra gift for each child. I was stunned and amazed, and my joy and excitement of Christmas had returned. It was going to be a great Christmas Day after all. It wouldn't be as lavish as those of my childhood, but it would be good enough.

I was curious. Where had the money come from? Could it be from a neighbor, a friend, a classmate, or the bishop? Logical deduction led me first to near neighbors. Visiting from house to house in our neighborhood proved embarrassing. As I attempted to thank neighbors, each stammered and then confessed, "It wasn't me." Calling friends and thanking them elicited clever expressions. "If you find out who is giving away money, tell them to send some my way." Classmates rendered similar comments.

It must be the bishop, I decided. He knew what I paid in tithing and would be aware that a less than exciting Christmas would be awaiting my family. The children and I walked to his house and knocked on the door. Enthusiastically, we thanked him for his generosity. However, he denied being our benefactor and assured us that he did not know who had been so kind.

Curiosity mounted as nightfall approached. I read the envelope again: "To a very, very, very, very, very special lady." This time I noticed that the "e" and "l" were misshapen letters produced by an old typewriter ribbon. I also observed that each dollar bill had been folded and unfolded many times, as if each one had been of infinite worth. My desire to discover the identity of the anonymous donor grew. Soon that desire was coupled with the gnawing resolve to return the money. The misshapen letters and folded dollar bills evidenced that the generous donor also had financial difficulties.

I couldn't sleep that night. Again and again I asked myself, "Who was it?" I had the clues of the old typewriter ribbon and the folded money, but not the answer. I can't really describe how I finally knew who the benefactor was, but about two o'clock in the morning, I knew. I knew who had a broken typewriter, and who needed to replace their ribbon, and who carefully folded and unfolded money, checking each dollar bill. It was my three sons.

With tears of love, I awoke the donors. Blurry-eyed they asked, "What's wrong?" I replied, "Nothing's wrong; everything is right! You gave me the money. You gave me all the money you possess!" Opening the bedroom closet door, I pulled out three empty jars that once had contained their treasured fortune. They sat silent for several moments until my nine-year-old, Brian, turned to his younger brother Todd and punched him. "You told!" he exclaimed. Attempting to fend off further blows, Todd yelled, "It wasn't me, it must have been John." Their five-year-old brother immediately said, "It wasn't me," as both boys landed on him. In unison they asked, "How did you know?"

I had searched outside my home for the answer—but the answer was within. I had seen generosity in all those around me, but had failed to recognize the generous hearts of my children. And now I more clearly knew why the Savior had said, "Suffer the little children to come unto me, and forbid them not: for of such is the kingdom of [heaven]." (Mark 10:14; Luke 18:16.) My house, with all of its material flaws, was my heaven on earth, and my sons were my greatest treasure. Christmas 1977 was indeed a merry Christmas worth remembering.

THE BON-BON BOMBER

GAIL HALVORSEN

I will never forget the Christmas I had over—not in—Berlin in 1948. Only a year before I could never have imagined I'd spend December shuttling 6,500 pounds of lollipops, candy bars and gobs of gum under armed guard to a jail cell for safe-keeping. Even now it is hard to believe it all really happened.

I was a lieutenant in the Air Force and a pilot when I volunteered to fly in food and fuel shortly after the Berlin Airlift began in 1948.

The West Berliners, our avowed enemies during World War II, were asking our help to preserve their freedom. They had been cut off from all land supplies by Russian troops.

At first I thought we'd only be there for a short time, that world opinion wouldn't allow the Russians to try to starve two and a half million people for that long. I didn't think the world would stand for blatant disrespect for human dignity.

Because a plane landed in Berlin with supplies every few minutes, there was no time to see the city. After my last flight one day, I hitched a ride back to Berlin on another plane, determined to use my "sleep time" to see the city.

Movie camera in hand, I walked two and a half miles from the landing point to the edge of Tempelhof Airport, expecting to take movies of the planes landing and departing.

I noticed a silent group of about thirty German children standing next to the barbed wire watching me. They were pale and quiet, their clothes patched in many places. I knew they had barely enough to eat.

The children began speaking to me in pretty good English, and after an hour of this I had to leave.

I walked about fifty yards before it struck me that these children had not asked me for anything. You see, everywhere else I had been—Africa, Great Britain, South America—the children figured an American was a soft touch. They'd all crowd around and say things like, "Any gum, chum?" or "Any bon-bon?" But these children were different, they didn't ask for anything.

So I reached into my pocket and was embarrassed that I only had two sticks of gum.

However, I broke them in two and gave them to the children in the front. I couldn't believe the grateful expression on all their faces. They didn't rush or push or shove, which I marveled at. The four who had taken the gum unwrapped the tiny pieces carefully and passed the paper around—the other children had sheer delight on their faces just to smell the wrappers.

An idea struck me. With only thirty cents, I could get a piece of gum for each of them. But how could I get it to them? I wouldn't likely have time to visit again.

So I told them to stand in a clearing near the airport to catch little parachutes with candy tied to them that I'd drop.

"How will we know which plane is you?" they asked.

I told them I'd come by the next day and wiggle my wings back and forth when I sighted them. (When I was learning how to fly out of Brigham City, I used to go over dad's beet field and say "Hi" to him that way.)

So I put together some candy bars and gum in three little handkerchief parachutes, saw the children, and dropped the candy through the flare chute behind the pilot's seat.

I was absolutely not going to drop any more after the first time. But other buddies in my squadron said they kept seeing a group of children looking up from the ground waving at them—as if they expected something. So I kept it up.

You see, what I was doing was against regulations and I was known as a stickler for going by the book. It was only a few weeks before I was "caught" and called in by the commander.

He said he had planned to chew me out but the general had called and congratulated the squadron for such a novel goodwill gesture.

A story about this candy bombing we were doing hit the German headlines when one of my chutes nearly struck a German reporter on the head. After the article was repeated all across America, I started getting massive amounts of candy and handkerchiefs for the squad's "sweet" flights. You must remember that this candy was in addition to the food and coal we were air-lifting.

Soon I began getting letters from grateful Berlin children addressed to "Uncle Wiggly Wings," "The Bon-Bon Bomber," "The Raisin Bombadier," and even "Schokoladenflleger."

I received one letter that had a beautiful map with it. The little girl said hers was the white house with chickens in the backyard and that she would be waiting there at 2 P.M. I never found her house so I mailed her some candy.

I even received letters from children in East Berlin who said they "didn't like Russians either, please drop some candy to us."

I'd estimate that by December, 90,000 miniature candy chutes had fluttered down into various parts of Berlin. It had become a massive operation that we dubbed "Operation Little Vittles" since the Berlin Airlift itself was "Operation Vittles."

With Christmas coming, my buddies and I wanted to do something special.

So when I went back to the U.S. for a brief visit in the fall, I met with the president of the American Confectionaires Association, who pledged he'd send me some boxes of candy.

During the first week of December a West German military policeman called and said he was forwarding a railroad car with 3,000 pounds of candy to the Rhein-Main air base!

It wasn't long before a second shipment of 3,500 pounds came in. The sum included contributions from the association and cities all over the U.S.—including a sizable amount from my hometown of Garland, Box Elder County.

The 6,500 pounds of candy was too much to drop but we knew we would get it to the children.

I contacted American authorities in Berlin who were setting up Christmas parties all over West Berlin. I told them I'd furnish dessert for the parties. The American Air Force colonel could hardly talk. "Gee," he said, "as bad off as they are, that would be great."

We boxed all of the candy and flew in 100 pounds each trip to Tempelhof. An officer would greet the plane and take the boxes to the Berlin jail where they steadily filled up two cells with the sweets.

The security was necessary because of the extreme black market value of the candy. For two candy bars, a West German lady did my laundry each week. At one Christmas show, Americans offered a stick of gum to each child who would come to the 1,800 seat theater. Some 3,500 children had to be turned away.

By December 23, all the candy was in Berlin being distributed to the party sites.

The parties began mid-afternoon December 24th, since the children had to be home by dark. West Berlin was under a mandatory blackout each night.

Myself? At first I thought it was unfair when I had to fly Christmas Eve. But it gave me time to think.

As I left the West German base for the last of my 450-mile round trips that night, fireworks exploded around me. But in West Berlin there was only darkness. On Christmas Eve, it was eerie.

What a people! I thought. Surrounded as they were, an island in an ocean of Russian troops, they fought on, living on half-rations. Just weeks before, during a general election, 99 out of 100 West Berliners had voted dramatically against acceptance of Communism.

How could I be anything but grateful for having known these people?

Some four dozen U.S. and British airmen died during the airlift in plane crashes and other accidents. Only two weeks after Christmas, when the airlift was 200 days old, shabbily-dressed Berliners brought modest gifts to the fliers at the airport, often breaking through informal police cordons to personally give their presents.

For me, Christmas 1948 had few of the little trinkets and symbols normally associated with that season. But I had learned what freedom was. I had memories enough for a lifetime and a joy it is difficult to describe. All for two sticks of gum.

THE CHRISTMAS SHOPPERS

LUCILE C. READING

The stores were gay with the glitter of Christmas and filled with exciting games and gadgets, and with warm and appealing clothing to tempt Timmy, age nine, and his seven-year-old brother Billy who, with Mr. Smith, were doing their Christmas shopping.

They had gone from store to store, looking at many possible gifts and then always shaking their heads when a clerk asked if she could help them. Billy had almost bought a game he wanted, and Timmy had paused an unusually long time before a display of books, but after whispered consultation with each other, the boys had decided in each case to look further. Finally impatient, Mr. Smith asked, "Where would you suggest we look next?" He was a member of a club that each year helped to make Christmas happier for poor families. He had given Timmy and Billy each four dollars and had taken them shopping for gifts they especially wanted.

"Could we go to a shoe store, sir?" asked Timmy. "We'd like a pair of shoes for our dad. He hasn't any to wear when he gets better and can go back to work."

When they reached the shoe store, Billy pulled something out of his pocket and handed it to Timmy, who smoothed a crumpled piece of brown paper before giving it to the clerk and explaining it was a pattern of their dad's foot. They had carefully drawn it while their father slept in a chair one evening. The clerk studied the pattern and then walked away. He returned in a few minutes, held out a box holding a pair of shoes, and asked, "Will these do?"

The shoes were so beautiful that the boys almost held their breath. Then Timmy saw the price on the box. "We only have $8.00," he said, disappointed, "and these shoes are $16.95."

The clerk cleared his throat. "They have been," he answered, "but they're on special today for Christmas gifts. They'll cost you just $3.98, and you'll have money left over for something for yourselves."

"Not for us," the boys exclaimed, "but we can get something for our mother and our two little sisters. Thank you, oh, thank you, sir!"

Over the boys' heads, the clerk and Mr. Smith exchanged meaningful looks. But Timmy and Billy, excited at being able to buy presents for the rest of the family, paid no attention to the men. They could hardly wait to finish their Christmas shopping.

THE VOICE ON THE PHONE

D . M . B R O W N

The fragrance of gingerbread always makes me think of Suzie and the year I was going to have a perfect Christmas. During past Christmas seasons, I had always been too busy to create the Christmas traditions I felt would build a lifetime of memories for my family. But that Christmas was going to be different. That year my time was my own, and I meant to make every minute of the holiday season count. I would make handpainted ornaments, home-sewn gifts, beautiful decorations, artistically wrapped packages, and baked goods to fill a freezer. I was baking gingerbread men for the tree the day my nine-year-old daughter brought Suzie home from school.

"Mama, this is my new friend, Suzie," Debbie announced, presenting a rather chubby, cheerful-looking little girl. Suzie reminded me of a California poppy, with her red-gold mop of curly hair and a freckled nose that twitched eagerly as she breathed in the spicy fragrance.

I took two warm gingerbread men from a pan and gave them to Suzie and Debbie. Soon the two girls were helping my seven-year-old son, Mark, hang gingerbread men on the tree. (Of course, the cookies never stayed long on the tree. The children and their friends ate all of them every few days, and we replenished the supply weekly. As a result, our house smelled gingery from Thanksgiving to New Year's Day.)

Later, Suzie's mother telephoned, and in a tired-sounding voice, she asked me to send Suzie home.

413

The Sunday after Thanksgiving, I was still working on my perfect Christmas. I had decided to mail my Christmas cards early, and so I had spread the dining-room table with Christmas cards, address books, stamps, and green- and red-ink pens with which to address the envelopes. I was all set to start when Mark came in.

"Mama, we talked in Primary today about helping other people," he told me. "Our Primary teacher said a lonely lady in our ward needs help."

"Oh? What's the lady's name?" I asked, wondering if I had met her.

"I can't remember . . . something long and hard to say," Mark said, "but Sister Jones wrote it on the blackboard, and I'd remember it if I saw it."

He went to the desk drawer and pulled out the ward list. After a moment he gave a shout of triumph. "Here it is!" he cried. He thrust the page under my nose, and I glanced at the name by his finger before turning back to address my Christmas cards. The name was difficult to pronounce.

Mark borrowed my pen and drew a green circle around the name in the ward list before putting it back in the drawer.

"I want to go visit that lonely lady and take something to her. Can we make something for her now?" Mark wanted to know.

"Not today, Mark. It's Sunday, and I don't bake on Sundays. Besides, this lady doesn't even know us. Surely she wouldn't want a visit from strangers," I explained. "Today we are going to start addressing our Christmas cards. For once I'm going to get our cards mailed before December twenty-third. If you want to help someone, you can help me."

In the days that followed, Mark persisted in reminding me about the lonely lady. Twice he asked to make something for the woman, but both times I was involved in other projects.

One Tuesday afternoon Suzie again came home with Debbie.

414

That day I was putting together my specialty: a gingerbread train. Each car carried tempting cargo such as breadsticks, candy canes, and cinnamon bears. Suzie's eyes sparkled when I gave her a few chocolate-chip cookie wheels to "glue" into place with frosting. She ate one of them.

"I wish my Mom made gingerbread trains," she said. "Last year she made a neat gingerbread house, but this year she said it was too much work."

"It is a lot of work," I agreed, remembering the year I had been too busy with church and community duties to make my gingerbread train. The children had been very disappointed that year, but not this year. This year everything would be perfect.

A week later Debbie came home from school just as I was taking a fresh batch of gingerbread men from the oven.

"Too bad Suzie isn't here," she said, biting off one cookie foot. "Suzie loves our gingerbread men. She wasn't in school today, though."

Debbie set down her cookie, suddenly serious. "They said Suzie's mama took too many pills, and she's in the hospital. She might die."

"Oh, Debbie, are you sure?" I asked in dismay.

Debbie nodded. "Sally Miller told me Sister Miller was at the hospital with Suzie's mama all night," she said. Sister Miller was our Relief Society president.

"I didn't know Suzie was a member of the Church," I said, surprised. "I've never seen her at meetings."

"Suzie said they used to come all the time before her dad died," Debbie said. "He got killed in a car accident this summer."

"Poor Suzie!" I said. "Her poor mother! And I don't even know her name."

I called Sister Miller to see if I could be of any help in caring for Suzie during the crisis. I also asked for Suzie's mother's name.

When she told me, it sounded vaguely familiar. I hung up the phone repeating the name when a devastating thought struck me. With a sinking feeling, I took the ward list from the desk drawer and turned some pages. Yes, there it was, circled in green ink— the name of Suzie's mother, the name of Mark's lonely lady whom I had never found time to help.

Suzie was with us that night when we received word that her mother had died.

I asked myself over and over: What if we had gone to visit her when Mark first wanted to? Would it have mattered that we were strangers? Would she have been a little less lonely, a little less desperate? I thought of the tired voice on the telephone, asking me to send Suzie home that first day we made gingerbread.

When Suzie went away a week later to live with her grandparents, we gave her our gingerbread train. The bright eyes that had sparkled as she helped make the train had lost some of their glow, but Suzie managed a little smile and a thank-you.

A gingerbread train. A very small gift. Too little. Too late. As Suzie took a halfhearted nibble from a breadstick, I saw more than a saddened little girl holding a cookie train. I saw myself with painful clarity: a woman so involved with the things of Christmas that I had lost touch with the very spirit of Christmas, without which there can never be a "perfect Christmas." I would never again forget.

Every holiday season since then, the fragrance of gingerbread reminds me of Suzie . . . and I cry.

The Worst Christmas Pageant Ever

ANN EDWARDS CANNON

I was fourteen and I wanted to die.

Part of the problem was that I was fourteen and female. My brother John, the doctor, says that being fourteen and female is a disorder actually recognized by the American Psychiatric Association, and that his professor once spent a whole day talking about it in his Introduction to Psychiatry class. Physical symptoms of the fourteen-and-female syndrome include slumping in chairs, standing with arms folded across the chest, and wearing the exact same clothes as other disturbed fourteen-year-old girls. Behavioral symptoms include crying, trying on lip gloss, crying, going to the mall, crying, talking to disturbed fourteen-year-old boys on the telephone—and crying.

It's a terrible disease, and so far there's no cure.

So being fourteen was definitely part of my problem. The other part was that I was supposed to be the featured Youth Participant in the ward Christmas program that Sunday. It wouldn't have been so bad if I had just been allowed to get up and deliver the standard Youth Talk, which runs something along these lines: "Today I'm going to talk about (fill in the blank). Webster's Dictionary defines (fill in the blank) as (fill in a couple more blanks). I hope that we can all (blank, blank, blank)." And so forth.

Well, I wasn't going to be allowed to give a Youth Talk. I had to participate with a bunch of adults in a special holiday program written and directed by Dr. LaVerl S. Wanship, professor of music.

Dr. Wanship was a roly-poly little man who could play the piano like nobody's business. In fact, he could play the piano so well that sometimes he would stop in the middle of bearing his testimony and say, "Why don't I just play my testimony for you?" Then he would stride up to the front of the chapel on his little legs, position himself in front of the piano, pause—and play. Whenever Dr. Wanship did this, I and the rest of the fourteen-year-olds in the ward would cringe. It was so *embarrassing*.

Actually, Dr. Wanship wasn't the only adult in our ward who did embarrassing things. There was Sister Miller, who wore white go-go boots even though she was seventy years old, and Brother Meacham, who sprayed spit every time he talked, and Sister Fisher, who loudly told everybody at a ward party that all it took to keep regular was a cup of bran and a glass of warm water every morning.

Even my own parents were embarrassing. Although they were always late to sacrament meeting, they breezed through the door at the front of the chapel and headed straight for the family pew instead of sitting circumspectly in the cultural hall, stealing Cheerios from babies with the rest of the stragglers. "You guys never come on time," a friend once whispered to me. "And why does your mother wear those black sunglasses in church, anyway?"

It was true. My mother, after arriving late, proceeded to sit through church meetings looking like Jacqueline Onassis avoiding the press at the airport. It didn't matter that she was the most terrific-looking mother in the whole ward, not to mention the universe—I still wanted to slip like so much loose change through the cracks of a sofa.

And now I was supposed to do something embarrassing, too.

Dr. Wanship called a practice the Saturday before the program so we could rehearse our parts. We met in the chapel and took turns reading our parts from the podium while Dr. Wanship sat on the front pew and flapped directions at us.

"It's your turn, Sister Edwards."

I schlepped over to the microphone like any self-respecting fourteen-year-old girl, plopped open my mostly unused Bible, and began to mumble.

"I am the light of the—"

Dr. Wanship leaped like a toad. "NO! NO! NO! Listen to the words you're saying." He placed his hands over his heart. "*Feel* the words you are saying."

I stared at Dr. Wanship. Putting too much Dippity-Do in my bangs was something to get worked up about. Reading scriptures wasn't.

"Try again."

I did. He flew at me again. And again and again.

"He wants me to make a total fool of myself," I wailed to my father that night.

My father looked like Job would have looked if the Lord had sent him a fourteen-year-old daughter along with the rest of the plagues. "Just do the best you can," he said patiently.

So the next afternoon I stood before the congregation, tossed my hair, and routinely read the words, "I am the light of the world: he that followeth me shall not walk in darkness, but shall have the light of life." (John 8:12.)

When I sat down, I saw a look of profound disappointment cloud Dr. Wanship's round little face.

Well, Dr. Wanship, that was more than twenty years ago, and it has taken me that long to understand why those words once made the night glad. So I want to apologize for letting you down and to tell you that I would try to read those words for you now the way you hoped I would then. I would make those glorious words ring from the chapel walls. I would make them crack stone.

Merry Christmas, Dr. Wanship.

THEN WE FOUND THE ROCKING HORSE

DEREK DIXON

The house was very quiet. My wife and three teenage daughters had gone to the first of the end-of-year sales in search of clothing bargains. I sat alone in a deep armchair, an unread book on my knees, looking at the snow-covered lawn where we had found the rocking horse fifteen days before. I was remembering those ten hectic days before Christmas when a simple Family Home Evening resolution had opened so many hearts in what had seemed an iron-hearted town.

We had sung and we had prayed; and then Wendy had said from the pinnacle of her twelve years, "Christmas isn't like it used to be, is it? There used to be a funny feeling around the house, all warm and cozy and safe, but I can't feel it any more." The others chimed in with their remarks, and a pattern began to emerge. Our recent Christmases had failed because of too much eating, too much television watching, too much wrangling over petty things, too many late nights and late risings, and too much concern for self.

And it looked as though the coming Christmas was going to be the same—a spiritual and family failure. The days would pass and again we would have that terrible, dried out, flat feeling. Was there no way to change the nature of the season in our home? No way to recapture the true spirit of Christmas?

A pause came in the council, and then my wife began to tell us about some young patients at the school for mentally handicapped children where she worked as a physiotherapist several hours a week. She spoke of emotional deprivation, of uncaring parents, of pinching poverty in many homes, of being forgotten because "they only smash things, don't they?" and of little hands empty at the time of giving. . . .

My wife proposed that we as a family gather toys for those forgotten children at the school. Approval of her suggestion was unanimous.

The following day we put our plan into effect. We explained to our friends about the children at the school and asked them for any little gifts they might care to contribute.

We received one or two stony stares and some half-promises—beyond that, nothing. We had only recently moved to that neighborhood and had scoffed at remarks that the town was a hard town, full of seemingly materialistic, hard-hearted people. Now it seemed to be more than true.

Disappointed at the lack of contributions, we decided that at least we would make a contribution of our own; and so for the next few evenings, after supper was over, we set to making little dolls' beds out of plywood and hardboard, which we then painted in bright glossy paint; my wife supplied miniature mattresses and covers. The kitchen began to look like a Lilliputian army supply base! We made six beds in all.

Still nothing from others. Still we asked. Only six days left to Christmas.

On the fifth day we found a rocking horse standing on the back lawn, shimmering in sunshine and frost, his mane worn but triumphant, his eyes wild with the sight of battle, and in his ears the thunder of the captains and the shouting. On the ground beside him stood a cardboard soapbox full of assorted toys. To this day their coming is a mystery to us. And yet it seemed to be a sign, for that very day people began arriving at the front door with gifts for the forgotten children at the school.

One distant neighbor, a single man, lonely and stiff, a man not even invited to contribute, crossed the street to my wife and blurted out:

"Look here, I haven't anything moneywise; but I have been saving little toy motor cars in matchboxes. I get them from the garage. Every time I buy six gallons of petrol they present me with another motor car. I've got twenty altogether. Well, no man has ever asked me to help in something like this, so I'd like to do my bit now. I'll bring the motor cars along to your house tomorrow night and you can be Santa Claus for me."

And he turned away to hide his embarrassment; but when the following evening came, he was there on the step with his twenty motor cars.

An even greater surprise waited at my office. One young man had been reared in London's harsh East End—a man of prejudice and heated temper to whom my attempts to live my religion were a waving flag to a bull. But that day he came to me and said:

"You and I are no great friends—in fact, I wouldn't help you to the end of the street if you had both big toes fractured; but those children at the school are something different. I see their faces everytime I close my eyes. Ginny and I were talking about them and wondering how we could help; and we've decided to give the best we have. In my spare moments, I model and paint airplanes. We hang them from the ceiling at home and admire them from time to time; but beyond that they do nothing, so we thought we would give those. And what does it matter if the kids do smash them up playing with them? An hour's pleasure for such a child is well worth the loss of a few models to us."

That very afternoon he produced a large selection of model airplanes.

When I arrived home that evening, my wife and children had similar experiences to relate—of shy strangers and generous enemies—and of friends, too—all of whom were haunted by visions of the empty-handed children; our front room overflowed with their gifts.

The following day the school van called at our home, and the gifts were loaded on board and delivered to the headmistress to distribute to the children. And that was that.

None of those who contributed gifts ever asked for or received recognition or thanks. At the school only the headmistress ever knew from where the gifts had come. The rest was silence.

But as I sit here in the twilight after Christmas, I wonder if the spirit that permeates our home permeates theirs. For we as a family found again in service to others the real spirit of Christmas. The very walls are alive with sweetness and calm.

And as the winter day moves toward its early close, and the cold stars stare down and the snow upon the lawn reflects back the light from my windows, I think upon the true nature of the universe; for from this small miracle at Christmas, I have learned that every act of man reaches out into the universe. Wheels turn, the gears mesh, eternal balances are set in motion, and the earth is changed by the little secrets of kindness that have no significance at all to any earthly historian.

Tragedy and the True Meaning of Christmas

LINDA GAPPMAYER REED

I t was going to be our best Christmas ever. Little did we know that a tragedy would make it one we would never forget.

Dad was a high school geography teacher, and money was scarce. We three children heard the words "We can't afford it" much too often. So we could hardly believe it—and certainly had little appreciation for the sacrifices involved—when Dad and Mom announced that we were going to take a vacation at Christmas-time.

Even more unexpected was the news that we would be buying our first-ever new car for the trip—a yellow 1963 station wagon with mock wooden trim and a luggage rack on top. The only items missing were the optional seat belts that Dad had wanted installed before the trip. But since they hadn't arrived at the car dealership in time for our departure, we left without them.

Time and scenery passed quickly as we listened to Christmas carols on the car radio and tried to stifle our giggles and whispers as we speculated about the gaily wrapped packages peeking out at us from their hiding places in the back of the car. I was hoping for what every ten-year-old girl was hoping for that year—a Barbie doll, complete with wardrobe and blue vinyl carrying case. Eventually the rhythm of the road and the stillness of the dark lulled us children into happy dreams.

I awoke instantly, with confusion all about me. I felt as if I were one of a hundred puzzle pieces, tossing and whirling, unable to come together as a whole. I remember screams and cries, the sound of the radio, darkness, and things flying past me and hitting me. When I reached out to try to avoid the jarring bumps, I briefly felt the smooth inside of the roof of the car.

Then, as suddenly as it had begun, everything stopped moving, and for just an instant, there was silence. The road had been covered with patches of black ice, invisible and treacherous. We had hit some ice, lost control of the car, and now we were at the bottom of a steep incline a few miles outside of Lovelock, Nevada In the darkness of the early morning, I could see that my father was conscious but was bleeding from several cuts in his scalp. Mother had been thrown free of the car and was unable to move. Paul, the baby, was screaming with fright. I was unhurt. Sam, my seven-year-old brother, was missing.

Dad wiped the blood from his eyes and prayed quickly for help. He and I began searching for Sam, while Mom called out continually, "Have you found him?" We did, finally, lying in a pile of shattered glass and rock. He had been thrown an incredible distance, taking with him the curved back window of the station wagon. He looked so small and cold, lying very still in his blood-soaked pajamas. The sight made Dad cry out in despair, "He's dead! We've lost him!"

As I looked about, I saw our belongings. One whole side of our beautiful new car was now smashed as flat as an aluminum can. Our luggage had been thrown open, and the contents were scattered all over the hillside. Christmas presents were everywhere, with wrapping paper torn or missing—and I could see the corner of a blue vinyl carrying case where the paper had been ripped away.

In those few moments I grew up quickly. I realized, with a growing sense of urgency, that none of those things mattered now. More than anything, I wanted my family around me, healthy and happy. I was already feeling the sense of loss and incompleteness Sam's passing would leave in my life.

It was not likely that we would be spotted from the highway by a passing car, so someone needed to climb the steep embankment to flag down help. Dad stayed at Sam's side while I climbed up. Ice and snow hurt my bare feet—I was wearing only pajamas—but I was warm inside as I considered the trust that Dad had placed in me. I prayed out loud as I waited several minutes with no sign of other traffic.

When help arrived, it was indeed an answer to prayer. The first car stopped. Inside were a doctor and his wife, a nurse, and they had blankets and medical supplies in the trunk of their car! Seconds later, a truck driver stopped and called ahead for an ambulance.

The doctor examined Sam and found faint, hopeful signs of life. His wife wrapped Paul and me in blankets and treated the worst of Mom's abrasions. Then, while we were waiting for the ambulance, they helped us sort out our belongings and packed them into their car for the trip into town. The ambulance arrived, and we were loaded inside, but the drive was no faster than a crawl because of the icy road.

The sun was just coming up as we came into Lovelock. Since a bus had overturned earlier, resulting in several deaths and critical injuries, the hospital was already filled to capacity. Paul was taken to an empty crib in the nursery, and Dad's cuts were quickly cleaned and stitched. Mom and Sam were examined on gurneys in the hallway: Mom had suffered severe ligament damage, and Sam had a badly fractured skull. His open head wound was filled with dirt and broken glass, and the doctors were concerned about possible infection, blood loss, and brain damage. Later, when Sam was conscious, Dad and I were allowed to see him briefly. The doctor asked him if he recognized us. Sam said nothing, but his eyes revealed his fear and confusion.

Dad and I collected our luggage, left the hospital, and checked into a nearby motel, where we washed our dirty, blood-stained clothing in the bathtub. I was still barefoot and in my pajamas, so we sorted through the remnants of our belongings for warmer attire. I found a sweater and a pair of jeans to wear but could find only one shoe. For the next three days, I walked to the hospital and back in my stocking feet—until my other shoe was discovered in the wreckage of the car.

That night at the hospital we were relieved to see that a room had been made available for Mom and Sam. But we were surprised to discover that they had company. Somehow, members of the Lovelock Branch had discovered our plight and had sent us the Christmas spirit. Two brethren had brought a small decorated Christmas tree and gifts for each of us. I received a pink powder mitt made of flannel with a blue satin bow. When I opened it, I cried for the first time since the accident and allowed myself, for a little while, to be a tired, frightened little girl.

Then the men assisted Dad in administering to Mom and Sam. Through their kindness, the priesthood blessing, and the whisper of love from the Lord, we finally found peace and reassurance. In less than twenty-four hours, our emotions had come full circle, and we were once again filled with Christmas hope.

Looking back, I realize that my father was younger then than I am now. Throughout the experience, he set an example for me of calm strength and faith in the will of the Lord. And although it must have been difficult to face each day with only the companionship of a ten-year-old child, he made me feel useful and important.

Mom and Sam were recovering slowly, but it would be some time before they would be able to travel. Since Dad had to get back home for work after a few days, he made the difficult decision to leave them in the hospital, borrow money to fly home with Paul and me, and then return for Mom and Sam when they were able to travel again.

At home, neighbors and ward members readily stepped in to help. Paul and I were taken into the homes of ward members, and someone loaned Dad a car so he could get to and from work.

Finally, Mom and Sam were strong enough to come home, but they couldn't travel by air. Some friends offered their station wagon and fitted a mattress into it. Another friend took time off work to be the driver.

What a joyous reunion we had! Mom was soon on her feet again, and Sam recovered quickly, showing no signs of the trauma he had so recently survived. During a routine checkup several months after the accident, the doctor couldn't believe that Sam had ever suffered a severe skull injury; there was only a small external scar, and the X rays revealed no internal scarring or damage. When he saw the original X rays, he said, "Well, I've seen a miracle!"

My blue vinyl Barbie case was one of the few gifts that survived that Christmas. But today, as I watch my four little girls playing with it, I wish I could pass on to them the other, more important gifts I received that year: a greater appreciation for life and family relationships, faith in my parents, faith in the compassion of friends and strangers, and, most important, faith in God and in the power of his priesthood.

If I could, I would shield my little ones from the hurts of life that will inevitably come to them. Certainly all of their trials may not have the happy outcome my tenth Christmas ultimately did. But I will watch over them and encourage them as they experience both the joys and the sorrows of this life. And I will pray that from their experiences, they too will recognize and accept the best gifts.

Two Dimes and a Nickel

RICHARD A. ROBB

During my first Christmas as bishop, a single mother with three small children lived in our ward. This young woman had a strong testimony of the gospel and lived it to the best of her ability. She cleaned homes and did sewing to try to make ends meet, but often she could not.

Single-handedly raising three boys under the age of eight was a real challenge. These active, energetic youngsters always seemed to be in some sort of trouble. I remember extricating them from more than one tussle with their classmates.

Several good people helped this struggling family. I'll never forget the brother who came into my office one Sunday just a couple of weeks before Christmas, asking to speak with me privately. He was concerned about the young mother and her family and wanted to do something for them. Would I accept his contribution and use it in the best way I could to help them? As we spoke, I hardly noticed his small son, who remained in the office with us.

The man explained that he did not know what the woman and her family needed. He just wanted to help and felt that I would be inspired to know what to do. He then entrusted to me quite a remarkable sum of money—not remarkable in the amount, but remarkable relative to his modest means, of which I was well aware. I knew that this gift meant a sacrifice of his own family's Christmas, at least in the temporal sense. But this wise brother knew where real rewards come from.

Seeing the resolve shining in his eyes, I protested only gently. Then I cleared my tightening throat, thanked him for his unselfish gift, then promised to do my best to make Christmas a little brighter for the young mother and her sons.

I also agreed to honor his request for anonymity.

The story might well end here and still be memorable. But the event that has etched this experience in my mind had yet to occur. It wasn't the way I was able to help the family with the contribution—although that turned out to be most gratifying—but rather what took place in my office one week following that brother's visit. It was just a few days before Christmas, and I was between tithing-settlement interviews when I heard a soft knock on the office door. I opened it to see, standing quite alone, the six-year-old boy who had sat quietly in my office while his dad and I had talked the Sunday before.

He asked politely if he could talk to me for just a minute. After we walked into the office—which I presume is always a bit of a frightening experience for youngsters—I invited him to sit down. He fidgeted with something in his pocket and, after some struggle, pulled out two dimes and a nickel and laid them on my desk. He apologized that the coins were all the money he had, and that they were a little old and dirty, since he had had them quite a while. The money, he explained, was for me to use to help his three friends, like his dad was helping their mother. As my heart swelled and my eyes became moist, he added that he felt I would know best how to divide his treasure among his friends and that he was sorry he did not have three dimes so that each could have one.

What lessons culminated in that moment! A father's unselfish example, the trust of a small boy in his bishop, and the humble, Christlike act of a child obviously without guile. Only a few weeks before I had pulled this boy from a scuffle involving the soon-to-be recipients of his forgiving love and charity.

I hugged him, partly to camouflage my now obvious tears and mostly to tell him how much I appreciated him and how much I knew his Father in Heaven loved him. I then walked him to the door, shook his hand, and assured him that I would do the best I could to help his friends this Christmas with his generous gift. As I turned to go back into my office, he whispered after me, "And remember, Bishop, don't ever tell anyone it was me."

Well, I never have told anyone until now, my young friend. I hope relating our special story in this way is all right so that others might feel a bit of the quiet Christmas spirit of love and charity that we felt that day.

UNEXPECTED STAR

MARGRETA SPENCER

In Belfast, in quieter times, I had two roommates—girls of another faith whom I had met through a mutual friend. None of us had any extra money. Carol and Anne were both midwifery students, and I was saving for a postgraduate nursing course.

Our apartment was dismal, faded, and hard to bear, but we could find no other place within our means.

Nevertheless, Carol and Anne decided to call the Society for the Prevention of Cruelty to Children and offer to give a

Christmas party for twelve needy children. Of course, I agreed to help with the work and the financing as did Carol's sister Marian.

I had seen some of the miseries of the slums. The most appalling thing I remembered was a little girl in a torn summer dress sitting on the cold, windy sidewalk molding a lump of filthy clay because she had no other toy. I could not now find and help that child, but I could try to help some others.

Our Christmas tree was two feet high, decorated with nine small glass balls, one package of tinfoil icicles, and a star we had made from the foil inside a cracker box. The room was decorated with a few streamers and a dozen balloons. The food was simple—fried potatoes and sausages, grilled tomatoes, cookies, and orangeade. Fancy food is almost unknown to ghetto children, and we were afraid they would not eat anything unfamiliar. Besides, we couldn't afford it. The twelve gifts were small and inexpensive: a string of plastic beads, a doll's feeding set, a young child's picture book, small toys and games. And, remembering the girl on the sidewalk, I bought a package of clay.

The children arrived semiclean and in their best rags. Eleven, twelve, thirteen! One of the girls had come with her toddler sister, who had refused to stay at home. That presented a problem.

In those days my annual project for the Relief Society bazaar was dressing little plastic dolls in sturdy clothes for girls to play with. Several such dolls were in my room. I quickly wrapped one of them in the last scrap of tissue paper for our extra guest and hurriedly put it under the tree.

Most of the children stood in a group at the door, but one determined boy about eight years old examined all the gifts through the paper.

"If you don't mind, Missus," he declared, "I'll have this game of blow football for me and me mates."

Carol smiled but was firm.

"We're giving out the presents at the end of the party. Right now we're going to play some games."

We played their games; they played our games. We told stories; they related past experiences. We sang songs and grew decidedly tired of the children's favorite, "Jingle Bells."

"Last year," announced the oldest girl, trying hard to be sophisticated in an ill-fitting sheath and high heels much too large, "I was to a party in the Linen Makers' Hall. Hundreds of us there was, and a tree thirty feet high."

"Was it grand, but?" asked a slightly envious voice.

"It wasn't, for no one had time to talk with us like these good ladies are doing."

We served the simple food, which first brought forth cries of delight and then the silence of serious eating.

"Ye've left food on your plate," objected our blow football elf to his neighbor.

"I can't eat it, but," she replied, "for I've never had this much food on me plate at once."

"Give it here, then, for 'tis a shame to waste good food."

He ate several children's leavings and then conceded defeat. He could not prevent a few scraps from going to waste.

We gave him the blow football game. We gave the twelve-year-old, would-be sophisticate the plastic beads. We gave the doll's feeding set to a seven-year-old Raggedy Ann.

"It's no use to me, Missus. I ain't got a doll."

So the Relief Society lost another plastic doll. This time it was wrapped in writing paper, and we pretended it had fallen behind the tree.

"'Tis the best party I was ever at," someone announced with satisfaction. "I felt right to home."

"Indeed it was grand, Missus," seconded another voice. "For whenever we'uns wanted something, one of you ladies was near."

I thought then that I had learned something about giving, but I was shortly to learn more. The sophisticate, I noticed, had traded her beads for the clay, the clay for a toy car, the toy car for the baby's picture book.

"Sure it'll do," she said, trying to rewrap it. The used cellophane tape wouldn't stick.

"And would you have a bit of string, Missus? And a pencil, please?"

I produced them, wondering. She tied the parcel awkwardly, and in large uneven letters she printed on it "TOMMY."

She saw me looking and she explained: "'Tis me wee brother, Missus. Nobody invited him to a party, and we can't afford him no present."

Ragged, messy little girl in your run-over, outsized high heels, I seem to remember that you are beautiful.

VENITE FEDELI:
CHRISTMAS IN BOLZANO

PATRICK SEAN HOPKINS

Elder Stout and I decided to have a prayer before going out again that Christmas Eve. We had arrived home from our last appointment, and I wasn't exactly eager to step into the freezing-cold Italian air again. But my companion thought we still had time for the Christmas project we had been planning.

"Please guide us to those with no special place to go," we asked. "Please help us to cheer those who are experiencing sadness and loneliness during the holiday."

I grudgingly rebuttoned the buttons I had so fervently unbuttoned minutes before as Elder Stout gathered up the Christmas gifts left over from what we had given our investigators—five Christmas candles decorated with construction-paper holly and aluminum-foil bases. We had made them ourselves during the weeks before while practicing *Venite Fedeli,* "O Come All Ye Faithful," to sing to those we found wandering around with no place to go on Christmas Eve.

We walked into the cold, deserted streets of Bolzano, and I apprehensively looked for someone to cheer up. I had only been in Italy for twenty days or so and, although enthusiastic about missionary work, still found it hard to approach strangers and talk to them in a barely learned language about things they didn't seem interested in.

A man started walking in our direction, avoiding our eyes. At least we weren't trying to stop him in the midst of a blizzard—the Dolomite Mountains protected the city and its Italian- and German-speaking inhabitants from the snow of the Alps. We managed to stop and talk with him, lit and gave him one of our decorated candles, and sang.

As we sang, the faraway look in his eyes faded away. Not only a smile, but genuine warmth came to his face. I felt good. The man walked away with new vitality, and my attitude about our plans for the evening changed. It wasn't going to be so bad after all.

Then, walking toward the center of the city, we met a gray-haired old man. He was wearing a thick jacket and hobbling over the Druso Bridge with the help of a crutch under his left arm.

Elder Stout recognized him as someone he had talked to before my arrival in Italy. We presented him a candle and sang our carol.

He was thrilled. "Won't you come with me?" he asked in Italian marked by a strong German accent. "I'm on my way to church." We agreed and proceeded into town slowly so as not to rush his broken pace. As we walked, Elder Stout and he continued talking. My tongue still hobbled as much as our new friend when it came to speaking Italian.

As they conversed, I studied our friend and realized that, notwithstanding the incredibly low temperature, the hand supporting his body on the crutch was gloveless. "Please take this glove for your left hand," I somehow forced out.

"No, no," he replied. "Many years ago I spent the winter in Russia as a soldier with less than what I'm wearing now. This is nothing compared to then."

We neared the church and noticed a large group of people waiting outside. Our friend yelled out, "Hey, these Americans want to sing for you and give you a present!" This wasn't exactly what we had planned to do, but we sang anyway and gave out one of the three remaining candles. Our friend stood off to the side and smiled.

The night was getting colder and colder, so when we finished, Elder Stout and I asked him to take a glove from one of us to protect his bare hand. Once again he explained that he had undergone winter in Russia many years ago and had suffered much worse.

Then a car stopped near the church, and a well-dressed woman and her young son stepped out. The boy was yelling, upset at the necessity of going to church on the night before his favorite day of the year. While the mother attempted to calm him down, our friend motioned us to them. As we followed his labored steps, he called out, "Hey, these American boys want to sing for you and give you a present!"

We knelt down eye-to-eye with the boy and made our presentation. As the boy, wide-eyed and silent, listened intently to our well-rehearsed carol, I could see our friend smiling and enjoying every minute. When we stood up to wish the mother a merry Christmas, we saw that she had been crying as we sang. She smiled at us, and, before we could say anything, our friend wished them a merry Christmas in a way that only Santa Claus could rival.

We echoed his wishes and turned back to tell our friend that we still had one more candle and planned to continue on until we found someone to give it to.

He looked at the ground and then turned back to us: "Well, it's too crowded here, anyway. Maybe I'll go on with you to a smaller church."

Happy to hear that we would still enjoy his company, we left to find another church. Our limping friend guided us through the quiet streets only to find the other chapel closed. As it got colder and colder, I kept remembering the hand of our friend, trying to sense what it would be like for my bare hand to remain frozen in one position, holding on to a crutch. We both offered our gloves, and again he refused.

As we walked away from the church, we saw two teenage girls walking dejectedly down the street. Within seconds, our friend was yelling, "Hey, these American boys want to sing for you and give you a present!" Remembering that we only had one candle left, not two for both, I became uneasy. But we lit the candle and gave it to one of them.

"What about the other girl?" our friend asked. After Elder Stout explained that we had just given away the last candle, our friend cried, "Wait!" and started fumbling through his pockets. He finally found the candle we had given him and handed it to the other girl. Elder Stout and I sang our carol while our friend stood by smiling. The girls began smiling, too.

When they walked away, Elder Stout said, "Well, that's the last of our candles. I guess it's time to go home." Our friend replied that he would accompany us as far as the other church. When we arrived, we wished one another a merry Christmas and went our separate ways.

Back in our apartment, Elder Stout and I knelt in prayer. We thanked the Lord for making it possible to touch a few hearts and shine a little light on saddened countenances. We also thanked him for the lesson that angels don't always wear white flowing robes but come in all different sizes, colors, and nationalities. Some walk with crutches.

THE WONDROUS GIFT

SPENCER W. KIMBALL

I often think of an experience in giving that occurred a number of years ago. In one of the stakes of Zion lives a family who gave to me a crisp fifty dollar bill, saying, "Today is the Lord's birthday. We always give gifts to our family members on their birthdays. We should like to give a gift to the Savior. Will you place this money where it will please the Redeemer the most?"

Two days later Sister Kimball and I were on our way to Europe for a six-month tour of all the missions. As we made hasty and extensive preparations, we kept thinking about the birthday gift entrusted to us, and then the thought came to us that perhaps in Europe we would find the most appreciative recipient.

For months we toured the missions, held meetings with the missionaries and Saints, and met many sweet folk. There were numerous opportunities to present the gift, for the majority of the Saints there could use extra funds. But we waited. Toward the end of the mission tour we met a sweet little woman in Germany. She was a widow—or was she? She had been alone with her family of children for ten years. Whether her husband was deceased or not, she did not know. A victim of war, he had disappeared, and no word had ever come from him. The little children, who were small when he was taken away, were now nearly grown, and the son was a full-time missionary among his people.

It was nearing the time of the temple dedication at Bern, Switzerland. I said to this sweet woman, "Are you going to the temple dedication?" I saw the disappointment in her eyes as she said how she would like to go but how impossible it was for her because of lack of finances. I quietly checked with the mission president as to her worthiness and the appropriateness of her going to the temple, and then I gave him half the gift, which he assured me would pay the bus transportation to Bern and return.

A few weeks later we were in southern France. We had driven from Geneva, Switzerland, south to the Riviera. The long circuitous route had taken most of the day. The crowds of fun-lovers along the beaches delayed us so that for some twenty or thirty miles we moved slowly, bumper to bumper, to reach our destination. When we arrived, we were one hour late for our meeting. It was a hot night. The building was filled to capacity. An elderly woman sat at the piano, entertaining this large crowd until our arrival. For one hour she had played. I was so embarrassed for our delay, and so grateful to her for what she had done to hold the group and entertain them, that I inquired concerning her. Her husband, a professor, had died, and the sweet little widow was making a meager living through her musical talents. She was a fairly recent convert. The mission president and the elders assured me that she was worthy, and so I left with the president the other half of the gift for her.

We completed our tours of the ten missions and finally arrived in Bern for the dedication service of the Swiss Temple. The prophet of the Lord was present, as were three of the apostles. After the glorious dedication meetings were over, the regular temple services were conducted in the various languages. As I assisted the French Saints in their session, I was conscious of the sweet little musician, and she literally beamed as she was enjoying the Savior's birthday gift. It had paid her transportation to the temple. Her eyes shone with a new luster; her step was lighter; she radiated joy and peace as she came through the temple with new light, new hope. And I whispered to myself, thank the Lord for good folk who remember the Redeemer on his birthday.

I was present again when the three German-speaking missions had their sessions in the temple. These faithful Saints were assembling for their first time in a holy temple of the Lord. Some of them had been in the Church for many years, and this was their first opportunity to be in a temple. And as these German Saints congregated, I saw a lovely mother rush over to a group of missionaries, single out her handsome missionary son, and embrace him. Their eyes were glistening as they were reunited after many months of separation. To meet in the temple of God, what a joy to them both! I whispered to the Prophet their story of devotion and sacrifice and uncertainties. He was touched by their tender affection. How they wished the lost father could be restored and that they all could be sealed this day! The light in this mother's eyes was like that of one of the other German sisters, who shook my hand warmly and with deep emotion said to me, "Now I can face anything. Now that I have been through the Lord's temple, have made my covenants with my Heavenly Father, and have had my own temple work done, I can meet any situation—hunger, cold, uncertainties. Even war with all its terrors will have less fear. Now I can take anything."

The light that shone in the eyes of these women reflected love and joy and the peace that are truly part of Christmas. In this season we need to listen carefully to the words of a glorious Christmas hymn that proclaims: "How silently, how silently, the wondrous gift is given! So God imparts to human hearts the blessings of his heaven." Our Savior who was the Babe in Bethlehem has given us the recipe for inner peace, for a soul that glows with joy, for a heart that loves life even though it may be strewn with trials.

SOURCES

Armour, Anobel. "Small Shepherd." *Improvement Era,* December 1951, 860.

Badger, Franklin. "A Surprise Visit from Santa." In *Treasures of Pioneer History,* compiled by Kate B. Carter, 3:168–69. 6 vols. Salt Lake City: The Daughters of the Utah Pioneers, 1952–57.

Black, Susan Easton. "The Anonymous Benefactor." In *Keeping Christmas,* 11–17. Salt Lake City: Deseret Book, 1996.

Brown, D. M. "The Voice on the Phone." *Ensign,* December 1989, 30–32.

Busath, Anne Castleton. "Seven Thousand Dollars by Christmas." *Ensign,* December 1981, 14–16.

Cannon, Anne Edwards. "The Worst Christmas Pageant Ever." In *Keeping Christmas,* 185–89. Salt Lake City: Deseret Book, 1996.

Cannon, George I. "A Soldier's Christmas in Italy." *Improvement Era,* December 1945, 732.

Carter, Kate B., comp. "Christmas in Orderville." In *Our Pioneer Heritage,* 18:160–61. Salt Lake City: The Daughters of the Utah Pioneers, 1975.

Chatterton, Aney B. "The Year of the Flexible Flyers." *Ensign,* December 1984, 60–61.

Clark, J. Reuben, Jr. "The Journey from Nazareth to Jerusalem." In *Behold the Lamb of God,* 137–47. Salt Lake City: Deseret Book, 1991.

Compton, Piers. "All Quiet for Christmas." In *Christmas Observed,* edited by Owen Dudley Edwards and Graham Richardson, 147–49. New York: St. Martin's Press, 1982.

Cornaby, Hannah. "Gingerbread Toys." In *Autobiography and Poems,* 45–46. Salt Lake City: J. C. Graham Co., 1881.

Davidson, Karen Lynn. *Our Latter-day Hymns: The Stories and the Messages,* 224. Salt Lake City: Deseret Book, 1988.

Day, Lillie Buhler. "The Christmas Our Parents Wept." *Ensign,* December 1981, 13–14.

Dixon, Derek. "Then We Found the Rocking Horse." *Ensign,* December 1973, 20–21.

Edersheim, Alfred. "Shepherds Watched Their Flocks." In *Life and Times of the Messiah,* 186–90. Iowa Falls: World Bible, 1971.

Ellsworth, Fae. "The Christmas We Gave Away." *Deseret News,* 24 December 1971.

Evans, Douglas W. "Mistletoe." *Friend,* December 1991, 28–30.

Farrar, Frederic W. "The Nativity." In *The Life of Christ*. Portland: Fountain Publications, 1964.

Griffiths, Thomas J. "Honesty's Reward." In *Christmas I Remember Best*, 39–41. Salt Lake City: *Deseret News*, 1983.

Halvorsen, Gail. "The Bon-Bon Bomber." In *Christmas I Remember Best*, 472–76. Salt Lake City: *Deseret News*, 1983.

Hansen, Alice Morgan. "Christmas Came Late." In *Treasures of Pioneer History*, compiled by Kate B. Carter, 3:175–76. 6 vols. Salt Lake City: The Daughters of the Utah Pioneers, 1952–57.

Harrison, Ted. "The Strangers." *Improvement Era*, December 1952, 894–95, 964–67.

Hatch, J. K. "Trapper." "One More Car." *Ensign*, December 1984, 62–63.

Hopkins, Patrick Sean. "*Venite Fedeli:* Christmas in Bolanzo." *Ensign*, December 1990, 12–13.

Horne, J. Arthur. "The Ways of Providence." *Improvement Era*, December 1923, 115.

Huffaker, Elizabeth. "First Christmas in Utah." In *Our Pioneer Heritage*, 14:204, compiled by Kate B. Carter. Salt Lake City: Daughters of the Utah Pioneers, 1971.

Hunsaker, Nettie [Lannette Hunsaker Francis]. "Papa's Song." *New Era*, December 1995, 36–38.

Keller, Cheryl. "One Shiny Dime and Three Pennies." *Ensign*, December 1983, 54–55.

Kimball, Spencer W. "The Wondrous Gift." In *Christmas Classics: A Treasury for Latter-day Saints*, 37–39. Salt Lake City: Deseret Book, 1995.

Larsen, Shauna Stewart. "This Is Christ's Birthday." In *Christmas—A Joyful Heritage*, compiled by Susan Arrington Madsen, 23–24. Salt Lake City: Deseret Book, 1984.

Lee, Harold B. "Are You Ready for Christmas?" *Improvement Era*, December 1968, 4–5.

McConkie, Bruce R. "Upon Judea's Plains." In *The Mortal Messiah, Book 1*, 339. Salt Lake City: Deseret Book, 1979.

———. "The Birth of the Mortal Messiah." In *The Mortal Messiah, Book 1*, 317–49. Salt Lake City: Deseret Book, 1979.

McKay, David O. "'Again It Was Christmas Eve': A Letter to Thomas E. McKay." In *Highlights in the Life of President David O. McKay*, edited by Janette McKay Morrell, 29–31. Salt Lake City: Deseret Book, 1971.

———. "The First Christmas." In *Steppingstones to an Abundant Life*, 422–23. Salt Lake City: Deseret Book, 1971.

McKay, Elaine S. "The Widow's Might." *Relief Society Magazine*, December 1970, 898–99.

Merrill, Harrison R. "Wise Young Santa Claus." *Improvement Era*, December 1931, 66.

Parry, Atwell J. "They Called Him Mordecai." Previously unpublished.

Pypher, George D. "Four Christmas Carols." *Improvement Era*, December 1936, 756–57.

Reading, Lucille C. "The Christmas Shoppers." *Children's Friend*, December 1969, 9.

Reed, Linda Gappmayer. "Tragedy and the True Meaning of Christmas." *Ensign*, December 1988, 34–36.

Richardson, Max B. "The King of Hearts." In *Christmas I Remember Best*, 17–19. Salt Lake City: *Deseret News*, 1983.

Robb, Richard A. "Two Dimes and a Nickel." *Ensign*, December 1986, 53.

Sadler, Juanita. "The Joy They Shared." *New Era*, December 1993, 24–25.

Schaar, Richard R. "A Chocolate Christmas." In *Christmas I Remember Best*, 91–92. Salt Lake City: *Deseret News*, 1983.

Scow, Anna Marie [as told to Jack M. Lyon]. "Food for Santa." In *Christmas Classics: A Treasury for Latter-day Saints*, 73. Salt Lake City: Deseret Book, 1995.

Shields, Jody. "The Broken Picture." In *Relief Society Magazine*, 1968.

Smith, Joseph F. "Christmas Reminiscences." *Improvement Era*, January 1919, 266–67.

Smith, Lila L. "Mama and the Magic Bag." *Relief Society Magazine*, December 1969, 894–97.

Soelberg, LaRue H. "A Gift of Friendship." *Deseret News*, 21 December 1970.

Spencer, Margreta. "Unexpected Star." *New Era*, December 1973, 14–16.

Staker, Matilda Y. Stolworthy. "One Christmas When Lorenzo D. Young Played Santa Claus." In *Heart Throbs of the West*, compiled by Kate B. Carter, 2:12–14. 12 vols. Salt Lake City: Daughters of the Utah Pioneers, 1939–51.

Stewart, Emily Smith. "Our Giving Christmases." In *A Story to Tell*, 460–65. Salt Lake City: Deseret Book, 1945.

Talmage, James E. "The Birth of Jesus Christ." In *Jesus the Christ*, 75–78, 79–80, 86–87. Salt Lake City: Deseret Book, 1983.

Wells, Susan. "My First Ball Dress Was Stunning." *Juvenile Instructor*, December 1918, 631.

Whitney, Orson F. "A Christmas Idyl." *Contributor*, January 1884, 151–53.

INDEX